Population
Resources
Environment

A Series of Books in Biology

EDITORS:
Donald Kennedy
Roderic B. Park

Paul R. Ehrlich
Anne H. Ehrlich
STANFORD UNIVERSITY

Population

Resources

Environment

ISSUES IN HUMAN ECOLOGY

 W. H. Freeman and Company
San Francisco

Printed in the United States of America

Library of Congress Catalog Card Number: 75-103067

International Standard Book Number: 0-7167-0680-6

3   4   5   6   7   8   9

*To Dorothy Decker
with love and thanks.*

Contents

Population

Resources

Environment

The Crisis

The explosive growth of the human population is the most significant terrestrial event of the past million millenia. Three and one-half billion people now inhabit the Earth, and every year this number increases by 70 million. Armed with weapons as diverse as thermonuclear bombs and DDT, this mass of humanity now threatens to destroy most of the life on the planet. Mankind itself may stand on the brink of extinction; in its death throes it could take with it most of the other passengers of Spaceship Earth. No geological event in a billion years—not the emergence of mighty mountain ranges, nor the submergence of entire subcontinents, nor the occurrence of periodic glacial ages—has posed a threat to terrestrial life comparable to that of human overpopulation.

Most of the members of modern societies have now seen pictures of the Earth as seen from the vicinity of the moon, and they must have a new awareness of the finite size of our planet. In comparison with many celestial bodies, it is a rather small ball of rock. It is also possibly a unique ball of rock, for its surface is populated by a vast variety of living organisms that depend for their existence on a thin film of atmosphere, which is itself, in part, a product of those living things.

If *Homo sapiens* is to continue as the dominant species of life on Earth, modern man must come soon to a better understanding of the Earth and of what he has been doing to it. Yet many people—as a result of the excitement over the successful landings of men on the moon—are better informed (and perhaps more curious) about conditions on the surface of that dead satellite than they are about the damage being done by overpopulation and overdevelopment to the only life-supporting planet we know.

Only recently have Americans been astounded to learn that many millions of their own fellow citizens go to bed hungry every night. Most of us, of course, have vague ideas about starvation in India or about Brazilians living in squalid *favelas,* but all too many of us have no real appreciation of the dimensions of the world food problem. Why should we? The concept of one or two *billion* people living on this planet without adequate diets truly staggers the imagination. How can it be that 10 or 20 million people, mostly children, are starving to death each year while we pay some of our farmers *not* to grow food? How many presumably well-educated Americans realize that their pets receive a better diet than hundreds of millions of their fellow human beings? How many are aware that many poor Americans resort to eating pet food as a cheap source of high-quality protein?

Look for a moment at the situation in those nations that most of us prefer to label with the euphemism "underdeveloped," but which might just as accurately be described as "hungry." In general, underdeveloped countries (UDCs) differ from developed countries (DCs) in a number of ways. UDCs are not industrialized. They tend to have inefficient, usually subsistence agricultural systems, extremely low gross national products and per capita incomes, high illiteracy rates, and incredibly high rates of population growth. For reasons that are made clear in this book, most of these countries will never, under any conceivable circumstances, be "developed" in the sense in which the United States is today. They could quite accurately be called "never-to-be-developed countries."

The people of the UDCs will be unable to escape from poverty and misery unless their populations are controlled. Today these countries have larger populations than they can properly support, given their physical and biological resources. Furthermore, their population growth rates make it clear that conditions are going to get steadily and rapidly worse. The populations of most UDCs are doubling every 20–30 years. Consider what it would mean for a country like the Philippines or Honduras to double its population in some 20 years. There would be nearly twice as many families in 20 years; today's children would be adults and have their own children. In order to maintain present living standards, such a country must, in two decades, duplicate every amenity for the support of human beings. Where there is one home today there must be two (or their equivalent). Where there is one schoolroom there must be two. Where there is one hospital, garage, judge, doctor, or mechanic, there must be two. Agricultural production must be doubled. Imports and exports must be doubled. The capacity of roads, water systems, electric generating plants, and so on must be doubled. It is problematical whether the United States could accomplish a doubling of its facilities in 20 years, and yet the United States has abundant capital, the world's finest industrial base, rich natural resources, excellent communications, and a population virtually 100 percent literate. The Philippines, Honduras, and other UDCs have none of these things. They are not even going to be able to maintain their present low standards of living.

Even if some UDCs should manage to maintain their living standards, this will not be acceptable to the people in those countries. The "have-nots" of the world are in an unprecedented position today: they are aware of what the "haves" enjoy. Magazines, movies, transistor radios, and even television have brought them news and pictures of our way of life—our fine homes, highly varied diet, and so forth. They have also seen in their own countries our automobiles, airplanes, tractors, refrigerators, and other appliances. Naturally they want to share our affluence. They have what Adlai Stevenson called "rising expectations." But, a few simple calculations show that they also have plummeting prospects. It takes no political genius to guess the results of not just a continual frustration of these expectations, but an actual deterioration of living standards as well. Population pressure has been described as numbers of people pressing against values. For many people in the UDCs there are relatively few values left to press against, and even these are doomed if mankind continues on its present course.

Many people in the UDCs—the Columbian mothers forced by hunger to practice infanticide, the Biafran children in the last stages of starvation, the Indian women who, during the recent Bihar famine, spent days sitting in the sun picking up grains of wheat one by one from railroad beds, and the several hundred thousand residents of Calcutta who live in the streets—have virtually nothing left to lose but their lives. The inhabitants of the DCs have much to lose. Overpopulation right now is lowering the quality of life dramatically in these countries as their struggle to maintain affluence and grow more food leads to environmental deterioration. In most DCs the air grows more foul and the water more undrinkable each year. Rates of drug usage, crime, and civil disorder rise and individual liberties are progressively curtailed as governments attempt to maintain order and public health.

The global polluting and exploiting activities of the DCs are even more serious than their internal problems. Spaceship Earth is now filled to capacity or beyond and is running out of food. And yet the people traveling first class are, without thinking, demolishing the ship's already overstrained life-support systems. The food-producing mechanism is being sabotaged. The devices that maintain the atmosphere are being turned off. The temperature-control system is being altered at random. Thermonuclear bombs, poison gases, and super-germs have been manufactured and stockpiled by people in the few first-class compartments for possible future use against other first-class passengers in their competitive struggles for dwindling resources—or perhaps even against the expectant but weaker masses of humanity in steerage. But, unaware that there is no one at the controls of their ship, many of the passengers ignore the chaos or view it with cheerful optimism, convinced that everything will turn out all right.

CHAPTER 2

Numbers of People

"The Generations pouring
From times of endless date,
In their going, in their flowing,
Ever form the steadfast State;
And Humanity is growing
Toward the fullness of her fate."

Herman Melville
(1819–1891)

"Prudent men should judge of future events
by what has taken place in the past,
and what is taking place in the present."

Miguel de Cervantes (1547–1616)
Persiles and Sigismunda

Assuming that the first "man" appeared between 1,600,000 and 600,000 years ago, we can estimate that between 60 and 100 billion representatives of *Homo sapiens* have lived on the planet Earth. Today some 3.6 billion people inhabit the Earth, roughly 4–5 percent of all those who have ever lived.

We do not have substantial historical data on which to base estimates of population before 1650; such estimates must be based on circumstantial evidence. For instance, we believe that agriculture was unknown before about 8,000 B.C.; prior to that date human groups made their living by hunting and gathering. No more than 20 million square miles of the Earth's total land area of some 58 million square miles could have been successfully utilized in this way by our early ancestors. From the population densities of the hunting and gathering tribes of today, we can estimate that the total human population of 8,000 B.C. was probably about 5 million people.

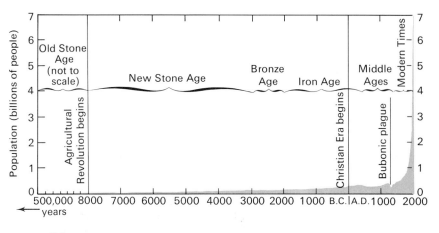

FIGURE 2-1

Growth of human numbers for the past one-half million years. If Old Stone Age were in scale, its base line would extend about 18 feet to the left. [After *Population Bulletin,* vol. 18, no. 1.]

Population sizes, at various times from the onset of the agricultural revolution until census data first were kept in the seventeenth century, have also been estimated. This was done by projection from census figures that exist for agricultural societies, and by examination of archaeological remains. Such data as number of rooms in excavated ancient villages prove especially useful for calculating village populations. It is thought that the total human population at the time of Christ was around 200 to 300 million people, and that it had increased to about 500 million (½ billion) by 1650. It then doubled to 1,000 million (1 billion) around 1850, and doubled again to 2 billion by 1930. The course of human population growth can be seen in Figure 2-1. Note that the size of the population has, with minor irregularities, increased continuously, and that *the rate of increase has also increased.*

Perhaps the best way to describe the growth rate is in terms of "doubling time"—the time required for the population to double in size. To go from

TABLE 2-1
Doubling Times

Date	Estimated world population	Time for population to double
8000 B.C.	5 million	
		1,500 years
1650 A.D.	500 million	
		200 years
1850 A.D.	1,000 million (1 billion)	
		80 years
1930 A.D.	2,000 million (2 billion)	
		45 years
1975 A.D.	4,000 million (4 billion)	
	Computed doubling time around 1970	35–37 years

5 million in 8,000 B.C. to 500 million in 1650 meant that the population increased 100-fold. This required between 6 and 7 doublings:

$$5 \text{ million} \rightarrow 10 \rightarrow 20 \rightarrow 40 \rightarrow 80 \rightarrow 160 \rightarrow 320 \rightarrow 640 \text{ million}$$

in a period of 9,000 to 10,000 years. Thus, on the average, the population doubled about once every 1,500 years during that period. The next doubling, from 500 million to a billion, took 200 years, and the doubling from a billion to 2 billion took only 80 years. Barring disaster, the population will reach 4 billion around 1975, having doubled in 45 years. The rate of growth around 1970 would, if continued, double the population in about 35 years. Table 2-1 summarizes our population history in these terms.

The sort of graph shown in Figure 2-1 does not reveal details of trends in the long, slow growth of the human population before the current millennium. But if population size and time are plotted against one another on logarithmic scales (a log-log graph), as in Figure 2-2, a greater range of time can be

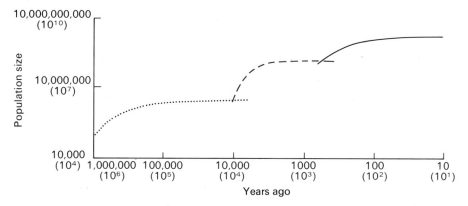

FIGURE 2-2

Human population growth plotted on a log-log scale. Plotted in this way population growth is seen as occurring in three surges, as a result of the cultural, agricultural, and industrial-medical revolutions, which are discussed later in this chapter. [After Deevey, "The Human Population." Copyright © 1960 by Scientific American, Inc. All rights reserved.]

shown, and more detail in the lower range of population sizes is revealed. Notice that the log-log graph shows three surges of population growth, one about 600,000 years ago, one about 8,000 years ago, and one about 200 years ago.

The reasons for the patterns shown on both graphs are reasonably clear, but before these reasons are examined, some details of population dynamics —the ways in which populations change size—must be considered. The size of a population is essentially the result of additions and subtractions. Additions to local human populations consist of births and immigrations; subtractions consist of deaths and emigrations. Demographers (scientists concerned with the statistical study of human populations) who are interested in the total population of the planet work primarily with birth and death rates, since there has been no migration to or from the Earth.

Birth and Death Rates

The birth rate is usually expressed as the number of babies born per thousand people per year. The total number of births during the year is divided by the estimated population at the midpoint of the period. For example, in the United States there were 3,453,000 live births during the 12 months ending with September 30, 1968. The population on March 31, 1968 (the midpoint of that period) was estimated to be 198,400,000. The birth rate for that period was therefore $3,453,000/198,400,000 = 0.0174$. There were 0.0174 births per person or $0.0174 \times 1,000 = 17.4$ births per thousand people. Similarly, there were 1,906,000 deaths during the period, giving a death rate of $1,906,000/198,400,000 = 0.0096 \times 1,000 = 9.6$ deaths per thousand people in the year from October 1, 1967 to September 30, 1968.

Growth Rate

Since birth rate represents additions and death rate represents subtractions, we can calculate the rate of growth (or shrinkage) of the population by subtracting the death rate from the birth rate. During the year ending September 30, 1968, the growth rate was 17.3 minus 9.6, or 7.7 per thousand. That is, in the period from October 1, 1967 to September 30, 1968, 7.7 people were added to each 1,000 people in the American population. Technically this is the "rate of natural increase," since migration is not considered. Demographers express this growth rate as a percent annual increase—that is, not as a rate per thousand but as a rate per hundred. In the example cited above the annual increase would be 0.77 percent, a typical rate for an industrialized nation. In 1968 the estimated world birth rate was 34, and the death rate 14. The population growth rate was thus $34 - 14 = 20$, or 2 percent.

If the world rate of increase is 2 percent and remains constant, then the population will double in 35 years. A 2-percent rate of increase means that 20 persons per thousand are added to the population each year. Note that if you simply *add* 20 persons per year to a population of 1,000 people, it will

TABLE 2–2

Annual percent increase	Doubling time (years)
0.5	140
0.8	87
1.0	70
2.0	35
3.0	24
4.0	17

take 50 years to double that population ($20 \times 50 = 1,000$). But the doubling time is actually much less, because populations grow in the way that money grows when interest is compounded. Just as the interest dollars themselves earn interest, so people added to populations produce more people. It is growth at compound interest rates that makes populations double so much more rapidly than seems possible (see Box 2-1). The relationship between the annual percent increase (interest rate) and the doubling time is shown in Table 2-2.

History of Population Growth

The story of human population growth is not primarily a story of changes in birth rate, but of changes in death rate. The populations of our ancestors one or two million years ago (*Australopithecus* and relatives) were confined to Africa and numbered perhaps 125,000 individuals. By that time, these ancestors of ours had already "invented" culture, the body of nongenetic information passed from generation to generation. The volume of culture is, of course, vastly greater today than in the days of *Australopithecus*. In those days human culture was transmitted orally and by demonstration from the older to the younger members of the group. It doubtless consisted of information about methods of hunting and gathering, rules of social conduct, dangerous enemies, and the like. Today, of course, human culture includes information transmitted and stored in such diverse places as books, phonograph records, photographs, videotapes, and computer tapes.

The possession of a substantial body of culture is what differentiates man from the other animals. During man's evolutionary history the possession of culture has been responsible for a great increase in human brain size (the australopithecines had small brains, with an average volume of only about 500 cubic centimeters). Early men added to the store of cultural information, developing and learning techniques of social organization and group and individual survival. This gave a selective advantage to individuals with the large brain capacity necessary to take full advantage of the culture. Larger brains in turn increased the potential store of cultural information, and a self-reinforcing coupling of the growth of culture and brain size resulted. This trend continued until perhaps 200,000 years ago, when growth of brain size leveled off at an average of some 1,350 cubic centimeters (Box 2-2).

The evolution of culture had an important side effect. Although the human birth rate remained around 50 per thousand, cultural advances caused a slight decline in the average death rate. Up until the agricultural revolution this decline produced an estimated average annual rate of population increase of only 0.002 percent. In prehistoric times there unquestionably were sizable fluctuations in birth and, in particular, death rates, especially during the difficult times associated with glacial advance. The end result, however, was a population of about 5 million around 8,000 B.C. Mankind had by that time spread from Africa to occupy the entire planet. It is thought that man first

BOX 2-1   INTEREST AND GROWTH RATES

If N_0 dollars are placed in a bank at a 2 percent rate of interest compounded semiannually, the principal plus the interest at the end of t years will be

$$N_t = N_0(1.01)^{2t} . \tag{1}$$

More generally, if the interest rate is expressed as a decimal r (where $100r =$ interest rate as a percent) and interest is compounded x times per year, then

$$N_t = N_0 \left(1 + \frac{r}{x}\right)^{xt} . \tag{2}$$

If interest is compounded continuously, then $x \to \infty$. Expression (2) may be rewritten, substituting $y = r/x$

$$N_t = N_0(1 + y)^{rt/y} = N_0(1 + y) \left(\frac{1}{y}\right)^{rt} . \tag{3}$$

Those who have had calculus will understand that as $x \to \infty$, $y \to 0$, and in the limit

$$\lim_{y \to 0} (1 + y)^{1/y} = e .$$

The base of natural logarithms, e, is approximately equal to 2.718. Therefore, when interest is compounded continuously (3) becomes

$$N_t = N_0 e^{rt} . \tag{4}$$

If

$$N_0 = \text{population at time 0,}$$

$$N_t = \text{population at time } t,$$

$$r = \text{growth rate (assumed to be calculated from}$$
$$\text{instantaneous birth and death rates),}$$

$$t = \text{time in years,}$$

then expression (4) will apply to population growth instead of to the accumulated sum of principal and interest. For instance, given the growth rate, the doubling time may be computed by setting $N_t/N_0 = 2$.

Then

$$2 = e^{rt}$$

Taking the natural logarithm of each side (and remembering that $\ln e = 1$) gives

$$\ln 2 = rt \quad \text{or} \quad \frac{\ln 2}{r} = t \quad \text{or} \quad \frac{0.6931}{r} = t .$$

For example, if the growth rate is 2 percent, then $r = 0.02$, and

$$t = \frac{0.6931}{0.02} = 34.65 \text{ years.}$$

entered the Western Hemisphere around 30,000 B.C. As he became ubiquitous, man's increased hunting and gathering efficiency may have led, among other things, to the extinction of many large mammals, such as the great ground sloths, sabre-toothed tigers, and woolly mammoths.

The consequences of cultural evolution for human population size and for man's environment were minor compared with those that were to follow in the agricultural revolution. It is not certain when the first group of *Homo sapiens* started to supplement their hunting and food gathering with primitive

---

BOX 2-2   NATURAL SELECTION

Natural selection is the prime mover of evolution. It is essentially the differential reproduction of genetic types. In all human populations, individuals differ from one another because each individual has a different hereditary endowment. For instance, people differ from one another in such traits as eye color, height, and blood type, which are at least partially hereditary. If people with one hereditary trait (that is, one kind of genetic information) tend to have more children than those with another, then natural selection is occurring with respect to that trait. Natural selection can cause one kind of genetic information—for example, that producing people with blue eyes—to become more and more common in the gene pool of a population. These changes in the gene pool are what is called *evolution*. Thus the statement that an evolutionary premium was placed on brain size is a convenient shorthand for a statement that might go like this: in early human populations there was variation in brain size. This variation was in part caused by differences among individuals in their genetic endowment. Individuals with slightly larger brains were better able to utilize the cultural information of the society. This permitted them more ready access to mates, a better chance of surviving, or perhaps a better chance of successfully rearing their offspring; and they reproduced more than did individuals with smaller brains. The result was a gradual increase in the genetic information producing larger brain size in the gene pools of human populations. In turn this increased the capacity for storing cultural information and produced a selective advantage for further increase in brain size. This reciprocal evolutionary trend continued until other factors, such as the difficulty of getting the enlarged brain case of a baby through the female's pelvis (which was not enlarged commensurately) at birth removed the selective premium on further increase in brain size.

Understanding natural selection will help to illuminate a number of other points in this book. Further on we will discuss the development of pesticide resistance in insect populations, a process that occurs through natural selection. The insect individuals vary in their natural resistance to a pesticide, and this variation has a genetic basis. Those that are naturally more resistant have a better chance of surviving, and thus of reproducing, than their less fortunate fellows. In this way the entire population becomes more and more resistant, as in each generation the most resistant individuals do most of the breeding.

The key thing to remember is that natural selection is *differential reproduction* of genetic types. It may involve survival, but differentials in reproduction may occur while the life expectancies of all genetic types remain identical.

farming. On the basis of studies of archaeological sites in the Middle East, there is firm evidence that established village-farming communities functioned between 7,000 and 5,500 B.C., and archaeologists estimate that agriculture began around 9,000–7,000 B.C. Around that time, certain groups of people in the hills flanking the Fertile Crescent, in what is now the border area of Iraq and Iran, gradually began to add a new dimension of security to their lives. Like modern Eskimos, these people practiced intensive food collection, and were presumably intimately familiar with the local flora and fauna. It was

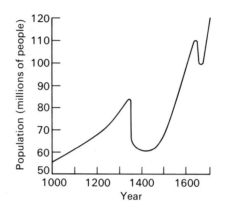

FIGURE 2-3

Effects of bubonic plague epidemics on European population size in the fourteenth and seventeenth centuries. Curve is an estimate based on historical accounts; actual data are scarce. [After Langer, "The Black Death." Copyright © 1964 by Scientific American, Inc. All rights reserved.]

a natural step from gathering food to producing it. This step, accompanied by settlement in one place with the consequent possibilities for storage of vegetable foods in granaries and bins, and meat on the hoof, freed men from the constant search for food. As a result some members of early agricultural communities were able to turn to other activities, all of which helped to raise the general standard of life. Wheeled vehicles appeared; copper, tin, and then iron were utilized; and dramatic sociopolitical changes occurred along with urbanization. Existence began to lose some of its hazards, and man's life expectancy began to creep upward from its primitive level of perhaps 25–30 years.

The growth of human populations was not continuous after the agricultural revolution. Civilizations grew, flourished, and disintegrated; periods of good and bad weather occurred; and those apocalyptic horsemen, pestilence, famine, and war, took their toll. Although the global trend, indicated in Figure 2-3, was one of accelerating increase, a great many local population "explosions" and "crashes" are concealed in that trend. For example, bubonic plague (Black Death) killed an estimated 25 percent of the inhabitants of Europe between 1348 and 1350. From 1348 to 1379 England's total population was reduced by almost 50 percent from an estimated 3.8 million to 2.1 million. Many cities lost half or more of their inhabitants in the second half of the fourteenth century. The effect of repeated visitations of plague on the population is shown in Figure 2-3.

Famine has also been an important periodic contributor to high death rates even after the agricultural revolution. Floods, droughts, insect plagues, warfare, and other causes often have pushed populations over the thin line between hunger and famine. One study, by Cornelius Walford, lists more than 200 famines in Great Britain alone between 10 and 1846 A.D. (Box 2-3). Another counts 1,828 Chinese famines in the 2,019 years preceding 1911, a rate of almost one per year. Some of these famines, and similar ones in India, have been known to result in many millions of deaths. Even in this century famine has killed millions. For example, perhaps 5–10 million deaths have been attributed to starvation in Russia (1918–1922, 1932–1934), perhaps as many as 4 million deaths in China (1920–1921), and 2–4 million deaths in West Bengal, India (1943).

Warfare has often created conditions in which both pestilence and famine thrived, but it is difficult to estimate what the direct effects of war on population size have been. In many areas of the world, wars must have made a major contribution to the death rate, even when the conflict was between "primitive" groups. Indeed, the effect of warfare on population size and distribution in New Guinea was rather dramatic until quite recently. For security, villages in many areas were placed exclusively on hilltops, some of them thousands of feet above the nearest available water. A likely demise for a New Guinean man, woman, or child was death at the hands of a hostile group. Throughout the history of Western Civilization, war has been essentially continual, which doubtless helped to maintain high death rates. Barbarian invasions of the Roman Empire (375–568 A.D.), the Hundred Years' War (1337–1453), and especially the Thirty Years' War (1618–1648) caused substantial increases in the death rate in Europe. To give a single instance from the last of these conflicts, the storming and pillaging of Magdeburg by Catholic forces in 1631 caused an estimated 20,000 deaths. Indeed, some historians feel that as many as a third of the inhabitants of Germany and Bohemia died as a direct result of the Thirty Years' War.

The Peace of Westphalia ended the Thirty Years' War in 1648, and a period of relative tranquility and stability began. At that time the commercial revolution was in full swing. Power was concentrated in monarchies, after having been decentralized in the loose feudal structure, and mercantilism was the economic order of the day. Perhaps the most basic idea of mercantilism was that of government intervention to increase the power of the state and (most important from our point of view) the prosperity of the nation. Planning by government was extended to provide economic necessities for the population.

In the mid-seventeenth century, then, a period of relative peace started in a post-feudal economic environment. Simultaneously, a revolution in European agriculture—a revolution that was largely a result of the commercial revolution—began to gather momentum, and it accelerated rapidly in the eighteenth century. Rising prices and increasing demand from the growing cities added to the commercial attractiveness of farming. The breakdown of the feudal system gradually destroyed the manorial estates. On these estates each serf had assigned to him several scattered strips of land and these strips were farmed communally. The peasants grew increasingly unhappy with the

---

BOX 2-3   FAMINES

A small sampling of quotes from Cornelius Walford's 1878 chronology of 350 famines will give some feel for the ubiquity in time and space of this kind of catastrophe. (Quotation marks indicate where Walford was quoting directly from his sources.) Those who have seen films of recent famines in Bihar (India) and Biafra (Africa) are unlikely to view scenes like those described below as things of the past.

B.C.	436	*Rome.* Famine. Thousands threw themselves into the Tiber.
A.D.	160	*England.* Multitudes starved.
	192	*Ireland.* General scarcity; bad harvest; mortality and emigration, "so the lands and houses, territories and tribes, were emptied."
	331	*Antioch.* This city was afflicted by so terrible a famine that a bushel of wheat was sold for 400 pieces of silver. During this grievous disaster Constantine sent to the Bishop 30,000 bushels of corn, besides an immense quantity of all kinds of provisions, to be distributed among the ecclesiastics, widows, orphans, etc.
	695–700	*England and Ireland.* Famine and pestilence during three years "so that men ate each other."
	1193–1196	*England, France.* "Famine occasioned by incessant rains. The common people perished everywhere for lack of food."
	1299	*Russia.* Ravaged by famine and pestilence.
	1412–1413	*India.* Great drought, followed by famine, occurred in the Ganges-Jumna delta.
	1600	*Russia.* Famine and plague of which 500,000 die.
	1769–1770	*India.* (Hindustan) First great Indian famine of which we have a record. It was estimated that 3,000,000 people perished. The air was so infected by the noxious effluvia of dead bodies that it was scarcely possible to stir abroad without perceiving it; and without hearing also the frantic cries of victims of famine who were seen at every stage of suffering and death.

communal farming, and strips were rearranged into single compacted hold-ings leased by individual peasants from the landholder.

As landowners wished to put more land to the plow there was an increas-ing trend toward the enclosing of old communal woodland and grazing lands with hedges and walls barring the peasants from resources essential to their subsistence. This movement was especially pronounced in Great Britain, where it was promoted by a series of special acts of Parliament. Furthermore, much of the peasantry was dispossessed, or forced out of agriculture by com-

1770	*Bohemia.* Famine and pestilence said to carry off 168,000 persons.
1789	*France.* Grievous famine; province of Rouen.
1790	*India.* Famine in district of Barda . . . so great was the distress that many people fled to other districts in search of food; while others destroyed themselves, and some killed their children and lived on their flesh.
1877–1878	*North China.* "Appalling famine raging throughout four provinces (of) North China. Nine million people re-ported destitute, children daily sold in markets for (rais-ing means to procure) food. . . . Total population of districts affected, 70 millions. . . ." The people's faces are black with hunger; they are dying by thousands upon thousands. Women and girls and boys are openly offered for sale to any chance wayfarer. When I left the country, a respectable married woman could be easily bought for six dollars, and a little girl for two. In cases, however, where it was found impossible to dispose of their children, parents have been known to kill them sooner than witness their prolonged suffering, in many instances throwing themselves afterwards down wells, or committing suicide by arsenic.
1878	*Morocco.* ". . . If you could see the terrible scenes of misery—poor starving mothers breaking and pounding up bones they find in the streets, and giving them to their famished children—it would make your heart ache."

petition from the more efficient large farming operations. Agriculture was transformed into big business.

Accompanying these changes were fundamental improvements in crops and farming techniques. For instance, the role of clover in renewing soil (by replacing lost nitrogen) was discovered in England by Lord Charles Townshend. This made the practice of letting fields lie fallow every third year unnecessary. Other improvements were made in methods of cultivation and in animal breeding. Agricultural output increased and, consequently, so did the margin over famine. It seems plausible that a combination of commercial and agricultural revolutions, a period of relative peace, and the disappearance of the Black Death* all combined to reduce the death rate and produce the European population surge which started in the mid-seventeenth century. Between 1650 and 1750 it is estimated that the populations of Europe and Russia increased from 103 million to 144 million. An additional factor that may have contributed to this burst of growth was the opening of the Western Hemisphere to European exploration. In 1500 the ratio of people to available land in Europe was about 27 per square mile. The addition of the vast, virtually unpopulated frontiers of the New World reduced the ratio for Europe plus the Western Hemisphere to less than five per square mile. As historian Walter Prescott Webb wrote, this frontier was, in essence, "a vast body of wealth without proprietors." Thus not only was land shortage in Europe in part alleviated, but several major European nations were enriched, both factors encouraging population growth.

Although we can speculate with ease about the causes of Europe's population boom between 1650 and 1750, it is somewhat more difficult to explain a similar boom in Asia. The population there increased by some 50–75 percent in this period. In China, after the collapse of the Ming dynasty in 1644, political stability and the new agricultural policies of the Manchu emperors doubtless led to a depression of death rates. Much of the Asiatic population growth during this period probably took place in China, since India was in a period of economic and political instability caused by the disintegration of the Mogul Empire. When the last of the Mogul emperors, Aurangzeb, died in 1707, India was racked by war and famine. Robert Clive and the East India Company established British hegemony in India during the period 1751–1761. At a time when China may have had the world's most advanced agricultural system under the efficient Manchu government, India was a battleground for the British and French. And the rapid increase in power of the British East India Company following the Peace of Paris in 1763 did not bring rapid relief. Indeed, in the famous famine of 1770 about one-third of the population of Bengal is reputed to have perished—a circumstance that did not prevent corrupt agents from increasing the East India Company's revenue from Bengal by more than 50 percent during that year!

---

* The disappearance was possibly due to the displacement of the black rat, which lived in houses, by the sewer-loving brown rat. This lessened rat-man contact, and thus reduced the chances of plague-carrying fleas reaching human beings. In London the great fire of 1666 destroyed much of the city, which consisted largely of rundown wooden buildings that provided excellent rat harborage. By orders of the King, the city was rebuilt with brick and stone, thus making it much more secure from plague.

World population grew at a rate of about 0.3 percent per year between 1650 and 1750. The growth rate increased to approximately 0.5 percent between 1750 and 1850. During this period the population of Europe doubled in response to a number of favorable changes: agricultural techniques advanced fairly rapidly, sanitation improved, the industrial revolution contributed to a general amelioration of the "rigors of life," and, at the end of the period, the introduction of smallpox vaccination initiated improvements in public health. Furthermore, this growth was achieved in the face of substantial emigration to the New World, where the population jumped from some 12 million to about 60 million in the same period. Growth in Asia between 1750 and 1850 was slower than in Europe, amounting to an increase of about 50 percent. Most of the developments that favored rapid increase in Europe's population were to appear in Asia only much later, if at all.

TABLE 2-3
Populations in Millions

	World	Africa	North America	Latin America	Asia (except USSR)	Europe and Asiatic USSR	Oceania
1850	1,131	97	26	33	700	274	2
1950	2,495	200	167	163	1,376	576	13

SOURCE: United Nations (1963) and estimates (somewhat modified) by Willcox, *Studies in American Demography* (1940) and Carr-Saunders, *World Population* (1936).

Little is known about the past population size of Africa, which truly remained unknown until the middle of the nineteenth century. It is generally accepted that the population remained more or less constant at around 100 million, plus or minus 5–10 million, between 1650 and 1850. Then European technology and medicine began to take effect in Africa, death rates started to drop, and the population increased some 20–40 percent between 1850 and 1900, doubling to 200 million by 1950.

The average growth rate of the world population between 1850 and 1950 was about 0.8 percent per year. Population increased in that time from slightly more than one billion to almost 2.5 billion. The estimated populations shown in Table 2-3 indicate that between 1850 and 1950 the population of Asia did not quite double, but population more than doubled in Europe and Africa, multiplied about fivefold in Latin America, and increased more than sixfold in North America.

The death rate continued to decline during the period 1850–1900 as a result of the industrial revolution and the accompanying advances in agriculture and medicine. Although the horrible conditions that prevailed in the mines and factories during the early stages of the rise of industry are well known to all who have read the literature of the period, the overall conditions in areas undergoing industrialization actually improved. Life in the rat-infested cities and rural slums of pre-industrial Europe had been grim almost beyond description. Advances in agriculture, industry, and transportation had, by 1850, substantially bettered the lot of Western man. Improved agriculture reduced the chances of crop failures and famine. Mechanized land and sea transport made local famines less disastrous when they occurred, and provided access to more distant resources. Great improvements in sanitation around the beginning of this century helped to reduce death rates further, as did knowledge of the role of bacteria in infection, which transformed medical practice and saved many lives. European death rates, which had been in the vicinity of 22–24 per thousand in 1850, decreased to around 18–20 per thousand and went as low as about 16 per thousand in some countries. For instance, combined rates for Denmark, Norway, and Sweden dropped from about 20 per thousand in 1850 to 16 in 1900.

In Western Europe in the latter half of the nineteenth century low death rates (and the resultant high rate of population increase) led to massive emigration. And, as the industrial revolution progressed, another significant trend appeared. Birth rates in Western countries began to decline. In Denmark, Norway, and Sweden the combined birth rate was around 32 per thousand in 1850; by 1900 it had decreased to 28. Similar declines occurred elsewhere. This was the start of the so-called "demographic transition"—a falling of birth rates which has characteristically followed industrialization.

The demographic transition carried on into the first half of the twentieth century. By the 1930's decreases in the birth rate had, in some countries, outpaced decreases in the death rate. By then the combined death rate of Denmark, Norway, and Sweden had decreased to 12 per thousand, but the birth rate had dropped precipitously to about 16. Populations in the industrial countries of Europe in the 1930's were in a demographic situation that, if continued, would have led to population declines. True, birth rates were still above death rates, but they would not have stayed that way for long. Death rates rise to meet declining birth rates. If the birth rates for women of each age class in these European populations (that is, the number of births per thousand women of a given age) had remained at the low levels reached during the 1930's, the growth rate of the population would have continued to decrease. This is because as the average age of the population increased, the proportion of women in their reproductive years—especially the years of highest fertility, from 20 to 29—would decrease, further lowering the overall birth rate of the population. At the same time, proportionately more and more people would enter the older age classes of the population and become subject to higher age-specific death rates, which would raise the death rate for the population as a whole. However, stimulated by improving economic conditions and World War II, birth rates rose again during the 1940's and 1950's. European growth rates have generally averaged between 0.5 and 1.0 percent since the War.

What is the cause of the lowered birth rates in industrialized countries? No one knows for certain, but some rather good guesses can be made. In agrarian societies, children are often viewed as economic bonuses. They serve as extra hands on the farm and as old-age insurance for the parents. This pronatalist point of view was beautifully expressed by Thomas Cooper in his book *Some Information Respecting America,* published in 1794. He says (p. 55) "In

America, particularly out of the large towns, no man of moderate desires feels anxious about a family. In the country, where dwells the mass of the people, every man feels the increase of his family to be the increase of his riches: and no farmer doubts about the facility of providing for his children as comfortably as they have lived. . . ."

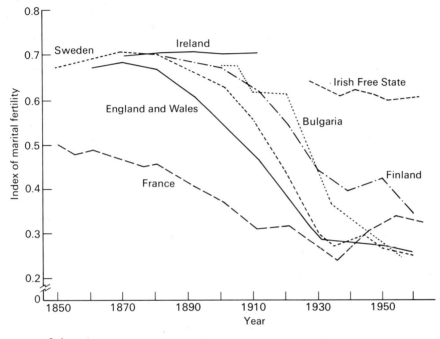

FIGURE 2-4

Demographic transition in selected European countries as indicated by changes in the index of fertility of married women. Scale on the abscissa indicates the number of births by married women divided by the number of births that a population of the same age structure would have if it were reproducing at the highest age-specific rates ever recorded for a population of substantial size. Highest value for the index would be 1. [After Coale, "Decline of Fertility in Europe." *In* Berelson et al., *Fertility and Family Planning,* Univ. of Michigan Press, 1969.]

In an industrial society these things are changed. Children are not potential producers; they are consumers. They require expensive feeding and education. Large families, which became more likely with lowered death rates, tended to reduce mobility and to make the accumulation of capital more difficult. The result of this in Europe was a trend toward later marriage (which, by reducing each woman's years of reproductive activity, reduces birth rates) and toward control of the number of births within marriage (Fig. 2-4).

The demographic transition was not, however, limited to the urban areas in Europe. Population increase created a squeeze in rural areas as well, a squeeze that was compounded by the modernization of farms. A finite amount of land had to supply a livelihood for more people. At the same time, mechanization, which reduced the need for farm labor, made it more and more difficult for a young couple to establish themselves on a farm of their own. As a result, rural birth rates dropped and many people moved to the cities.

There was, of course, no demographic transition outside the industrialized countries. For instance, the Indian birth rate in 1891 was estimated to be 49 per thousand per year, but in 1931 it was still 46 per thousand. In the decade 1930–1940 the rate of population growth in North America and Europe was 0.7 percent, whereas that of Asia was 1.1 percent; Africa 1.5 percent; and Latin America 2.0 percent; even though the death rates were relatively higher in the last three areas. The world growth rate for the decade was 1.1 percent.

Thus far two principal demographic trends in the modern world have been discussed. The first was a decline in the death rate in countries undergoing industrialization, and the second was a decline in the birth rate following industrialization. The first of these trends resulted in a relatively rapid growth rate in Western countries, a growth rate above the world average. The second trend moved the growth rate of these countries below the world average, Europe making the demographic transition around the turn of the twentieth century, and North America more recently.

A third major demographic trend began around the time of World War II. A dramatic decline in death rates occurred in the underdeveloped countries. In some areas, such as Mexico, the decline started before the war. In others, such as Ceylon, it did not start until the end of the war. Compare, for instance, the trend for Sweden since 1860 with that in Mexico since 1930 (Fig. 2-5). This decline was caused primarily by the rapid export of modern drugs and public health measures from the developed countries to the underdeveloped countries. The consequent "death control" produced the most rapid, widespread change known in the history of human population dynamics.

The power of exported death control can be seen by examining the classic case of Ceylon's assault on malaria after World War II. Between 1933 and 1942 the death rate due directly to malaria was reported as about two per thousand. This rate, however, represented only a fraction of the malaria deaths, as many were reported as being due to "pyrexia," a fancy name for fever. Actually, in 1934–1935 a malaria epidemic may have been directly responsible for fully half of the deaths on the island, about 17 per thousand. The death rate at that time rose to 34 per thousand. In addition, malaria, which infected a large portion of the population, made many people susceptible to other diseases and thus contributed to the death rate indirectly as well as directly.

The death rate in Ceylon in 1945 was 22 per thousand. The introduction of DDT in 1946 brought rapid control over the mosquitoes that carry malaria. As a result, the death rate on the island was reduced by about 50 percent in less than a decade. It dropped 34 percent between 1946 and 1947 and moved down to 10 per thousand in 1954; it has continued to decline since then, and in 1969 stood at 8 per thousand. Although part of the drop is doubtless due

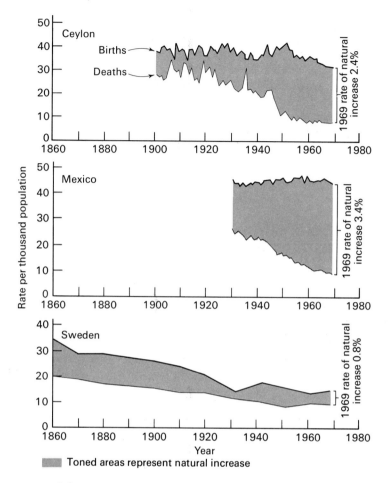

Rate per thousand population

FIGURE 2-5

Different patterns of change in birth and death rates and rate of natural increase. Death rates dropped gradually in western industrial countries such as Sweden and precipitously in UDCs such as Ceylon and Mexico. [Courtesy of the Population Reference Bureau.]

to the killing of insects that carry nonmalarial diseases and to other public health measures, most of it can be accounted for by the control of malaria.

Victory over malaria, yellow fever, smallpox, cholera, and other infectious diseases has been responsible for similar decreases in death rates throughout most of the UDCs. The decline in death rate has been most pronounced among children and young adults. These are the people with proportionately the highest death rates from infectious diseases—the diseases most efficiently dealt with by modern medical and public health procedures. Congenital problems in infants and degenerative diseases of older people reduce the propor-

TABLE 2-4
Change in Age-specific Death Rates of Males in Two UDCs

| Age class | 1950–1952 rate as a percentage of 1920–1922 rate | |
	Jamaica	Ceylon
0–1	45.1	39.8
1–5	38.3	34.7
5–10	34.6	21.7
10–15	28.7	15.6
15–20	25.9	16.1
20–40	31.7	21.4
40–60	59.2	32.4
60–70	73.1	48.2

SOURCE: Kingsley Davis, *Population Review* (1965).

tionate effects of infectious disease in those age brackets. This differential reduction of mortality can be clearly seen in data from Jamaica and Ceylon (Table 2-4).

In the decade 1940–1950 the death rate declined 46 percent in Puerto Rico, 43 percent in Formosa, and 23 percent in Jamaica. In a sample of 18 undeveloped areas the average decline in death rate between 1945 and 1950 was 24 percent. Figure 2-6 shows the dramatic change in death rates from the 1945–1949 average to 1960–1961 in selected Asian nations.

A critical point to remember is that this decline in death rate is different in kind from the long-term slow decline that occurred throughout most of the

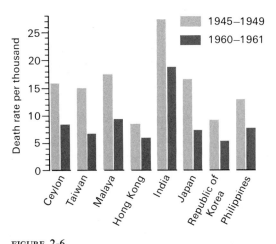

FIGURE 2-6

Change in death rates in selected Asian Nations. The average rates of 1945–1949 are compared with those of 1960–1961. [After *Population Bulletin,* vol. 20, no. 2.]

world following the agricultural revolution. It is also different in kind from the comparatively more rapid decline in death rates in the Western World over the past century. The difference is that it is a response to a spectacular environmental change in the UDCs, largely through control of infectious diseases, not a fundamental change in their institutions or general way of life. Furthermore, the change did not originate within these countries, but was brought about from the outside. The factors that led to a demographic transition (to low birth rates) in the DCs were not and are not present in the UDCs. Instead, a large proportion of the world's population has moved rapidly from a situation of high birth and death rates to one of high birth and low death rates. As a result, the annual rates of increase have risen sharply. Egypt, for instance, moved from a growth rate of slightly more than 1.5 percent before 1945 (birth rate 40–45, death rate about 28) to 2.5–3.0 percent after 1945 (1969 birth rate 43, death rate 15, growth rate 2.9 percent).

Because of the death rate reduction in the UDCs, the world growth rate moved from 0.9 percent (doubling time 77 years) in the decade 1940–1950 to a rate of 1.8 percent (doubling time 39 years) in the decade 1950–1960. The world's population grew from a total of about 2.3 billion in 1940 to 2.5 billion in 1950 and 3.0 billion in 1960. According to the Population Reference Bureau's *1969 World Population Data Sheet* (reproduced here in Appendix 1), the world's population size in mid-1969 was estimated to be 3.55 billion, the growth rate 1.9 percent, and the doubling time 37 years. During the 1960's the world growth rate fluctuated between 1.8 and 2.0 percent. These figures are only approximations (because census data from many countries are inadequate—see introduction to Appendix 1), but they are more than sufficient for the purposes of discussion in this book. If there were actually only 3.3 billion people or as many as 3.7 billion in the world as of mid-1969, or if the world growth rate were actually 1.7 or 2.1 percent, our conclusions would not change one iota.

Bibliography

Agarwala, S. N., 1967. *Population*. National Book Trust, India.

Braidwood, Robert J., 1960. The agricultural revolution. *Scientific American,* vol. 203, no. 3 (Sept.).

Carr-Saunders, A. M., 1936. *World Population*. Oxford Univ. Press, Fairlawn, N.J.

Dalrymple, Dana G., 1964. The Soviet Famine of 1932–34. *Soviet Studies,* vol. 14, pp. 250–284. An excellent and detailed account.

Davis, Kingsley, 1956. The amazing decline of mortality in underdeveloped areas. *Am. Econ. Rev.,* vol. 46, pp. 305–318.

Davis, Kingsley, 1963. Population. *Scientific American,* vol. 209, no. 3 (Sept.)

Davis, Kingsley, 1965. The population impact on children in the world's agrarian countries. *Population Review,* vol. 9, pp. 17–31.

Deevey, Edward S., 1960. The human population. *Scientific American,* vol. 203, no. 3 (Sept.).

Ehrlich, P. R., and R. W. Holm, 1963. *The Process of Evolution.* McGraw-Hill, New York. See especially Chapter 12.

Keyfitz, Nathan, 1966. How many people have ever lived on Earth? *Demography,* vol. 3, pp. 581–582.

Langer, William L., 1958. The next assignment. *American Historical Review,* vol. 63, pp. 283–305. Includes an excellent discussion of the long-term effects of the Black Death on society.

Langer, William L., 1964. The Black Death. *Scientific American,* vol. 210, no. 2 (Feb.).

Martin, Paul S., 1967. Pleistocene overkill. *Natural History,* pp. 32–38 (Dec.). Describes early man's effects on other large animals.

Population Reference Bureau, 1962. How many people have ever lived on Earth? *Population Bulletin,* vol. 18, no. 1. Contains a good brief summary of population growth. An arithmetic error in the calculation of the total number of people who have lived is corrected by Keyfitz (see ref. above). *Population Bulletin* is a major source of information for the educated layman on all aspects of demography. The Bureau also produces an invaluable annual "Population Data Sheet." For more information write Population Reference Bureau, 1755 Massachusetts Avenue, N.W., Washington, D.C. 20036.

Thompson, Warren S., and David J. Lewis, 1965. *Population Problems,* 5th ed. McGraw-Hill, New York. An excellent, comprehensive source.

United Nations, Statistical Office. *Demographic Yearbook.* This annual compilation is *the* source for world data on population.

Walford, Cornelius, 1878. The famines of the world: past and present. *Royal Stat. Soc. Jour.* vol. 41, pp. 433–526.

Waterbolk, H. T., 1968. Food production in prehistoric Europe. *Science,* vol. 162, pp. 1093–1102.

Willcox, Walter F., 1940. *Studies in American Demography.* Cornell Univ. Press, Ithaca, N.Y.

Wrigley, E. A., 1969. *Population and History.* McGraw-Hill, New York.

CHAPTER 3

Population Structure and Projection

"We shall see finally appear the miracle of an animal society, a complete and definitive ant-heap"

Paul · Valéry
(1871–1945)

The discussion of population so far has dealt mainly with population sizes and growth rates, but there is more to demography than just sizes and growth rates. Populations have structure, by which demographers usually mean age structure and sex ratio. Distribution (the position and relative spacing of individuals) is also a factor in the structure of populations. Both age structure and distribution will be considered in the first part of this chapter. The second part is a discussion of projections of future population sizes—projections that usually depend on various assumptions about population structure.

Age Structure

During the Depression in the 1930's, some European countries were in an interesting demographic situation. If age-specific birth and death rates had held constant, the populations in these countries would have stopped growing and begun to decline. But in fact they continued to increase, although slowly. This increase was due to the *age structure* of the population—the percentage of people in different age classes.

Contrast, for instance, the age structures of the populations of Mauritius (an island in the Indian Ocean) and the United Kingdom in 1959 as shown by their population profiles (Fig. 3-1). These profiles are a graphic means of showing the age structure of the populations. Because the profiles are based on proportions, they both have the same area in spite of the great difference in the absolute sizes of the populations. This permits one to focus easily on their

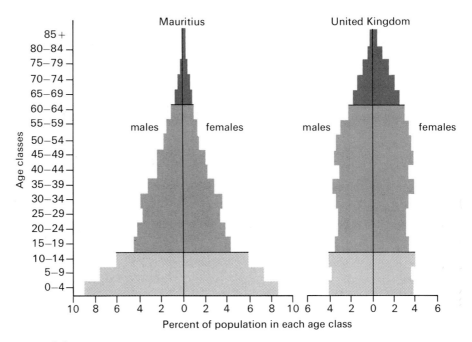

FIGURE 3-1

Age structure of population of Mauritius and United Kingdom in 1959. These age profiles contrast the age distribution in a rapidly growing UDC with a very slowly growing DC. In Mauritius young people predominate; in the United Kingdom the population is more evenly distributed over the age spectrum. Note that in each profile the percentage of males of each age class in the population is shown to the left of the center line and that of females to the right. In Figures 3-1 to 3-5 the working ages (15–54) are shown in medium gray, the young dependents (0–14) in pale gray, and the elderly dependents (65 or over) in dark gray. [After *Population Bulletin*, vol. 18, no. 5.]

comparative shapes, which, of course, are an indication of their comparative age structures. Mauritius' profile exemplifies rapidly growing countries with high birth rates and declining death rates. Most of its people are young; 44 percent are under age 15. The U.K., however, has had low birth and death rates for many decades. It has a much narrower population profile than Mauritius. Only 23 percent of the population of the United Kingdom in 1959 was under age 15.

In Mauritius (Box 3-1) and many other UDCs high birth rates and increasing control over infant and child mortality have greatly inflated the younger age groups in the population. There has not yet been sufficient time

BOX 3-1   MAURITIUS, CHILDREN, AND THE DEPENDENCY LOAD

Mauritius, one of the Mascarene Islands in the Indian Ocean, has one particular claim to fame—it was once the home of the now-extinct dodo, a flightless bird larger than a turkey. By 1969 more than 800,000 people were jammed onto the island, more than 1,100 per square mile, and the island's population had a growth rate of 2 percent a year. The story of Mauritius' postwar population growth is similar to that of other UDCs, and the result has been a dependency load of 47 percent; that is, 47 percent of the population is either under 15 (44 percent) or over 65 (3 percent). The society is faced with a tremendous burden in the form of vast numbers of children who are non-productive or relatively unproductive.

The huge proportion of young people in the population has put a tremendous strain on Mauritius' school system. Many primary schools had to go on double shifts, and an extreme shortage of teachers developed. In order to staff the schools, teachers had to be put in charge of classes before their training could be completed. Most of the country's educational effort went into primary schools; as of 1962 only one out of seven elementary school students went on to high school.

The education problem in Mauritius is a good example of what demographer Kingsley Davis meant when he said that children "are the principal victims of improvident reproduction." Many UDCs simply cannot afford to educate their children adequately. The governments of DCs are able to spend almost twice as much proportionately on education as opposed to health as are governments of the UDCs. The government of Mauritius spent more on both health and public assistance in 1958–1959 than it did on education, yet, after the first five years of life, children in the UDCs enter the portion of the population that has the lowest mortality rates. These children desperately need education, for their own good and for the future of their society, but the sorry fact is that in the absence of population control, solving the problems of health in the UDCs makes solving the problem of education extremely difficult.

High fertility and low income also tend to force children out of school and into the labor pool as early as possible. Even the chances for education in the home are reduced when families are large and mothers overburdened. Child labor is used at a very high level in underdeveloped countries, although the productivity of that labor may be quite low. United Nations statistics, which may understate the case, show that 31 percent of males between 10 and 14 years of age are economically active in UDCs, in contrast to only 5 percent in DCs.

It is a brutal irony that children must bear the brunt of the suffering caused by the population explosion. As Davis says, "the old philosophy that their coming is a just and divine punishment for their parents' sexual indulgence, and therefore not to be mitigated by deliberate control is one of the cruelest doctrines ever devised by a species noted for its cruel and crazy notions."

for individuals born in the period of "death control" to reach the older age classes, whose death rates are higher than those of the younger age classes. In most of these countries the greatest decreases in death rates among infants and children occurred in the late 1940's, and the large numbers of children born in that period will be in their peak reproductive years in the early 1970's. Their children will in turn further inflate the lower tiers of the population

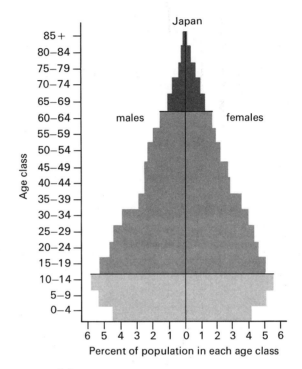

FIGURE 3-2

Age structure of population of Japan in 1960. Note narrow base of profile, caused by a sharp decrease in the birth rate. [After Thompson and Lewis, *Population Problems*, 5th ed. McGraw-Hill, 1965.]

pyramid. Eventually, either population control will lower birth rates in these countries, or famine or other natural checks on population will once again increase mortality in the youngest age classes—or possibly in all age classes. If birth rates are lowered, there will also be a rise in the death rate as the population ages. In the absence of both birth control and natural checks, however, death rates in the extraordinarily young populations of these UDCs may temporarily fall below those of the DCs. For instance, in 1969 the death rate in the United Kingdom was 11.2 per thousand, in Belgium 12.2, and in the United States 9.6. In contrast, the death rate in Costa Rica was 7.0, Trinidad 8.0, Ceylon 8.0, Singapore 5.0, and Hong Kong 5.0.

Rapid and substantial decreases in birth rate, which can be produced by the onset of a successful population-control program, may temporarily produce a population profile that is sharply constricted at the base. Such is the shape of Japan's 1960 profile (Fig. 3-2), which shows the effects of an extremely rapid postwar decline in the birth rate. Japan is a DC today, but the profile resembles that of a typical UDC from the 10–14 age class upward. However,

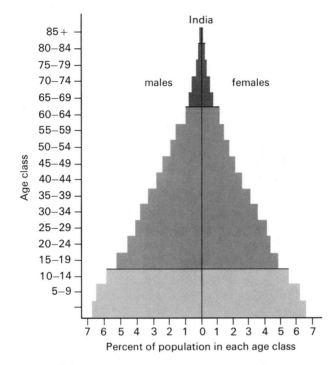

FIGURE 3-3

Age structure of population of India in 1951. Declining death rates have not yet produced the "pinched profile characteristic of rapidly growing UDCs such as Mauritius. [After Thompson and Lewis, *Population Problems,* 5th ed. McGraw-Hill, 1965.]

the 0–4 and 5–9 classes are considerably smaller than in most UDCs, so that only 30 percent of the population is under 15.

Two additional profile shapes are commonly found. One is the more or less equilateral triangle characteristic of countries that have both high birth rates and high death rates. Such profiles must have typified most human populations until fairly recently. They lack the extremely broad base of profiles like that of Mauritius (Fig. 3-1) and most other UDCs today. India's profile was essentially triangular in 1951 (Fig. 3-3). Since then, however, India's death rate has dropped by about 10 per thousand, and the base of her profile has broadened to give her the sort of "pinched triangle" shape of the other UDCs. The second additional profile is exemplified by that of the United States in 1950 (Fig. 3-4); such bell-shaped profiles result when a population that once had low birth and death rates undergoes a subsequent rise in birth rate and starts growing again at a relatively rapid rate.

One of the most significant features of the age structure of a population is the proportion of people who are economically productive in relation to those

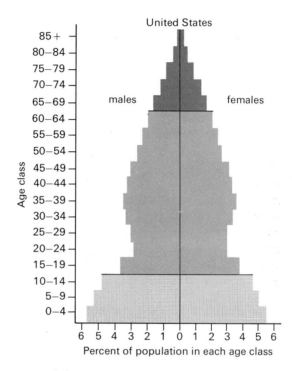

FIGURE 3-4

Age structure of population of United States in 1960. Large "bulge" in 0–14 age class represents the age group that will be reproducing in the 1970's. [After Thompson and Lewis, *Population Problems,* 5th ed. McGraw-Hill, 1965.]

who are dependent on them. For purposes of convenience the productive part of the population is arbitrarily considered to be those in the age class 15–59 (Fig. 3-5). In the population profiles (Figs. 3-1 to 3-4) and in Figure 3-5, the working ages are shown in medium gray, the young dependents in pale gray; and "senior citizens" in dark gray. Figures 3-1 to 3-5 provide a comparison of the proportion of dependents in these same populations. The proportion of dependents in UDCs is generally much higher than in the DCs, primarily because a large fraction of the population is under 15 years of age. Thus the ratio of dependents to the total population size is higher in the poor countries, and lower in the rich countries, although the ratio is somewhat biased because of the heavier utilization of child labor in UDCs (Box 3-1). This unfortunate dependency ratio is an additional heavy burden to the UDCs, as they struggle for economic development.

The high percentage of people under 15 years of age is also indicative of the explosive growth potential of their populations. In most UDCs this percentage is 40–45; in a few as high as 50. By contrast, the percentage under

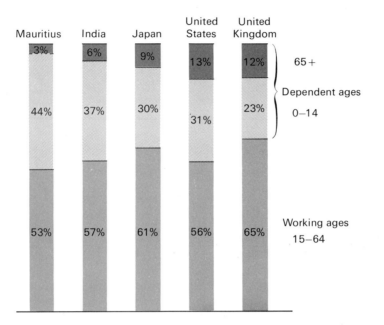

FIGURE 3-5

Dependency loads in Mauritius (1959), India (1951), Japan (1960), United States (1960), and United Kingdom (1959). Note contrast in proportions of economically active people in a typical UDC, Mauritius, and a typical DC, the United Kingdom. [After *Population Bulletin,* vol. 18, no. 5; and Thompson and Lewis, *Population Problems,* 5th ed., McGraw-Hill, 1965.]

age 15 in DCs is usually 20–30. Thus UDCs have a much greater proportion of people in their prereproductive years. As these young people grow up and move into their reproductive years, the size of the childbearing fraction of the population will increase astronomically. In turn their children will further inflate the size of the youngest age groups. These masses of young people in the UDCs are the gunpowder of the population explosion. Their existence means that, even if great progress were made immediately in reducing the number of births per female in those countries, it would be *some 30 years before such birth control could significantly slow population growth.*

The birth and death rates used thus far, which are expressed in births and deaths per thousand population, are known technically as *crude birth rates* and *crude death rates.* They are called "crude" simply because they do not account for differences in the structure of populations. They are the most readily available (and thus most widely quoted) figures, and although they are often quite useful, comparison of crude rates may be quite misleading.

An outstanding example was the recent highly publicized drop in the birth rate in the United States, which some people and publications misinterpreted as heralding the end of the U.S. population explosion. The birth rate in 1968 was 17.4, a record low for the country, going below the previous low of the depression year 1936. Note the trend in birth rates between 1959 and 1968 shown in Figure 3-6. In this period the crude birth rate declined about 25

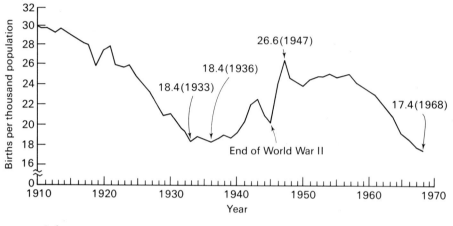

FIGURE 3-6

Birth rate in United States, 1910–1968. [After *Population Profile,* Population Reference Bureau, March 1967.]

percent. This could, of course, have been caused by a decrease in the number of women in the childbearing years rather than by a change in the desired family size of individual women. One check on this may be made by looking at another demographic statistic, the *fertility rate.* The fertility rate—the number of births per 1,000 women 15–44 years of age—is a more refined indicator of birth trends, because it compensates for differences in sex ratio (such as are sometimes the result of wars) and for gross differences in age structure. Differences in age structure might be revealed if two populations had identical crude birth rates but widely differing fertility rates. This might mean, for instance, that one had a relatively low proportion of its people in the 15–44 age group and a high fertility rate, while the other had a relatively high proportion in the 15–44 age group and a lower fertility rate.

As is shown in Figure 3-7, the fertility rate in the U.S.A. *was also declining* during the period 1959–1968, and at just about the same rate as the crude birth rate. So not only were fewer babies being born in proportion to the entire population, but fewer babies were being born in relation to the population of females in their childbearing years. But does this mean that the population explosion in the United States was coming to an end in the late 1960's?

The fertility rate *has* been on a downward trend, but the 1968 fertility rate of about 85 was still higher than the lows reached during the Depression (when it was well below 80). The crude birth rate reached a record low because a smaller proportion of the total population were women in the 15–44 age group in the late 1960's than in 1936. In 1936, 24 percent of the population consisted of women in those childbearing years; in 1967, only 20 percent. In 1967 there were an estimated 40.2 million women in the 15–44 age class. By 1970 the U.S. Census Bureau predicted that there would be about

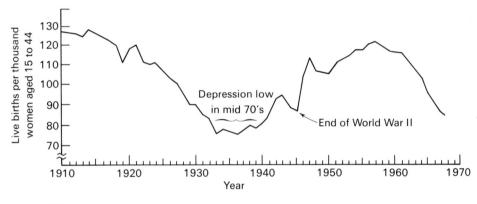

FIGURE 3-7

Fertility rate in United States, 1910–1968. [After *Population Profile,* Population Reference Bureau, March 1967.]

42.3 million women in this class. In 1975 the number of women of childbearing age is projected to be about 46.9 million, an increase of 17 percent over 1967.

Of the women in the 15–44 age group, those in the 20–29 subgroup bear most of the children. This subgroup, which accounted for some 60 percent of the children born in 1967, is projected to increase from 14.3 million in 1968 to 15.5 million in 1970, to 18.3 million in 1975, and to 20 million by 1980. After that the size of the subgroup will begin to decline as the babies of the low-birth-rate 1960's enter their reproductive years. From these data it is apparent that, barring a tremendous drop in the fertility rate, a considerable rise in the American *crude birth rate* can be expected in the 1970's. Unless the death rate also rises this will result in an increase in the growth rate of the population.

Many other factors influence birth rates in addition to the number of women in their childbearing years. Severe economic conditions, epidemics, and wars may cause declines. For instance, the shipment of young men overseas during World War I and the great influenza epidemic of 1918 led to a drop in the American birth rate from 28.2 in 1918 to 26.1 in 1919. Similarly, improvements in economic conditions and the return of World War II servicemen led to a birth rate jump from 20.4 in 1945 to 26.6 in 1947.

The optimists who greeted the decline in birth rates in the 1960's with pronouncements about the end of the population explosion would probably interpret a December thaw as a sign of Spring. It is too early at this writing to predict the magnitude of the baby boom of the 1970's, which will result from the increased number of women in their prime reproductive years. But 1968 surveys indicate a rising preference among Americans for large families, and this is not an encouraging sign. Gallup polls periodically ask the question, "What do you think is the ideal number of children for a family to have?" In 1936, 34 percent of Americans answered "four or more." In 1945 the percentage was up to 49, from which point it descended to 35 percent in 1966. In 1968 it was back up to 41 percent. That figure is itself 70 percent higher than the highest equivalent figure in 11 European countries where similar surveys have been conducted. Results there, for those wanting four or more children, ranged from 7 percent in Austria to 24 percent in the Netherlands. There is often, of course, a substantial difference between opinions or plans expressed about family size and actual reproductive performance. Moreover, both ideals and plans are subject to change during a period of time. A wide variety of factors could lead either to larger or smaller family sizes in the 1970's than those now voiced as "ideal."

Distribution

Mankind is not uniformly distributed over the face of the Earth. Figure 3-8 shows the rough pattern of population density in 1965. Population density is the number of individuals per unit area. For human populations this figure is normally expressed as people per square mile or per square kilometer. Some rough estimates (people per square mile) of population densities in the 1960's are:

Earth (land area)	65
United States	55
Japan	700
Tokyo	20,000
New York City	25,000
Manhattan	75,000

In contrast, before the arrival of Europeans in the continental United States, its population density was about 0.33 people per square mile; the density rose to 5 people per square mile by about 1800. Of course, one must be cautious in picturing densities in terms of people per square mile because of man's tendency to gather in clusters. Although the U.S.A. may today have about 55 people per square mile *on the average,* there are of course many square miles that have no people. Furthermore, within any given square mile people will not ordinarily be uniformly distributed.

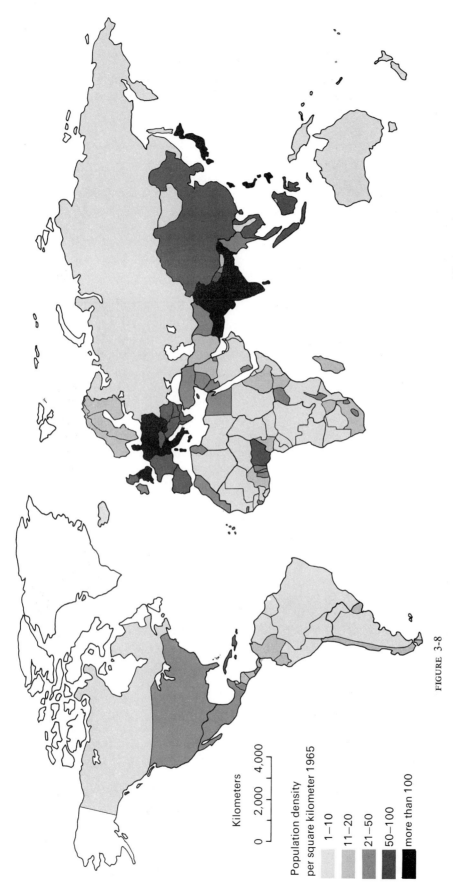

Kilometers

0   2,000   4,000

Population density
per square kilometer 1965

1–10

11–20

21–50

50–100

more than 100

FIGURE 3-8

Patterns of population density, 1965. Figures are given in persons per square kilometer. A square kilometer is 0.3861 square miles. [Data from Bogue, *Principles of Demography*, Wiley, 1969].

The densities and distributions of populations, especially in relation to resources, have played critical roles in many important events in human history. Densities that are perceived by the members of populations themselves as "high" generate what is generally referred to as "population pressure." Overpopulation is usually thought of in relation not to the absolute size of a population but to its density. There must have been many thousands of occasions in prehistory when one tribe or another decided that it had pretty much exhausted the berries and game in its home territory, and moved in on its neighbors. Many of the famous migrations of history, such as the barbarian invasions of Europe in the early Christian era, may have been due to population pressures. In 1095 when Pope Urban II preached the First Crusade, he referred to the advantages of gaining new lands. The crusaders were mainly second sons who were dispossessed because of the growing European trend toward primogeniture (inheritance by the first-born son only).

Considerable evidence indicates that population pressures were building up in fifteenth-century Europe. There is, for instance, evidence of attempts at land reclamation. The population density of Europe in 1500 is estimated to have been about 27 people per square mile. The addition of the New World frontier to Europe reduced the overall population density of Europe plus the Western Hemisphere to less than 5 people per square mile. European exploitation of the spatial, mineral, and other material wealth of the New World led to the creation of a basic set of institutions attuned to frontier attitudes. The economic boom that ensued lasted for 400 years. As far as land is concerned, the boom is now plainly over. The population density of the European metropolis (Western Europe and the Western Hemisphere) exceeded 27 per square mile before 1930. Since all of the material things on which the boom depended came ultimately from the land, the entire boom is clearly limited. In fact, the institutions and attitudes that evolved in the frontier setting now constitute a major threat to the survival of mankind.

Many wars were fought by European nations as they scrambled to occupy the Western Hemisphere. They warred among themselves and against the small native populations in the New World. More recently, population pressure contributed to Nazi Germany's famous drive for "Lebensraum" (literally, room for living), especially in the East, where it reached its climax in "Operation Barbarossa"—the ill-fated invasion of the Soviet Union. Historian D. L. Bilderback comments that in the early years of Hitler's power, "large numbers of intelligent and humane persons believed that the Eastern adventure was a matter of necessity for their own survival." Whether Germany in 1941 was overpopulated in some absolute sense is not the point. The nation perceived itself as overpopulated. Germany is probably more pressed for space today than she was then. The Bonn Government, however, in contrast to Hitler, is not calling attention to overpopulation as a problem; indeed, it almost certainly does not realize that by many standards Germany today *is* overpopulated.

Japan's expansionist moves in the 1930's and early 1940's can be traced in part to the high population density on her small islands. The population growth of Japan in the last third of the nineteenth century and the first third of the twentieth century was unprecedented among industrialized nations. It doubled in size (from 35 to 70 million) and therefore in density during the 63 years between 1874 and 1937. When the attempt to conquer additional territory failed, and population growth continued to accelerate, Japan moved to take drastic steps to limit her population (see Chapter 10). Japan is now again feeling the pinch, and is looking toward the continent of Asia for at least economic Lebensraum.

Population pressures are certainly contributing to international tensions in the world today. Russia, India, and other neighbors of grossly overpopulated China guard their frontiers nervously. Chinese forces have already occupied Tibet. Population growth in China will leave her little long-range choice but to expand or starve. Australians are clearly apprehensive about the Asian multitudes. Their attitude is reflected in Australia's immigration laws and foreign policy. They have reason to be fearful, since the generally unfavorable and unreliable climate over much of Australia, together with its history of disastrous agricultural practices, mean that the entire continent lacks the resources for absorbing even a single year's increment to the Asian population. Such an increment would *quadruple* Australia's population from 12.2 million to 52 million. The number of people added *annually* to India's population alone is more than the entire population of Australia today.

Urbanization

One of the oldest of all demographic trends is the one toward urbanization. Preagricultural man, by necessity, had to be dispersed over the landscape. Hunting and gathering required perhaps a minimum of two square miles of territory to produce the food for one person. Under such conditions, and without even the most primitive of transportation systems, it was impossible for people to exist in large concentrations. But the agricultural revolution began to change all that. Because more food could be produced in less area, people began to form primitive communities. The ability of a farmer to feed more than his own family was obviously a prerequisite of urbanization. A fraction of the population first had to be freed from cultivation of the land in order to form cities. But the division of labor and specialization of a nonfarming population does not in itself seem to have led immediately to urbanization. For example, some scholars hold the view that a considerable segment of the Egyptian population had been freed from the land for almost a full 2,000 years after the founding of the first dynasty (ca. 3200 B.C.), but that even though they produced monumental public works, a governmental structure, writing, and science, they developed no true cities. Similarly it is doubted whether the Mayan civilization produced cities. It is thought that, in ancient Mesopotamia at least, the development of large and complex irrigation systems helped lead to the formation of cities. Then, as today, shortage of water formed the basis of political disputes, and people may have gathered together in cities for defensive purposes. Mesopotamian cities also would have served as storage and redistribution centers for food.

As anthropologist Robert M. Adams has said, ". . . the complexity of subsistence pursuits on the flood plains may have indirectly aided the movement toward cities. Institutions were needed to mediate between herdsman and cultivator; between fisherman and sailor; between plowmaker and plowman." Whatever the actual impetus for urbanization was, the first cities arose along the Tigris and Euphrates rivers between 4000 and 3000 B.C.

The trend toward urbanization continues today, as it generally has since those first cities were formed. The move to the cities has at times been accelerated by agricultural advances that have made possible the establishment of larger, more efficient farms. It seems also to have been accelerated by growth in rural areas, which necessitated either the subdivision of farms among several sons, or the migration of "surplus" offspring to the cities. This movement into large urban concentrations has been especially accelerated in the last century. For instance, in the United States about 6 percent of the population lived in urban areas in 1800, 15 percent in 1850, 40 percent in 1900; today, more than 70 percent live in cities or their suburbs (Fig. 3-9).

Rapid urbanization has not been confined to industrialized countries, however. Between 1950 and 1960, the populations of cities in the DCs increased 25 percent, those of cities in the UDCs, 55 percent. In Latin America, especially since the close of World War II, there has been an increasing flood of impoverished peasants into urban areas. A result of this has been the development of characteristic huge shanty-towns, given different names in each country: *favelas* in Brazil, *tugurios* in Colombia, *ranchos* in Venezuela, and *barriadas* in Peru. In Peru some three-quarters of a million squatters live in such settlements—a substantial fraction of Peru's population of 13 million.

The trend in Africa has been similar, with hundreds of thousands migrating to the cities annually in search of a better life. Nairobi, the capital of Kenya, had a 1968 population of 460,000 and is growing at a rate of 7 percent per year. That is more than double the growth rate of Los Angeles in the decade 1950–1960. Accra, the capital of Ghana, is growing at almost 8 percent per year; Abidjan, capital of the Ivory Coast, at almost 10 percent; Lusaka, capital of Zambia, and Lagos, capital of Nigeria, both at 14 percent. In both Latin America and Africa the trend to the cities seems to be caused in large part by the kind of hope for a better life that has drawn many people from rural areas of the southern United States and Puerto Rico to New York, Chicago, and other Northern metropolises. And in the cities of underdeveloped countries, the opportunities are much more limited than in the United States. Yet, miserable as their condition is, nearly all evidently prefer to remain in the cities rather than return to what they left. Of course, many may also have burned their bridges behind them and have no way of successfully returning to their former homes.

The rate of urbanization in Asia has also been rapid in this century, but in many areas the increases have been from a rather low base. For instance, at the turn of the century about 11 percent of India's population was urban. Today more than 20 percent of India's people live in cities. Most of this

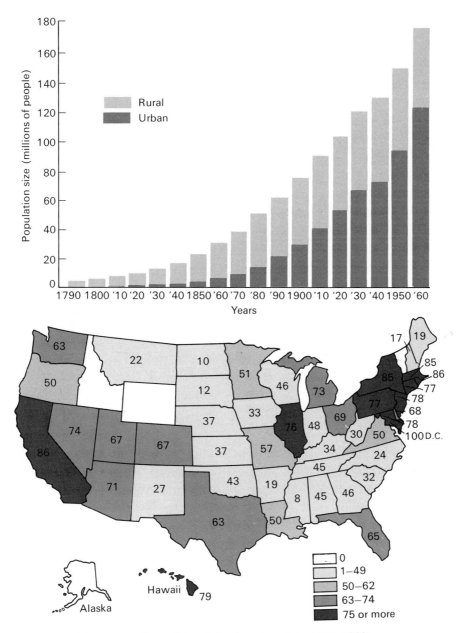

Percentage of population living in metropolitan areas, 1960

FIGURE 3-9

Urbanization of the United States. In 1960, 70 percent of Americans were living in towns or cities and 63 percent were living in large cities and their surroundings (metropolitan areas). The 1970 census will certainly show these percentages increased. [After *Population Bulletin,* vol. 19, no. 2.]

increase has occurred since 1931, with the largest percent increase occurring in the decade 1941–1951 and the largest absolute increase in the decade 1951–1961. Data for the period since the 1961 census are not available, but the figure 20 percent is based on the 1961 figures corrected for comparability with previous censuses and projected. Even under the new, more restricted definition of "urban," the figure would be close to 20 percent today.

One problem that is inevitably encountered when discussing urbanization is the definition of "urban area." This varies from country to country, and from time to time. And, of course, urban areas in different countries or different areas of the same country often are quite dissimilar. Los Angeles, New York, and Chicago have certain features (and problems) in common —good art museums, major universities, slums, disadvantaged minorities, numerous TV stations, dangerously congested airports, diverse specialty shops, and air pollution, to name a few. But their differences are as apparent as their similarities. The air-pollution problems of Los Angeles and New York are fundamentally different in that the "smogs" over each city have different compositions. Water supply problems are unique in each of the three cities. Los Angeles has a hopeless surface transportation problem and smoggy "sunshine slums." Mexican-Americans are one of its largest minority groups. Chicago has substantial problems with a "hillbilly" minority. New York has been unable to absorb satisfactorily the masses of immigrants from Puerto Rico and has been overwhelmed with welfare recipients migrating from the rural South. The problems of government in all three cities have their own peculiar twists.

Historically, urbanization seems to have one almost universal effect and that is the breaking down of the traditional cultures of those who migrate to the cities—a loss of roots, or alienation. In rural or tribal societies each individual had a well-defined role in the organization of the society, a role that he or she matured into and that was recognized by all other members of the society. In contrast, anonymity is the main feature of the city. City-dwellers tend to know well only about the same number of people as village-dwellers, and they tend to go to great lengths not to "get involved" with the vast majority of the human beings with whom they come into contact.

Urbanization in the United States differs dramatically from urbanization in most UDCs. For instance, the difference between city-dwellers and country-dwellers in the United States has become increasingly blurred, especially in recent years, with urban culture becoming dominant. Rapid transportation and mass media have exposed the country folk to the ways of the city. The image of the hick has less and less validity today, especially when some "hicks" fly their wives several hundred miles to the city in their private aircraft for shopping sprees and a night at the theater. Furthermore, in the United States especially, the phenomenon of suburbanization has developed. Suburbanites, who take advantage of high-speed transport and general affluence, attempt to enjoy the advantages of city and countryside simultaneously, working in the former and living in the latter.

In the UDCs, communications and transportation are much less efficient, and the peasant culture is less influenced by the urban. According to sociologist Nathan Keyfitz of the University of California, the overwhelming majority of urban dwellers in the UDCs are migrants from the countryside who have brought their peasant culture with them. Unlike the typical DC urbanite, whose specialized education, training, and skills assure him of a place in the city's complex social web, the UDC immigrant has no such talents to offer. Cities in developed countries are a source of wealth and power, generated through technology and manufacturing. The goods they produce are exchanged for food from the countryside. In contrast, many UDC cities subsist primarily on food imported from other countries. Attracted by the opportunity to obtain a share of the imported food, inhabitants of the countryside move into these cities when the countryside can no longer support them. Inevitably, they find that their limited skills render them incapable of contributing to the economy, and as a consequence they are not much better off than they were where they came from. In many UDC cities these unproductive squatters now make up a majority of their populations, and their number in most places is growing very rapidly.

Many migrants to the UDC city maintain contact with their home villages or form modified village societies within the city, and thus tend to transfer the village culture to the city. This may explain why the reproductive rates and attitudes of the inhabitants of these cities closely resemble those of their rural relatives.

Demographic Projections

Once there was a young man who proposed a novel pay scheme to a prospective employer. For one month's work he was to receive one cent on the first day, two cents on the second, four on the third, and so on. Each day his pay was to double until the end of the month. The employer, a rather dull-witted merchant, agreed. The merchant was chagrined, to say the least, when he found that the young man's pay for the 15th day was more than $160. The merchant went bankrupt long before he had to pay the young man $167,733 for the 25th day. Had he remained in business he would have had to pay his new employee wages of more than $10 million for the month.

This is just one of many stories that illustrate the astronomical figures that are quickly reached by repeated doubling, from even a minute base. Another is about a reward that consists of a single grain of rice on the first square of a chessboard, 2 on the second, 4 on the third, and so forth, until the board is filled. It turns out that completing the reward takes several thousand times the world's annual rice crop.

Similar horrendous figures may be generated by projecting the human population of the world into the future. After all, the doubling time for that population is now only about 35 years. If growth continued at that rate the world population would exceed a billion billion people about 1,000 years from now. That would be some 1,700 persons *per square yard* of the Earth's surface, land and sea! Even more preposterous figures can be generated. In a few thousand more years everything in the visible universe would be converted into people, and the diameter of the ball of people would be expanding with the speed of light! Such projections should convince all but the most obtuse that growth of the human population must stop eventually.

Of primary interest and significance to us are predictions of population sizes in the next few decades. The best known of these are the low, medium, and high population projections for the period 1965–2000 made by the

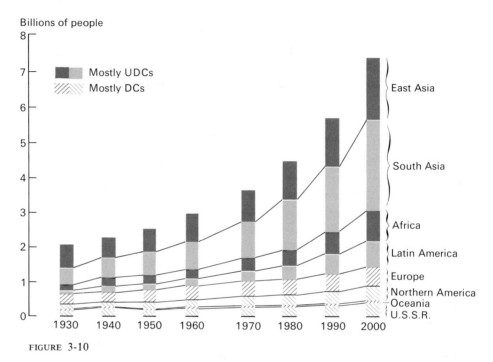

FIGURE 3-10

Projected growth of world population, based on the United Nations "constant fertility" projection. [After *Population Bulletin,* vol. 21, no. 4.]

United Nations. These are not simple extrapolations of past trends or present rates into the future. Instead, these population projections are computed on a component basis. That is, specific forecasts are made of trends in age-specific fertility, death rates, migration, and so forth. These are based on the best possible demographic data for the nations or regions of the world, and the scope of future variation in these rates is estimated on the basis of past trends in developed and undeveloped areas. Possible major disasters, such as thermonuclear war, are not considered. All of these data are integrated to provide medium, low, and high projections, the last two of which the demographers hope will bracket the actual figures. The accuracy of the projections depends, of course, on the degree to which the various realized rates differ from the predicted rates. Another projection, called the "constant fertility, no migration" projection, is made on the simpler assumption that current trends in fertility and mortality will continue and that there will be no migration between areas (Fig. 3-10).

The low U.N. forecast projects a world population of about 5,449 million in the year 2000, the medium forecast 6,130 million, and the high 6,994 million. Data for the regions denoted in Figure 3-11 are given in Table 3-1. The map also indicates level of development of the areas. If, however, present high birth rates should continue and be accompanied by a continuing decline in death rates, the constant-fertility projection would be for 7,522 million people at the turn of the century. The U.N.'s low, medium, and high projec-

TABLE 3-1
Estimate of Population in the Year 2000 (in millions)

Region	1969 population	Projection			
		Low	Medium	High	Constant Fertility, No Migration
World Total	3,551	5,449	6,130	6,994	7,522
Developed regions	1,078	1,293	1,441	1,574	1,580
Underdeveloped regions	2,473	4,155	4,688	5,420	5,942
East Asia	1,182	1,118	1,287	1,623	1,811
South Asia	809	1,984	2,171	2,444	2,702
Europe	456	491	527	563	570
Soviet Union	241	316	353	403	402
Africa	344	684	768	864	860
Northern America	225	294	354	376	388
Latin America	276	532	638	686	756
Oceania	19	28	32	35	33

SOURCE: United Nations, *World Population Prospects as Assessed in 1963.*

tions all rest on an assumption that fertility rates will be lowered in those areas where they are now dangerously high. For convenience in comparing future trends against the projected figures, detailed tables for each of these areas appear in Appendix 2. Note in the appendix that the 1970 world population size will slightly exceed that predicted by the U.N.'s medium projection.

The history of population projections in the past few decades has been that they have erred fairly consistently on the low side. For instance, in its November 8, 1948 issue, *Time* magazine quoted the opinions of unnamed "experts" who felt then that a prediction (by the U.N. Food and Agriculture Organization) of a world population of 2,250 million in 1960 was probably too high. The actual population in 1960 was about 3,000 million. In 1949 economist Colin Clark projected a world population in 1990 of 3.5 billion, and in 1950 demographer Frank Notestein projected that by the year 2000 there would be 3.3 billion people alive. Both figures were exceeded well before 1970. In 1957 the demographers of the United Nations offered the

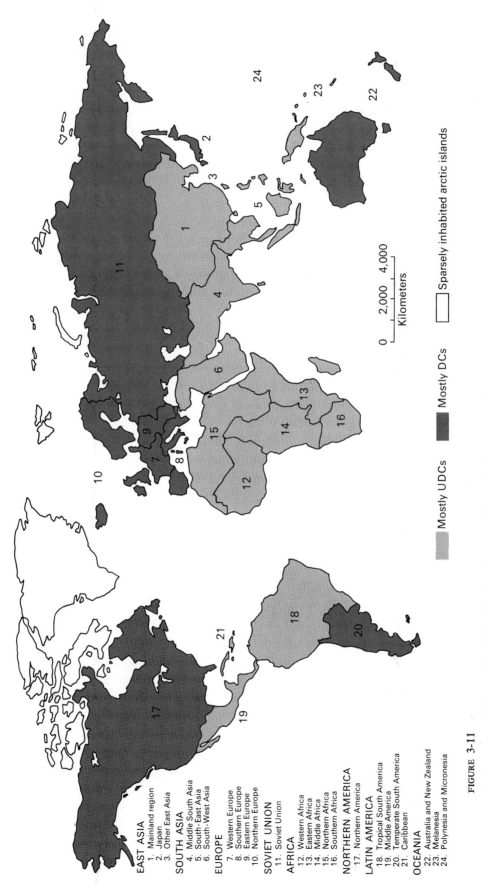

EAST ASIA
1. Mainland region
2. Japan
3. Other East Asia

SOUTH ASIA
4. Middle South Asia
5. South-East Asia
6. South-West Asia

EUROPE
7. Western Europe
8. Southern Europe
9. Eastern Europe
10. Northern Europe

SOVIET UNION
11. Soviet Union

AFRICA
12. Western Africa
13. Eastern Africa
14. Middle Africa
15. Northern Africa
16. Southern Africa

NORTHERN AMERICA
17. Northern America

LATIN AMERICA
18. Tropical South America
19. Middle America
20. Temperate South America
21. Caribbean

OCEANIA
22. Australia and New Zealand
23. Melanesia
24. Polynesia and Micronesia

Mostly UDCs ▨   Mostly DCs ▰   Sparsely inhabited arctic islands ▢

0   2,000   4,000
Kilometers

FIGURE 3-11

Regions of world for which United Nations demographic projections are made.

following population projections for 1970: low, 3,350 million; medium, 3,480 million; and high, 3,500 million. The actual population size passed the high projection for 1970 sometime near the end of 1968. In the depression years it was common for demographers to show great concern over the possibility of population declines. Their apprehensions were based on projections of trends in both the birth rate and the death rate. Depression declines in birth rates were more than compensated for by the baby boom of the 1940's and 1950's. And the unprecedented effect of death control exported from DCs to UDCs was not foreseen.

Since prediction is a favorite sport of almost everyone concerned with the population problem, we might as well stick our necks out. Along with some professional demographers, we feel that the 1963 U.N. projections for the year 2000, with the possible exception of the low forecast, are too high. This is not, however, because we share their optimism about the impact of family planning programs on birth rates. Instead, for reasons explained in subsequent chapters, we predict that a drastic rise in the death rate will either slow or terminate the population explosion.

Regardless of whether today's trends continue, it is instructive to assess the effects of their continuation on various regions of the world. All current figures used below are from the Population Reference Bureau's mid-1969 estimates (see Appendix 1), and projections are those of the U.N.

North America. Canada and the United States have a population of 225 million. A growth rate of 1.1 percent per year gives a doubling time for the area of 63 years, which is fast for DCs. If catastrophe is avoided, North America could have as many as 375 million people in the year 2000 or as few as 300 million.

Latin America. This area has a population of 276 million and a growth rate of 2.9 percent, the highest rate for any major region. As a whole the population of the area is doubling every 24 years. Some Latin American countries have incredibly high growth rates and rapid doubling times. Costa Rica holds the current record with a growth rate of 3.8 percent and a doubling time of 18 years. Other representative doubling times are for Mexico, 21 years; Peru, 23 years; Brazil, 25 years; Jamaica, 28 years; Bolivia, 29 years, and Cuba, 35 years. According to various projections, the population of this area in the year 2000 will be 550–750 million (see Fig. 3-12); but our prediction is that it won't even get close to 650 million because of rising death rates.

Europe. The demographic antithesis of Latin America is the continent of Europe. Today's European population (excluding European Russia and Turkey) is 456 million, more than two-thirds again that of Latin America. The growth rate for the continent is 0.8 percent, which gives a doubling time of 88 years. The more rapidly growing countries, such as France, Switzerland, and the Netherlands, have doubling times of about 60–80 years. But most European countries are doubling much more slowly than that: Italy every 100 years; the United Kingdom, 117 years; Czechoslovakia, Austria, and

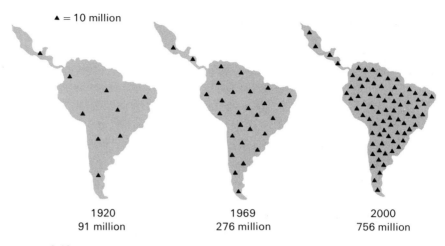

▲ = 10 million

1920
91 million

1969
276 million

2000
756 million

FIGURE 3-12

Population growth in Latin America, 1920–2000. If fertility rates do not drop, the population of the area will undergo a more than 8-fold increase in 80 years. [After *Population Bulletin,* vol. 23, no. 3.]

Ireland, 140 years; West Germany, 175 years; Hungary, 233 years; and East Germany, 700 years. In the year 2000 Europe's population is projected to be about 550 million.

The Soviet Union has a present population of 241 million, a growth rate of 1.0 percent, and a doubling time of 70 years. For several years its growth rate has been similar to that of the U.S. Its population is projected to reach some 350 million by the year 2000.

Africa. The present population of Africa is 344 million people. Its current rate of population growth is 2.4 percent, and its doubling time 28 years. The pattern of doubling times is not unlike that of Latin America, except that generally higher death rates result in a somewhat lower growth rate. Sample doubling times are for Morocco, 23 years; Kenya and Zambia, 23 years; the United Arab Republic, 24 years; Nigeria, 28 years; South Africa and Madagascar, 29 years; the Congo, 31 years; and Angola, 50 years. Projections for the year 2000, based on the optimistic assumption that the death rate will not increase, give Africa a population of 700–850 million, second only to the projected high for Asia.

Asia. Today's population giant, Asia, has a population of 1,990 million— almost two billion people. That figure, which amounts to more than half of the world's population, does not include the population of Asiatic U.S.S.R. Asia's current growth rate is 2.0 percent, and her doubling time is 35 years. Among the Asian nations, only Japan shows a pattern similar to that of Europe and North America. Japan's growth rate is 1.1 percent, and the doubling time is close to that of North America, 63 years. For the rest of

Asia the doubling times tell the same old story of the UDCs: Philippines 20 years; Pakistan, 21 years; Malaysia, 23 years; India, 28 years; and Afghanistan, 31 years. Mainland China presents a special problem. The size and growth rate of its population are uncertain. Estimates of size range from 700 to 950 million persons, the U.N. figure being 740 million. The Population Reference Bureau's growth rate estimate is 1.4 percent (50-year-doubling time), and this is basically an informed guess. Projections for the year 2000 put Asia's population between 3,000 and 4,500 million, and uniformly predict that she will continue to be the home of more than one-half of all *Homo sapiens.*

Projected Changes in Density and Distribution

Aside from changes in population size one may also examine trends in population distribution (Figs. 3-13, 3-14). Obviously changes in density, calculated by nation or by region, are directly proportional to projected size changes, assuming that borders remain constant. More interesting are projections of trends in urbanization. For instance, one projection leads to a population estimate for Calcutta in the year 2000 of 66 million people, more

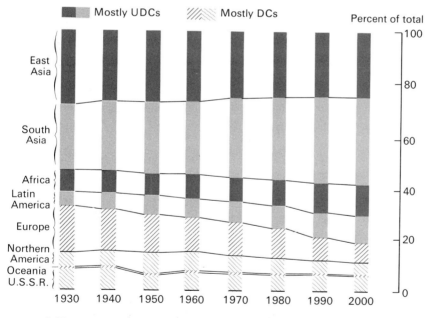

FIGURE 3-13

Percentage distribution of world population, 1930–2000. Future figures are those of the United Nations "constant fertility" projection. In 1930, DCs had 32.7 percent of the people. In 1965 they had 27.5 percent, and if the United Nations constant fertility projection is the one that holds, that percentage will shrink to 18.8 by the year 2000. [After *Population Bulletin,* vol. 21, no. 4.]

than eight times today's population. Needless to say, this will not be reached. But there is a realistic expectation that the population of this festering city, which has several hundred thousand people living homeless in its streets today, will increase from 7.5 million to 12 million in the next two decades. Calcutta is already a disaster area, and the consequences of further growth at such a rate are heart-rending to contemplate. The population of relatively prosperous Tokyo is projected to reach 40 million in the year 2000 (as opposed to perhaps 16 million in 1970). Tokyo is using 7,000 tons of garbage a day to fill Tokyo Bay, in a desperate attempt to create land for expansion.

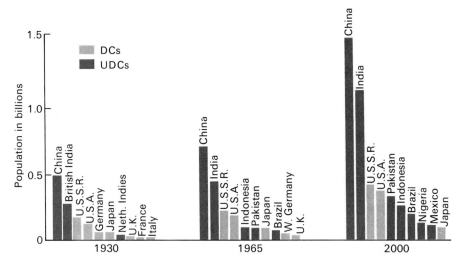

FIGURE 3-14

"Top Ten" nations in population size: 1930, 1965, 2000. China and India are each projected to have populations of more than a billion by the year 2000. Japan will have dropped to tenth place by then, and Nigeria and Mexico will have joined the "Top Ten," replacing the U.K. and West Germany. [After *Population Bulletin,* vol. 21, no. 4.]

Flat, empty land is at a premium in mountainous, overpopulated Japan. Middle-class apartments are already so scarce that there is a 2-year waiting list. Tokyo's incredible crowding seems destined only to get worse.

Demographer Kingsley Davis has recently made some extrapolations of urbanization trends, and has produced some startling statistics. If the urban growth rate that has prevailed since 1950 should continue, half of the people in the world would be living in the cities by 1984. If the trend should continue to 2023 (it cannot!), everyone in the world would live in an urban area. Most striking of all, in 2020 most people would not just be in urban areas; half of the world's human beings would be in cities of over one million population, and in 2044 *everyone* would be existing in "cities" of that size. At that time the largest "city" would have a projected population of 1.4 billion people (out of a projected world population of 15 billion). The word "city" is in quotes because, should such a stage be reached, world living conditions would make the term meaningless in its usual sense.

Bibliography

Adams, Robert M., 1960. The origin of cities. *Scientific American,* vol. 203, no. 2 (Sept.).

Bogue, D. J., 1969. *Principles of Demography.* Wiley, New York.

Davis, Kingsley, 1965. The population impact on children in the world's agrarian countries. *Population Review,* vol. 9, pp. 17–31. Contains details of the argument that children get a disproportionately bad deal in the UDCs.

Keyfitz, Nathan, 1966. Population density and the style of social life, *BioScience,* vol. 16, no. 12, pp. 868–873 (Dec.). Information on the origin of cities and differences between DC and UDC cities.

Mangin, William, 1967. Squatter settlements. *Scientific American,* vol. 217, no. 4, (Oct.). Provides some insight into recent migrants into UDC cities.

Marshall, A. J. (ed.), 1966. *The Great Extermination.* Heinemann, London. This book details much of the destruction of the Australian environment.

Population Reference Bureau, 1962. The story of Mauritius from the Dodo to the stork. *Population Bulletin,* vol. 18, no. 5. This issue details a UDC "population explosion" in a microcosm and is the basis of Box 3-1.

United Nations, 1966. World population prospects as assessed in 1963. *Population Studies,* no. 41. This is the major source for detailed population projections.

United States Public Health Service, National Center for Health Statistics. *Monthly Vital Statistics Report.* These provide current statistics on live births, marriages, deaths, and infant deaths, both "provisional" and "final." They are available from Health Services and Mental Health Administration, Washington, D.C. 20201.

CHAPTER 4

The Limits of the Earth

"The power of population is infinitely greater than the power in the earth to produce subsistence for man."

Thomas Malthus, (1766–1834)

"The image of the frontier is probably one of the oldest images of mankind, and it is not surprising that we find it hard to get rid of."

Kenneth E. Boulding, *The Economics of the Coming Spaceship Earth,* 1966.

Photographs of the Earth taken from the vicinity of the moon make the finite nature of our planet apparent to us in a way that no writing can. What is the capacity of the Earth to support people? Unfortunately, there is no simple answer to this question, although certain theoretical limits may be calculated. More than 100 years ago Justus von Liebig established a principle that has become known as the "law of the minimum." It says, in essence, that the size of a population or the life of an individual will be limited by whatever requisite of life is in the shortest supply. It is not yet clear what that requisite will be for the human population, which, as we have seen, is growing at an increasingly faster rate. In this chapter and the next the following potential limiting factors are considered: space, heat, available energy, nonrenewable resources, water, and food.

Outer Space

Because this chapter deals with the limits of the Earth, it is important to demonstrate clearly that we are for practical purposes limited to our own small planet. To do this let us examine for a moment the possibilities of shipping surplus people to other planets, a solution that has been seriously proposed more than once. To Americans who see science fiction dramas on television, as well as real-life performances by astronauts on the moon, it may seem entirely reasonable to regard Space as the next frontier. Nevertheless, the obstacles to interplanetary or interstellar migration are stupendous and far beyond present or foreseeable technological capabilities to overcome. Even if the technology should become available, in the end we would be defeated by the very source of our present difficulties: numbers. For the sake of this discussion, let us ignore the virtual certainty that the other planets of the solar system are uninhabitable, and consider some interesting calculations that have been made on how much time we could gain if we insisted on postponing direct action against the population explosion by occupying the planets of our solar system. For instance, at any given time, and at current population growth rates, it would take only about 50 years before Venus, Mercury, Mars, our moon, and the moons of Jupiter and Saturn all had the same population density as Earth.

What if the fantastic problems of reaching and colonizing the larger and more distant planets of the solar system, such as Jupiter, Uranus, and Pluto, could be solved? It would take only about 200 years of time to fill them "Earth-full." So we could perhaps gain 250 years for population growth in the solar system after reaching an absolute limit on Earth. Then, of course, we would still have the problem, but in greater dimensions.

A fundamental aspect of such a migration scheme would be the cost of the venture. Let us make some optimistic assumptions. Suppose that a small modern spaceship like Apollo, instead of carrying three men to the moon, could transport 100 people to one of the planets for the same cost. In order to hold the present population of the Earth constant, we would have to export about 70 million people per year (assuming no change in the growth rate). To do so would require the launching of very nearly 2,000 spaceships each day, year in and year out. The cost, not counting the expense of recruiting and training migrants, would exceed $300 billion daily. Three days' launches would equal the present annual gross national product of the U.S.

The optimists who think migration can help relieve the population explosion simply have not examined the numbers involved in the transportation game. For comparison, let us consider migration on a much simpler level. Suppose the U.S. and India agreed to "solve" India's present population crisis by moving Indians to the U.S. The entire long-range jet transport fleet of the United States (about 600 planes with an average capacity of 150 passengers), averaging two round trips per week, could transport only about nine million people per year from India to the United States; that is, only about 75 percent of India's annual population *growth*. Ocean liners and transports, although larger, are less numerous and much slower, and over long distances they could not do as well as aircraft. In short, if there were a place *on the Earth* to send our surplus people, we could not even send them there now.

On the optimistic grounds that anything is possible, though, let us suppose that the immense problems of reaching and colonizing the planets of our own solar system are somehow solved. What then? The optimists would have us next expand to occupy the planets of *other* stars. Interstellar transport for surplus people presents an amusing prospect. Since the ships would take generations to reach most stars, the only people who *could* be transported would be those willing to exercise strict birth control. Population explosions on spaceships could not be tolerated.

We could continue to outline other speculations and fantasies, but hopefully you are now convinced that the extremely remote possibility of expanding into outer space offers no escape from the laws of population growth. The population will have to stop growing sooner or later.

Heat

A British physicist, J. H. Fremlin, has calculated an ultimate terrestrial population density of some 100 persons per square yard of the Earth's surface. At that point a "heat limit" would be reached. People themselves, as well as their activities, convert other forms of energy into heat, which must be dissipated. Indeed, whenever energy is put to work, heat is produced. This is a basic law of the universe, one of the Laws of Thermodynamics (Box 4-1). According to Fremlin, at about the density described, the outer surface of the planet (by that time an artificial "world roof" covering the entire planet) would have to be kept around the melting point of iron to radiate away the excess heat.

Fremlin, however, made a series of extremely unlikely assumptions to permit the population to build to the 60,000,000,000,000,000 people of his limit. He assumed, for instance, that all social, political, and technological problems of crowding people into a 2,000-story building, covering the entire surface of the Earth, would be solved. It is more likely that a different sort of heat limit would prevail long before any such astronomical population size is reached. Meteorologists caution that world climates could be drastically altered if the additional heat that man dissipates in his global environment reaches about one percent of the solar energy absorbed and re-radiated at the Earth's surface. Since energy consumption is at present increasing at about 5 percent per year, such a climatological heat limit could be reached in less than a century. The consequences of altering the heat balance, locally and globally, are discussed in detail in Chapter 7.

In *all* aspects of population, resources, and environment, the restrictions imposed by the laws of thermodynamics can be critical. Many futuristic proposals for expanding energy supplies, utilizing new resources, and increasing food production lose their luster in the cold perspective of the efficiencies to which these laws restrict us.

Energy

Will the availability of energy impose a limit on human population growth? The energy situation is uncertain and complex, but it can be summarized as

BOX 4-1   THE LAWS OF THERMODYNAMICS

Essential to an understanding of a number of important environmental problems is a grasp of the two fundamental laws of thermodynamics. It should be noted at the outset that these laws apply to all known phenomena—no exception to either has ever been observed. The first law is the formal statement of "conservation of energy": energy can neither be created nor destroyed. The law makes sense only when it is realized that energy takes on a myriad of forms, and it is only the *total* of the energy in all its guises which is required to be constant. Examples of the various forms are energy of motion (kinetic energy), potential energy (gravitational, elastic), chemical energy, heat, nuclear energy, and the energy associated with mass itself (given explicitly by Einstein's famous formula, $E = mc^2$). Although physicists concern themselves with the details of relations among the kinds of energy (actually some of the "different" forms listed above are identical), the reader need remember only that physical processes change just the *distribution* of energy among its various categories, never the sum in all of the categories. Apparent violations of the first law invariably stem from overlooking a category.

The second law of thermodynamics is subtler and more difficult to grasp, but fully as important in its implications. It specifies the *direction* in which physical processes proceed. General statements of the second law tend to be inscrutable; it is more fruitful to begin with specifics. In spontaneous processes, for example, the second law declares that heat flowing between two objects moves from the hotter to the colder, that concentrations (of anything) tend to disperse, that structure tends to disappear, that order becomes disorder. Thus, if a partitioned container is filled with hot water on one side and cold water on the other and is left to itself, the hot water cools and the

cold water warms—heat flows from hotter to colder. Note that the opposite process (the hot water getting hotter and the cold getting colder) does not violate the first law, conservation of energy. It does not occur because it violates the *second* law. Indeed, many processes can be imagined that satisfy the first law but which, because they violate the second, do not occur. As another example, consider adding a drop of dye to a glass of water. Intuition and the second law (both based on experience) dictate that the dye will spread, eventually coloring all the water—concentrations disperse, order (the dye–no-dye arrangement) disappears. The opposite process, the spontaneous concentration of dispersed dye, is consistent with conservation of energy, but *not* with the second law.

Unfortunately, the second law is this simple only for spontaneous processes with isolated and obvious effects. It applies as well to the most complicated biological and technological phenomena, but for each application must usually be restated in a different form: one is, "the disorder of the universe is always increasing"; another is, "no process is possible whose *sole* result is the flow of heat from a cold body to a hot one." The first formulation also applies to localized phenomena, as long as no effects are left out. For instance, both biological organisms and the technology of man are capable of filtering and concentrating dispersed substances from their environment. But when all the consequences of this activity are considered, including the expenditure of energy and the disposition of the heat produced, the "disorder" in the system as a whole (pond, planet, universe, depending on how far-reaching the activity) invariably increases. As an example of the other formulation of the second law, consider a refrigerator, which certainly causes heat to flow from cold bodies (contents of the refrigerator) to a hot one (the room). The "catch" is that this heat flow is not the *sole* result of the operation of the refrigerator: a motor, which is *hotter* than the room, has been doing work, which requires energy, and has been giving off heat in addition to that removed from inside the refrigerator. As in the case with the first law, apparent violations of the second law can always be traced to leaving something out of the accounting.

Another, and for our purposes more pertinent, perspective on the second law of thermodynamics comes from relating disorder to the degradation of energy. Order, it seems, is related to the ability of energy to do work, and while the first law insists that the total *amount* of energy in the universe remains constant, the second law requires that the fraction of *energy available to be used* is continually being diminished. For this reason it is often said that the second law tells us that the universe is "running down." This idea can be understood from the fact that energy is most usable where it is most concentrated—for example, in highly structured chemical bonds (gasoline, sugar) or at high temperature (steam, incoming sunlight). Since the second law says that the *overall* tendency in all processes is *away* from concentration, *away* from high temperature, it is saying that, overall, more and more energy is becoming less and less usable. Typically, the manifestation of this degradation of energy is the production of heat at relatively low, hence relatively useless, temperatures—for example, the heat of a car's exhaust, the heat of tire friction against the road, the heat radiated by your body, the heat of a decomposing animal carcass.

The laws of thermodynamics often can be used quantitatively to determine the minimum loss of useful energy (ideal efficiency) associated with a given process. But the reader need note only that, on thermodynamic grounds alone, such losses *always* occur, even in the complete absence of friction. In the real world, of course, some sort of friction or its equivalent is always present, so the losses are even larger. For instance, in the basic process by which cells extract energy from the chemical bonds of food molecules, almost half the useful energy is lost: more than one food-molecule bond must be broken for each equivalent bond synthesized in the organism eating the food. Thus the laws of thermodynamics tell us why we need a continual input of energy to maintain ourselves, why we must eat much more than a pound of food in order to gain a pound of weight, and why the total weight of plants on the face of the earth will always be much greater than the weight of the plant-eaters, which will in turn always be much greater than the weight of flesh-eaters. They also make it clear that all the energy used on the face of the earth, whether of solar or nuclear origin, will ultimately be degraded to heat. Here the laws catch us both coming and going, for they put limits on the efficiency with which we can manipulate this heat. Hence they pose the threat (discussed elsewhere) that man may make this planet uncomfortably warm with degraded energy well before he runs out of high-grade energy to consume.

It has been asked whether a revolutionary development in physics, like Einstein's theory of relativity, might not open the way to circumvention of the laws of thermodynamics. The answer is no: knowledge will expand and theories will change, but the practical consequence of the laws of thermodynamics will persist—just as Newton's Laws of classical physics remain valid for describing the vast majority of human activities and observations today, in the age of relativity.

follows: we are not yet running out of energy, but we are being forced to use the resources that produce it faster than is probably healthy. Our supplies of fossil fuels—coal, petroleum, and natural gas—are finite and will probably be consumed within a few hundred years, possibly much sooner. Coal will probably be the last to go, perhaps 300–400 years from now. Petroleum (including that in oil shales) will go much sooner. The most recent and thorough estimate, by geologist M. King Hubbert, gives us about a century before our petroleum reserves (including recent Alaskan discoveries) are depleted. Already we are being forced to consider more expensive mining techniques to permit utilization of the oil shales. We are living beyond our means, "spending our capital," depleting what are essentially nonrenewable resources. Furthermore, some organic chemists consider the burning of fossil fuels for energy production to be one of the least desirable uses for these large organic molecules. Petroleum and coal have many other uses in areas as diverse as lubrication and the production of plastics.

The world's potential production of hydroelectric power is roughly equivalent to the amount of power now produced by fossil fuels. There are, however, serious problems in utilizing it to the utmost. Much of the potential lies in UDCs, where the power could not be used unless those countries become industrialized, and global ecological factors and shortages of resources will prevent industrialization in most of them. Furthermore, hydroelectric power depends on dams, which under present conditions of technology are temporary structures. In a few hundred years, sometimes much less, their reservoirs fill with silt and become useless. Finally, there is an aesthetic question. Do we wish to impound and control all of the wild rivers of the Earth?

For many years men have speculated about the sun as a source of nondepletable power, but large-scale utilization of solar energy presents serious technological problems, especially in a crowded world. Sunlight must be gathered over large areas; the collecting device for an electric generating plant with a capacity of 1,000 megawatts (enough power to supply electricity to a city of perhaps 1.5 million people) would have to cover an area of about 16 square miles. Tidal power, also the subject of some speculation, does not have more than a minute fraction of the potential of water power, and will presumably never be of more than local importance. There is some dispute about the power potential of the heat of the Earth's core (geothermal energy). This energy is nuclear in the sense that the heat is produced by radioactive decay. Some experts say that geothermal energy will never supply more than a very small fraction of the power used by man; others connected with companies attempting to harness this energy are much more optimistic. Some predict that toward the end of this century geothermal production of electricity will supply as much as one-half of America's electrical power.

Many people who are aware of the approaching end of our fossil fuel resources assume that uranium-based nuclear power will soon simply replace the fossil fuels. Unfortunately, the continued availability of high-grade uranium ore reserves is not proven, nor are the direct or environmental costs of nuclear power well established. Contrary to a widely held misconception, nuclear power is not now "dirt cheap," and does not represent a power panacea for either DCs or UDCs. The largest nuclear generating stations now in operation are, even with their massive hidden subsidies (Chapter 6), just competitive with or marginally superior to modern coal-fired plants of comparable size (in areas where coal is not scarce). At best, both produce power for approximately 4 or 5 mills (one mill = one-tenth of a cent) per kilowatt-hour. Smaller nuclear plants are less economical than small plants that operate on fossil fuels. In this connection it is important to note that UDCs rarely can use the outputs of large power plants. There are simply not enough industries, lightbulbs, appliances, neon signs, electric trains, buses, streetcars, and so on to utilize that much electricity. Significantly, the cost of the modernization and industrialization required to utilize the electrical power exceeds the cost of the power itself by several orders of magnitude. For example, economist E. S. Mason has calculated that the output of capital necessary to consume the output of a relatively small (70,000 kilowatt) plant—about 1.2 million dollars worth of electricity per year at 40 percent utilization and 5 mills/kwh—would be 111 million dollars per year if the power were consumed by metals industries, and 270 million dollars per year if it were consumed by petroleum products industries. All things considered, only those UDCs that are now short of fossil fuels or have problems in transporting them would have reason to choose nuclear power.

Prospects for major reductions in the cost of nuclear power in the future hinge on the possibility that safe and economical "breeder" reactors can be developed, and on the more remote possibility that a successful thermonuclear (fusion) reactor can be produced. The time scale for availability and the ultimate cost of energy are uncertain for both possibilities. The breeder reactor would convert more nonfissionable uranium and thorium to plutonium than it would consume as fuel for itself. Although breeder reactors would effectively extend our fissionable fuel supply by a factor of approximately 400, they are not expected to become economically competitive with conventional reactors until the 1980's. Whenever they do, there is no guarantee that the cost per unit energy beyond that time can be reduced, because of their probable continued high cost and the probable increase in the cost of the ore that the breeders will convert to fuel. In the latter regard, although crushing granite for its few parts per million of uranium and thorium has been suggested as a source of nuclear fuel, and is possible in theory, the problems and cost of doing so are far from resolved. Not the least of these problems is what to do with the leftover granite! It is too soon to predict the costs associated with fusion reactors, but few scientists active in the field of plasma physics today are willing to predict whether such a device can be developed to generate *useful* power within the next 25 years—and it is plasma physicists who must solve the critical problems. One guess puts the unit energy cost at more than one-half that for coal or a fission power station of comparable size, but this is pure speculation. Possibly the major benefit of controlled fusion will be to extend the energy supply rather than to cheapen it.

A second common misconception about nuclear power is that it can reduce our dependence upon fossil fuels to zero as soon as that becomes necessary or desirable. In fact, nuclear power plants produce only electrical energy; and electrical energy constituted only 19 percent of the total energy consumed in the United States in 1960. Thus the length of time that nuclear fuels can postpone the exhaustion of our coal and oil depends on how much the use of electrical energy can be increased. The task is immense and revolutionary! It will require a conversion from engines fueled by petroleum products to electric or fuel-cell-powered transportation, conversion from coal and oil to electric heating, and conversion to electrically powered industries. All such conversions will take time and will be extremely expensive.

Nuclear energy, then, is a panacea neither for the DCs nor the UDCs. It may relieve, but not remove, the pressure on fossil fuel supplies, and may provide reasonably priced power in certain parts of the world where these fuels are not abundant. It has substantial, if expensive, potential applications in increasing food production, which are discussed in the next chapter.

It is clear that mankind, if it survives for another century or so, will witness drastic changes in the use of energy sources. It does not appear, however, that availability of energy itself will place a limit on population growth, although difficulties accompanying the transition from one source to another might well do so. The ultimate limits to the use of energy (assuming radioactive pollution and other safety problems associated with nuclear energy can be solved) come not from its shortage, but from the problem of dissipating the heat to which all useful energy is ultimately degraded.

Nonrenewable Mineral Resources

Geologist T. S. Lovering wrote in 1968 for the Texas Quarterly: "Surprisingly enough, many men unfamiliar with the mineral industry believe that the beneficent gods of technology are about to open the cornucopia of granite and sea, flooding industry with any and all metals desired." Lovering was responding to the outpouring of propaganda from technological optimists who discount the problems posed by the unprecedented consumption of nonrenewable resources and by their sporadic distribution. How well fixed is mankind for the fossil fuels, the metals, and the other minerals he extracts from the Earth? Should we believe the technological optimists, who hold that science and technology can solve resource problems? Or should we listen to those who argue that mineral resources, whether they be extracted from undiscovered rich deposits or from such common rocks as granite, are exhaustible and irreplaceable? The answer goes something like this: for the next 30 years, the DCs will probably not fare too badly, since most of the UDCs will be unable to industrialize on any more than a modest scale. For approximately a century after that, mankind in general will do rather poorly, especially if any of several current trends continue. Beyond that time, the costs of energy required to extract whatever resources remain will tax far more than man's ingenuity.

The resources of the Earth's crust are very unevenly distributed—a result of the uneven distribution of the processes that led to their deposition and concentration. The distribution of coal, for instance, presumably represents the pattern of distribution of certain types of swamp plant communities that existed several million years ago. Some minerals have been formed by sedimentation; others have been deposited in fractures in the Earth's crust. The concentration of some minerals varies more or less continuously from very high-grade ores to below the average abundance of the element in the crust of the Earth. Certain types of copper ores exhibit such a pattern of deposition, as do the ores of other important metals, such as iron and aluminum. Many others, including ores of lead, zinc, tin, nickel, tungsten, mercury, manganese, cobalt, precious metals, and molybdenum do not. They show sharp discontinuities in concentration.

This frequent discontinuous distribution, as well as other factors, makes untenable the views of certain economists who think that only economic considerations determine the availability of mineral resources. They have the idea that as demand increases, mining will simply move to poorer and poorer ores, which are assumed to be progressively more and more abundant. These economists have misinterpreted a principle called the "arithmetic-geometric ratio" (A/G ratio)—a principle that geologists developed for application to certain types of ore deposits within certain limits. It is valid only for those ores (such as porphyry copper deposits) and only within those limits. The idea is that as the grade of ore decreases arithmetically, its abundance will increase geometrically until the average abundance in the Earth's crust is reached. It is further assumed that the additional cost of mining the low-grade ores can easily be absorbed, since the dollar value of mineral resources is at present only a small part of the gross national product. But, as noted above, the geological facts of mineral distribution do not support the simplistic views of the cornucopians any more than the physical and biological facts of life support their views about the imagined panacea of unlimited power from atomic energy. Although some ores approximate a distribution where the A/G ratio may be applied, most do not.

Our present level of affluence depends on much more than the availability of relatively common substances, such as iron, aluminum, zinc, phosphate rock, coal, and oil. Also necessary are such "mineral vitamins" as vanadium, tantalum, tungsten, molybdenum, and helium. Although these are little known to the layman, they are critically important to industrial processes. Like the familiar vitamins in our diets, these minerals are often required only in small amounts, but they are indispensable, which by analogy gives them the "vitamin" label.

Figure 4-1 gives estimated time spans for depletion of various mineral reserves. Implicit in the chart are certain assumptions: these are that the population will remain constant at 3.3 billion, that consumption will not increase above 1965 rates, that no ore now uneconomical to mine will be exploited, and that there will be no discovery of presently unknown reserves. These assumptions, of course, had to be made to reduce variables; otherwise the chart could not have been made up.

Population and consumption have obviously both grown since 1965. Some low-grade ores have become economically competitive, and perhaps more will. Nor is there any doubt that new reserves of at least some of the minerals will be found. But how future developments will interact (or counteract) is totally unknown, so the chart is probably as good an estimate of today's reserves as is possible.

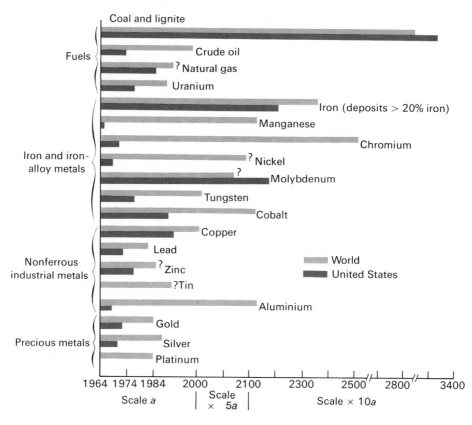

FIGURE 4-1

Lifetimes of estimated recoverable reserves of mineral resources. Reserves are those that are of high enough grade to be mined with today's techniques. Increasing population and consumption rates, unknown deposits, and future use of presently submarginal ores are not considered. [After Cloud, *Realities of Mineral Distribution,* 1968.]

Clearly, these estimates hardly give us reason for optimism. A considerable amount of substitution and extraction from low-quality ores will be necessary well before the end of this century. Unless oil exploration is extraordinarily successful we will be well into our reserves of oil shale, and we may even need to convert coal to liquid fuels. There has been a rather gradual rise in domestic oil production from 318,535 metric tons in 1953 to 409,170 metric tons in 1966. In the same period, world oil production more than doubled —from 657,800 metric tons to 1,641,400 metric tons. At present the United States produces about one-fourth of the world's oil, but consumes about eight times the per capita figure for the "free world"—about 900 gallons per year for every man, woman, and child in this nation. Nuclear energy will possibly relieve some of the demand on oil reserves, but even so, in 1967 Charles F. Jones of the Humble Oil Company estimated that during the thirteen years between 1967 and 1980 the consumption of oil in the United States would be more than twice the amount of our known reserves. We will of course continue trying to supplement these reserves by importing oil. Unfortunately, however, we have already experienced some trouble in making trade agreements for oil and minerals with foreign countries.

By 1961 we were importing more than 90 percent of our nickel and 30 percent of our copper. In general, the United States is highly dependent on foreign sources for most of its basic industrial raw materials, except bituminous coal (for instance, in 1966 we mined 52,209,000 metric tons of iron ore, but we consumed 131,314,000 metric tons of steel). At the same time, our industrial production and affluence have reached unprecedented levels, far beyond the highest levels theoretically possible for the UDCs. Our national per capita income is some 33 times that of India, and both our per capita gross national product and our per capita steel production are more than 50 times that of India. Our per capita steel *consumption* (production plus imports minus exports) is some 667 times that of Indonesia, 133 times that of Pakistan, 83 times that of Ceylon, 23 times that of Colombia, 10 times that of Mexico, 2 times that of France and Switzerland, 1.8 times that of Japan, 1.7 times that of the United Kingdom and Russia, and marginally (3 percent) higher than that of our nearest rival, Sweden. The United States in 1966 accounted for well over a third of the world's tin consumption, well over a fourth of its phosphate, potash, and nitrogenous fertilizer consumption and half of its newsprint and synthetic rubber (produced from a variety of resources), more than a fourth of its steel, and about a fifth of its cotton. Estimates of the total American utilization of raw materials currently run as high as 50 percent of the world's consumption, with a projection of current trends to about 80 percent around 1980. Probably 30 percent and 50 percent would be more realistic figures, but in any event our consumption is far beyond our "share" on a basis of population. We number less than 6 percent of the world's people!

The availability of critical resources has a considerable bearing on the possibilities of industrialization in the UDCs. Even if world population growth stopped in 1970, world iron production would have to be increased about sixfold, copper production almost sixfold, and lead production about eightfold to bring global per capita consumption to the current American level. And these figures neglect the enormous amounts of these metals already mined, refined, and in use in the railroads, automobiles, girders, electrical wiring, and so on in the United States. To raise all of the 3.6 billion people of the world of 1970 to the American standard of living would require the extraction of almost 30 billion tons of iron, more than 500 million tons of copper and lead, more than 300 million tons of zinc, about 50 million tons of tin, as well as enormous quantities of other minerals. That means the extraction of some 75 times as much iron as is now extracted annually, 100 times as much as copper, 200 times as much lead, 75 times as much zinc, and 250 times as much tin. The needed iron is theoretically available, and might be extracted by tremendous efforts over a long period of time, but a serious limit could be imposed by a shortage of molybdenum, which is needed to convert iron to steel. Needed quantities of the other materials far exceed *all* known or inferred reserves. Of course, to raise the standard of living of the projected world population of the year 2000 to today's American standard would require doubling all of the above figures. But, far from concentrating on ways to help UDCs while making a maximum effort to husband limited resources, economists in the DCs want to *increase* the rate of domestic consumption of nonrenewable resources far above that of 1970, while population growth continues. Our environment cannot stand "world industrialization," partly because of the thermal limits mentioned earlier; but even if it could, the problem of supplying the raw materials alone staggers the imagination.

It is questionable whether the DCs will be able to obtain the steadily increasing amounts of critical resources that are projected as future "needs." In the short term, say until the end of this century, the United States *might* do all right by increasing its imports, assuming that the UDCs will continue to let us exploit their mineral resources, and by developing substitutes. Maintaining imports will be especially important. In common with almost all industrial nations, with the possible exception of the U.S.S.R., we are already net importers of most of the metals and ores we use (Fig. 4-2). Obviously, should any unforeseen events limit our access to imports, we would be in trouble immediately. Unfortunately, such "unforeseen events" are likely in our future, as is shown in later chapters.

The long-run solution to world shortages of most mineral resources is seen by technological optimists to be in extracting them from such common rock as granite and from sea water, where 63 out of 92 naturally occurring elements have been found (although the important metals dissolved in sea water are present only in extraordinarily low concentrations). They further assume that in an era of cheap energy this will be feasible, but they are apparently unaware of the problems of thermal pollution and other ecological consequences of such a program. Both the geological and the economic facts of life make it probable that, as one knowledgeable geologist put it, "average rock will never be mined."

It is unlikely that cheap nuclear energy can greatly reduce the cost of mining, mainly because most mining will presumably continue to be subterranean; there are definite limits to the feasible depth of open-pit mining. Most plans call for underground nuclear blasts to fragment the rock, followed by hydrometallurgical or chemical mining. These techniques present enormous problems. Rocks must be fractured to the proper particle size, and then brought into contact with special solvents (which must also be derived from natural resources). Ways must be found to contain the solvents and to prevent them from being consumed by dissolving unwanted materials. In attempting to extract low concentrations underground, electrolysis also seems very unpromising, as are biologically catalyzed metallurgical reactions. If extraction below ground is successful, then the reagent and the dissolved material must be pumped to the surface, both possibly hot and extremely radio-

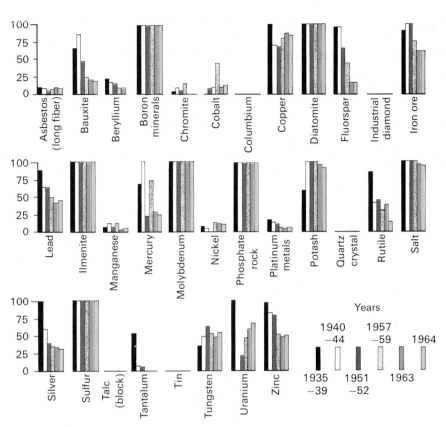

FIGURE 4-2

Self-sufficiency of the United States in selected minerals, calculated as the percentage of primary consumption mined in the country. [Data from the U.S. Department of the Interior, Bureau of Mines, Division of Minerals, 1965.]

active. After the separation both the waste rock and the solvent must be disposed of.

In reality, labor costs would probably remain quite high in any futuristic programs to extract desired minerals from low-grade deposits. It seems likely that it will remain much cheaper to search out mineral concentrations well above the average than to mine average rock, even if it means keeping human miners with picks at the mining face. As geologist Preston Cloud has observed: "The reality is that even the achievement of a breeder reactor offers no guarantee of unlimited mineral resources in the face of geologic limitations and expanding populations with increased per-capita demands, even over the middle term. To assume such for the long term would be sheer folly."

Water

"Water is the best of all things," said the Greek poet Pindar. It is also, in the broad sense, a renewable resource. It circulates on the Earth in a complex series of pathways known collectively as the hydrologic cycle (Fig. 4-3). The oceans serve as the principal reservoir, from which an estimated 875 cubic kilometers (ck) evaporate per day. About 775 ck return to the ocean through condensation and precipitation, there being a net windborne transfer of some 100 ck from the seas to the land. About 260 ck daily fall upon the land, 100 ck of which are blown in from the sea and 160 ck have been previously evaporated from the land. The cycle is balanced by about 100 ck of daily runoff from land to sea via the streams, rivers, and flow of groundwater. But even though it circulates, the finite supply of fresh water still places limits on the numbers of people that can be supported, both in specific locations and on the Earth as a whole.

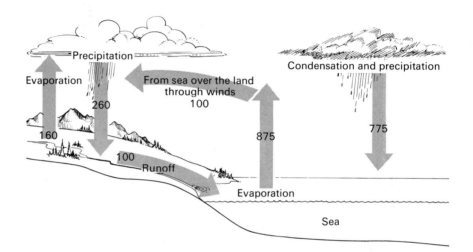

FIGURE 4-3

Hydrologic cycle (in cubic kilometers per day). [Data from Borgstrom, *Too Many*, Macmillan, New York, 1967].

Water is needed in prodigious quantities just to produce food. Plants are constantly absorbing water from the soil and evaporating it from their leaves, which is the basic reason for the extreme water requirements of vegetable food production and the even greater requirements of meat production. A single corn plant may take from the soil, and evaporate, as much as 200 quarts of water in a growing season. The water needed for the production of one pound of meat includes that necessary for growing about 10 pounds of forage plants, plus the water required by the animal directly for drinking, and further water for meat processing. To produce a pound of dry wheat requires some 60 gallons of water; a pound of rice, 200–250 gallons; a pound of meat, 2,500–6,000 gallons; and a quart of milk, about 1,000 gallons. Industrial processes are even more water-greedy. Directly and indirectly, it takes an estimated 100,000 gallons of water to produce a single automobile. Each American's share of all the water disposed of in the United States in

1900 was about 525 gallons daily. This increased to almost 1,500 gallons per capita in 1960, and is expected to reach almost 2,000 gallons by 1980. These figures do not include the use of rainwater by crops, but roughly 50 percent of the consumption given here is for irrigation.

Some 97 percent of the world's water is salt water, stored in the ocean basins. Of the remaining 3 percent, which is fresh water, almost 98 percent is tied up in the ice caps, principally of Antarctica and Greenland. Since freeing all of this water would raise the sea level some 200 feet, inundating many of our cities and much of our crop land, it would seem best to leave most of that water tied up as it is, even if it were feasible to free it. Some of the water in the hydrological cycle is subject to reuse; in fact, the water in some river systems of the DCs is reused up to 50 times. But the huge amounts of water required by living plants are returned to the cycle directly and cannot be reused by man immediately.

The rather small total supply of fresh water is now being reduced. Man is removing fresh water from the continents faster than the hydrologic cycle replaces it. Michigan State's Georg Borgstrom, an authority on food production, estimates that the people of Europe extract three times what the cycle returns to accessible reserves, and that North Americans take out about twice what is returned. Groundwater reserves, our "water capital," have been depleted at a shocking rate. The groundwater supply will soon be below that necessary to meet withdrawal demands, and the water bank will fail. Projected American water requirements in 1980 will be about 700 billion gallons. Even on the basis of the most optimistic technological and economic assumptions, only an estimated 650 billion gallons can be made available. Similar shortages will occur in many areas of the world, especially in connection with the immense water needs related to agriculture. For instance, India, in her desperate struggle to grow more food, has greatly increased her tapping of groundwater. Between July 1968 and June 1969 the government drove 2,000 new tube wells, and private enterprise drove 76,000. In addition, 246,000 new pumps were installed. It is no wonder that scientists with such diverse interests as agriculturalist Borgstrom and Stanford geologist Richard Jahns feel that the world faces an extremely grave water crisis.

Food and Nutrition

The most pressing factor now limiting the capacity of the Earth to support *Homo sapiens* is the supply of food. In the rest of this chapter, man's needs for food and his current nutritional situation are discussed. The next chapter takes up the all-important subject of our attempts to meet these needs today, and our prospects for meeting them in the future.

Despite the emphasis on the need for a "balanced diet," which has been a part of school curricula and general public information in the United States since the 1920's and 1930's, some Americans are still convinced that the typical Asian can live happily and healthily on one bowl of rice per day. The truth is that an Asian's nutritional requirements are essentially the same as his American counterpart's, although the total amount of some nutrients needed may be less owing to his smaller size (itself probably the result of poor nutrition during his years of growth). The Asian, however, meets his needs through a quite different assortment of foods from those an American would choose. The traditional diets of various peoples of the world differ tremendously, from the East African Masai diet of berries, grain, vegetables, milk, and blood from cattle, and sometimes sheep or goat meat, to the Polynesian diet of coconut, fish, breadfruit, taro, and tropical fruits, and occasionally pork or poultry. American and European diets—once based on a relatively few foods, such as beef, mutton, poultry, dairy products, eggs, wheat (bread) and other grains, potatoes (more recently), and vegetables and fruits—have grown in the past generation to include a fantastic array of foods from all parts of the world. Nevertheless, the relatively limited traditional diets of most of the people in underdeveloped countries, where undernutrition and malnutrition are today very widespread, could be basically adequate to meet their needs. The existing nutritional deficiencies result either from insufficient supplies of some or all of these foods, or from poverty or ignorance.

To comprehend fully the nutritional problems of today's hungry millions, one must be conversant with problems of agricultural development and production, agricultural economics, food distribution patterns, cultural food preferences, and even public health situations. But above all, the nutritional needs that are common to all people, regardless of what they recognize as "food," must be understood.

Some 45 compounds and elements found in foods are considered "essential nutrients," necessary for life and health in human beings (see Appendix 3 for details). These nutrients fall into five general categories: carbohydrates, fats, proteins, vitamins, and minerals. Each nutrient can be found in a wide variety of foods, although no one food contains all of them. Each performs some particular function or functions within the body, providing energy, building and repairing tissue, or maintaining the physiological processes of life.

Human nutritional requirements can be met by eating some foods from each of four groups daily. These are:

1. Milk and dairy products for calcium, protein, vitamins, and other minerals. In some countries soybeans are substituted for milk, but they are not as rich in calcium. Using lime in the preparation of foods, and eating whole small fishes or pickled pigs' feet are ways in which some people without dairy products obtain their calcium (the acid in the pickling fluid dissolves the calcium from the pig's bones and makes it available).

2. Meat, fish, poultry, or eggs for protein, fats, and vitamins. These are luxury foods for most of the world. They are more expensive both in terms of the price the purchaser pays and in terms of the agricultural and environmental cost of producing them.

3. Grains and starchy vegetables for carbohydrates, vitamins, and some protein. This category includes the staple foods, such as wheat, rice, potatoes, and corn. Among poor people these foods make up the bulk of the diet, and provide a large proportion of the protein intake.

4. Fruits and vegetables for carbohydrates, vitamins, minerals, and some protein. These are often absent in the diets of poor people in both DCs and UDCs because of their expense, and sometimes as a result of faulty distribution. Peas, beans, and other of the legumes are important protein sources for people living in poverty.

A Hungry World

"Basically there are not many oases left in a vast, almost worldwide network of slums; about 450 million well-fed people living in comparative luxury . . . as against 2,400 million undernourished, malnourished, or in other ways deficiently fed and generally poor . . ." This vivid description of the present world situation appears in Georg Borgstrom's 1969 book, *Too Many*.

In 1967 the President's Science Advisory Committee Panel on the World Food Supply estimated that 20 percent of the people in the underdeveloped countries (which include two-thirds of the world population) were undernourished (that is, were not receiving enough calories per day) and that 60 percent were malnourished (seriously lacking in one or more essential nutrients, most commonly protein). This means that as many as a billion and a half people are either undernourished or malnourished. Other estimates place the number of "hungry" people at more than 2 billion. Of these, an estimated half billion can be described as either chronically hungry or starving. These numbers do not include the hungry and malnourished millions in the lower economic strata of developed countries such as the United States or the number of people who can afford to eat well but are malnourished because of their ignorance of elementary nutrition. Figure 4-4 shows the areas of the world where hunger is most widespread.

Even in the face of such staggering numbers, one might be tempted to shrug and say, "Oh well, there have always been famines and hungry people." The truth is that today's situation is totally unprecedented, and not simply because of the magnitude of the suffering. Famines, which have existed throughout human history, have generally been cataclysmic, short-term events caused by weather or human intervention and have been limited to relatively small, local populations. Though such famines are undeniably tragic affairs that result in a great deal of human suffering and death, they are an entirely different phenomenon from the unceasing privation now endured by more than one billion people around the globe. But, most important of all, today's hunger is unprecedented because the multitudinous hungry are increasingly aware of the dietary condition of the affluent few, and have high hopes of emulating them.

Biafra's present famine represents the traditional type; the relatively ade-

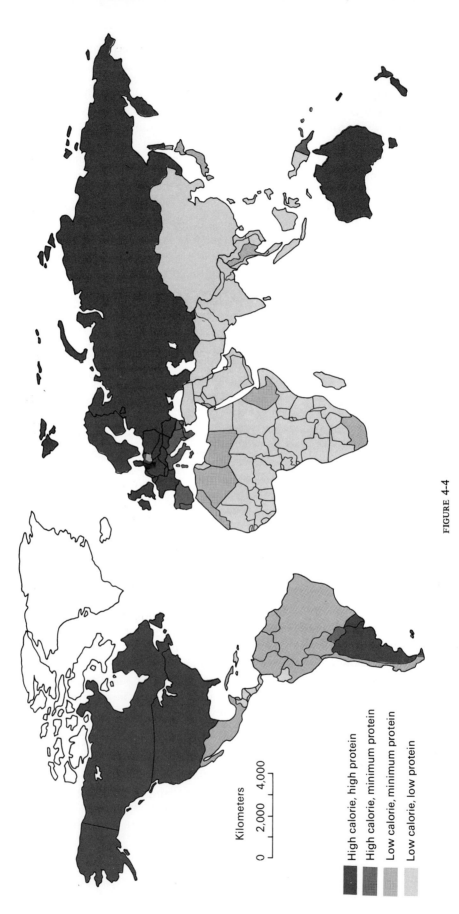

FIGURE 4-4

The geography of hunger.

Kilometers

0   2,000   4,000

High calorie, high protein

High calorie, minimum protein

Low calorie, minimum protein

Low calorie, low protein

quately nourished population of Biafra was suddenly faced with a cata-strophic reduction in food supply. The political upheaval that produced the shortage may prolong the period before food production can be re-established, but the famine will nevertheless probably be a temporary affair. Except in the cases of severest deprivation, most adults who survive will probably not have suffered permanent harm from hunger, although many very young and vul-nerable children unquestionably have, and older children will have suffered some retardation of physical growth. The worst effects on the younger chil-dren will be permanent mental deficiency due to a lack of protein during critical stages in brain development (discussed later in this chapter).

Contrast this situation, which is sad enough, with the sort of grinding pov-erty in some other underdeveloped areas, which has been gradually worsening for a number of years. Population growth has outstripped increases in food production in many areas. Before World War II, many countries in Africa, Asia, and Latin America were grain exporters. By the mid-1960's, they were importing grain in far greater quantities than they had ever exported it. The per capita food production in most of Asia, Africa, and Latin America dropped during the early 1960's; final data for the late 1960's are not yet available, but undoubtedly will show some improvement after the disastrous years of 1966 and 1967 in Asia.

Although individual needs for calories vary according to body size and activity, the United Nations Food and Agriculture Organization (FAO) has established standard "reference" body weights and standard daily per capita caloric requirements for estimating a population's caloric food needs. Chil-dren's caloric needs, which are higher than those of adults in proportion to their body weights, are standardized according to age groups. For adults, al-lowances are also made for pregnancies and age differences. On the basis of these FAO standards, the President's Science Advisory Committee has placed current world average caloric needs at 2,354 per capita per day. The FAO estimates that an average of 2,420 calories per capita per day in food is cur-rently available at the market level. When the inequities of distribution within and between countries and average loss of at least 10 percent before consump-tion are taken into account, the reality of the gap between needed and availa-ble calories becomes clear.

Individual protein requirements also vary with body size and age, although activity makes very little difference. These needs must be calculated according to the quality of the protein sources. Where animal foods are a rare element in the diet, more protein is needed to compensate for the lower quality of the protein in vegetable sources (see Appendix 3). Maldistribution of proteins in UDCs, even within households, is an even more serious problem than maldistribution of calories (Figs. 4-5, 4-6).

Conflicting accounts of the actual food situation sometimes result from different ways of comparing figures. Food production figures are usually quoted only in calories and take no account of whether adequate protein or other nutrients are available. In addition, there is a vast difference be-tween what is produced and what reaches the marketplace. Estimates of losses to insect and rodent pests and to spoilage range from 20 percent to as high as 50 percent in some areas.

To feed the projected population of 1985 even at the inadequate 1965 level, the President's Science Advisory Committee Panel estimated that world food production must be increased between 43 and 52 percent over 1965 production. The low estimates assume that effective population-control measures will have reduced fertility by 30 percent by 1985 and that food distribution will have been improved. The greatest increase in food needs will occur in the poor countries, which are growing most rapidly. For example, the requirements of India, Pakistan, and Brazil for calories will virtually double. The increase in protein requirements will be somewhat higher. In some UDCs the protein increase may need to be as much as 150 percent. If the world is successful in making these prodigious increases in available food, and its dis-

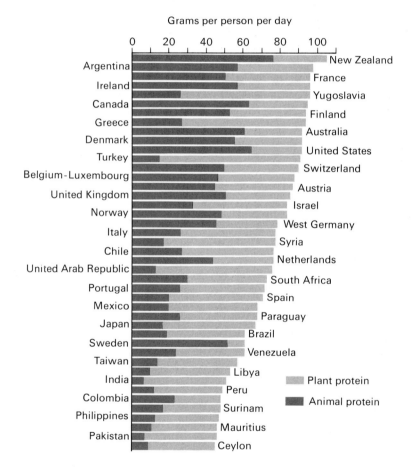

FIGURE 4-5

Daily per capita total protein supplies in 43 countries. [After *Introduction to Livestock Production*, by H. H. Cole. W. H. Freeman and Company. Copyright © 1966.]

tribution is improved, in 1985 we will have a population of around 5 billion, perhaps 15 percent of which will still be undernourished and 40 percent still malnourished.

The present failures of food distribution are the result of a number of interacting factors, including poverty, ignorance, cultural and economic patterns, and lack of transport systems. Although the worldwide average diet might theoretically be adequate, the average diet within many countries in Southern Asia and tropical Latin America is significantly below FAO minimum nutritional standards. Within these countries individuals in the poorest quarter of the population may be receiving only three-fourths of the calories and proteins of even this inadequate average diet. These shortages show up in widespread malnutrition and hunger to an obvious degree, especially among

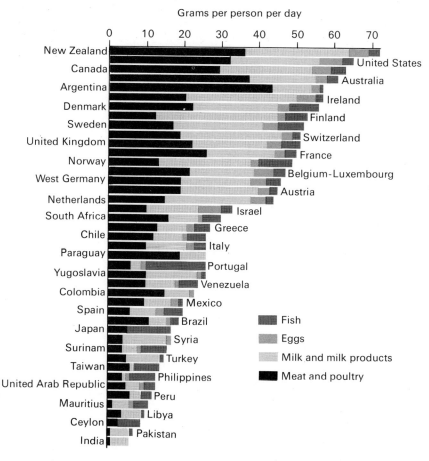

FIGURE 4-6

Daily per capita animal protein supplies in 43 countries. [After *Introduction to Livestock Production,* by H. H. Cole. W. H. Freeman and Company. Copyright © 1966.]

TABLE 4-1
Infant Mortality Rates, Under 1 Year, 1964

Continent and country	Rate per 1,000 live births	Continent and country	Rate per 1,000 live births
Africa		*Europe*	
Mauritius	56.7	Austria	29.2
Réunion	76.4	Belgium	25.3
United Arab Republic	117.3	Bulgaria	32.9
		Czechoslovakia	21.4
North and Central America		Denmark	18.7
Barbados	52.1	Finland	17.0
Canada	24.7	France	23.3
Costa Rica	82.5	Germany, East	28.8
Dominican Republic	79.0	Germany, West	25.2
Guatemala	87.9	Greece	35.8
Mexico	64.5	Hungary	40.0
Puerto Rico	51.6	Ireland	26.7
Trinidad and Tobago	35.3	Italy	36.1
United States	24.8	Netherlands	14.8
		Norway	16.4
South America		Poland	47.7
Argentina	59.2	Portugal	69.0
Chile	108.5	Spain	39.2
Colombia	83.3	Sweden	14.2
Ecuador	94.0	Switzerland	19.0
Peru	83.5	United Kingdom—England	
Venezuela	48.7	and Wales	19.9
		Yugoslavia	75.8
Asia			
China (Taiwan)	23.9	*Oceania*	
Hong Kong	26.4	Australia	19.1
Israel	28.2	Fiji	30.5
Japan	20.4	New Zealand	19.1
Kuwait	51.2		
Philippines	70.5		
Thailand	37.8		

SOURCE: United Nations, *Demographic Yearbook 1967.*

such vulnerable groups as infants, preschool children (ages 1–4), and pregnant and nursing women.

Deaths from starvation and malnutrition are commonplace. Of the 60 million deaths that occur each year, between 10 and 20 million are estimated to be the result of starvation or malnutrition. In most countries the cause of death is usually officially attributed to some infectious or parasitic disease, which in most cases only dealt the final blow. Diseases that are usually only minor nuisances in well-nourished individuals are devastating to the malnourished. Even if they do not kill, they tend to intensify the malnourishment by draining the individual's reserves. Cases in which normally minor diseases have precipitated a severe deficiency disorder are often seen by public health workers. Extremely poor sanitary conditions further complicate the picture; dysentery and infestations of various kinds of worms are commonplace. Diarrhea, dangerous even in a well-fed, protected baby, is disastrous to an ill-fed one. *For our purposes, any death that would not have occurred if the individual had been properly nourished may be considered as due to starvation, regardless of the ultimate agent.*

These interacting factors are a major cause of the high infant and even higher child mortality rates in the UDCs compared with those of the DCs (Tables 4-1 and 4-2). Infants are somewhat protected from both parasites and severe nutritional deficiencies while they are nursing. Mother's milk is extremely nourishing and does not transmit parasites. Nevertheless, the infant mortality rate in poor countries is 4 to 8 times higher than that in the United States, which is by no means the world's lowest (Table 4-1). The preschool mortality rate has been considered the best indication of the nutritional level of a population, since children of this age are usually no longer protected by nursing and are therefore the most susceptible segment of the population (Table 4-2). In many parts of Latin America, Asia, and Africa these rates are 10 to 40 times higher than in the U.S. There is no question that at least half of these deaths are basically due to malnutrition (usually protein starvation).

TABLE 4-2
Child Mortality Rates 1–4 Years, 1960–1962 (Average Annual)

Continent and country	Rate per 1,000 children (ages 1-4) per Year	Continent and country	Rate per 1,000 children (ages 1-4) per Year
Africa		*Europe*	
Mauritius	8.7	Austria	1.3
Réunion	9.6	Belgium	1.0
United Arab Republic	37.9	Bulgaria	2.4
North and Central America		Czechoslovakia	1.2
Barbados	3.7	Denmark	0.9
Canada	1.1	Finland	1.1
Costa Rica	7.2	France	1.0
Dominican Republic	10.8	Germany, East	1.6
Guatemala	32.7	Germany, West	1.3
Mexico	13.8	Greece	1.9
Puerto Rico	2.9	Hungary	1.6
Trinidad and Tobago	2.5	Ireland	1.2
United States	1.0	Italy	1.9
South America		Netherlands	1.1
Argentina	4.2	Norway	1.0
Chile	8.0	Poland	1.6
Colombia	17.4	Portugal	8.0
Equador	22.1	Spain	2.0
Peru	17.4	Sweden	0.8
Venezuela	5.9	Switzerland	1.2
Asia		United Kingdom—England, and Wales	0.9
Ceylon	8.8	Yugoslavia	5.2
China (Taiwan)	7.2	*Oceania*	
Hong Kong	4.4	Australia	1.1
Israel	1.8	Fiji Islands	3.7
Japan	2.2	New Zealand	1.2
Kuwait	3.6		
Philippines	8.4		
Syria	8.3		
Thailand	9.1		

SOURCE: United Nations, *Statistical Series,* K/3, 1967.

Common Deficiency Diseases

The most commonly encountered deficiency diseases in UDCs are marasmus and kwashiorkor (Fig. 4-7). Marasmus is probably indicative of overall undernutrition, but it is often referred to as a "protein-calorie deficiency." It seems to be related to early weaning or to a failure in breast-feeding that results in the provision of inadequate substitutes for mother's milk, and it often appears following a bout of diarrhea or some other disease. Most victims are babies less than a year old. Since poor people in the UDCs (particularly those who migrate to cities and fill up the shanty towns) have begun to adopt from the wealthier urban classes the habit of early weaning, marasmus is on the increase. Unfortunately when these babies are weaned, the mothers have no adequate substitute to offer for their milk. Out of ignorance and poverty combined, the babies are likely to receive corn flour, sago, or arrowroot gruels, with a tiny amount of milk added "for color," or, if they are luckier, dried or condensed milk that has been diluted. The child with marasmus is very thin and wasted, and has wrinkled skin and enormous eyes. Many of the children of Biafra exhibit these symptoms.

Kwashiorkor is a West African word that means "the sickness the child develops when another baby is born." Kwashiorkor is the result of protein starvation, and can occur even if calories are abundantly provided. It most frequently follows weaning, when the child of one or two years is offered mainly starches or sugars for his diet (the Jamaican "sugar baby" is an example). In mild cases the child's physical growth is retarded, the hair and skin are discolored, and he has a pot-belly. He may also lose his appetite. When the disease is more acute, the discoloration is more pronounced, hair is loosely rooted and pulls out in tufts, legs and feet swell with fluids, digestive problems arise, and the child becomes markedly apathetic. After this stage is reached, death will follow unless the best medical care can be provided. The President's Science Advisory Committee reports that the high mortality rates of children 1–4 years old in UDCs "suggest that moderate protein-calorie malnutrition affects at least 50 percent of these children."

Vitamin A deficiency often accompanies protein malnutrition and shows up in a drying of eye membranes (xerophthalmia) or softening of the cornea (kerotomalacia), which soon leads to blindness if not treated. Supplementing protein-deficient diets with high-protein foods without adding vitamin A, as has been done under American food-aid programs in which non-fat dry milk was distributed, will cause a previously unsuspected deficiency to be manifested in an acute form. Since 1965 American non-fat dry milk shipped overseas has been fortified with vitamin A. Vitamin A deficiency is widespread in most of the underdeveloped world and most frequently afflicts preschool children.

Beriberi is a disease caused by a deficiency of thiamine. It often accompanies a high-carbohydrate diet, usually one based on polished rice. The thiamine in rice is in or just under the outer skin of the grain, which is removed in milling. Where rice is hand-pounded, undermilled, or parboiled

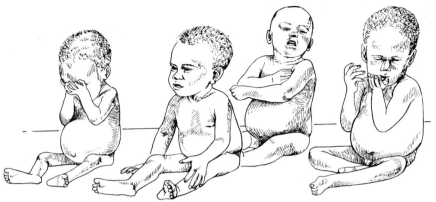

FIGURE 4-7

Symptoms of kwashiorkor (protein deficiency) in African children.
[Drawn from a photograph by Eva D. Wilson.]

(soaked and partly cooked) before milling, at least some of the thiamine is preserved. But polished rice is preferred in many countries for its keeping qualities and because the product of milling (the polishings or husks) may be used as feed for stock. Infantile beriberi, an acute form of the disease, strikes suckling infants and soon leads to death unless it is treated promptly. Severe thiamine deficiency in the mother is the cause of infantile beriberi.

Beriberi is widespread in Southeast Asia and the Philippines, and it appears to be increasing. This is partly due to the introduction of modern community rice mills, which eliminate the need for hand-pounding, formerly done at home. Pregnant and nursing women in these areas are often, by tradition, restricted to very limited diets, which further curtails their intake of thiamine as well as that of other vitamins and proteins.

Another prevalent form of malnutrition in poor countries, particularly among women and small children, is anemia, usually iron-deficiency anemia. Lack of protein, vitamin B_{12}, or folic acid can also play a part in anemia. During pregnancy, a fetus absorbs from the mother's stored reserves a large supply of iron, which it needs during the months after birth (mother's milk contains very little iron). Successive pregnancies can very quickly lead to exhaustion of a mother's reserve supply; if her diet does not replenish it, the result is anemia for both mother and child. This not only produces a lack of energy and low productiveness in the mother but can increase the likelihood of stillbirth and premature birth. The incidence of death from anemia in poor countries ranges from 6 to 16 times higher than that in the United States. It is common wherever poverty and poor sanitation prevail, where it is often aggravated by such parasitic infections as hookworm. These parasites consume large amounts of blood.

Rickets and osteomalacia (softening of the bones) are due to lack of vitamin D or calcium, or both. Like many other deficiencies, this syndrome also affects both mother and child, for the calcium deprivation may begin in the prenatal period. During pregnancy, the fetus draws from the mother's body minerals and vitamins that may not be replenished by her food. Lactation draws still greater amounts of calcium. Successive cycles of pregnancy and lactation may leave the mother virtually crippled by the drain on her bone structure. She may even be unable to leave her house. Thus she is denied the sunlight that would help replenish her vitamin D and is denied the chance of working to obtain better food.

Rickets, the childhood form of osteomalacia, is not very common in tropical countries, where sunshine is abundant. Nevertheless, it does exist, more often in the cities and towns. It is found also in India, Pakistan, China, and parts of the Middle East. Customs of keeping children indoors and of keeping women secluded or heavily veiled undoubtedly contribute to the incidence of both diseases.

Scurvy, pellagra, and ariboflavinosis are deficiency diseases which are less widespread than the others. Scurvy (deficiency of vitamin C), which is prevented by eating fresh fruits and vegetables, occasionally appears in arid countries during drought or famine, or among urban poor, especially the elderly. Pellagra (deficiency of niacin) usually occurs among people whose staple food is corn. In Latin America it somehow seems to be avoided through the practice of soaking the corn in lime-water before grinding it. Ariboflavinosis (lack of riboflavin) usually seems to accompany other forms of malnutrition, especially vitamin A deficiency. (See Appendix 3 for details of these diseases.)

Implications of Severe Malnutrition and Hunger

The serious malnutrition prevalent in our overpopulated world causes incalculable suffering, wasting of human life, and loss of human productivity. Malnourishment, especially protein deficiency, inhibits the development of protective antibodies and lowers resistance to diseases. Even more alarming is the growing body of evidence which shows that protein malnutrition has permanent effects, especially on small children. It has been known for a long time that malnourishment during the years of growth and development will result in a certain amount of dwarfing and delayed physical maturity, even if the deficiency is temporary and a normal diet is later restored. What is far more ominous is the evidence that protein deficiency in infancy and early childhood may result in permanent impairment of the brain.

A child's body grows to 20 percent of its adult size in the first three years, while the brain grows to 80 percent of its adult size. This rapid brain growth is primarily a result of protein synthesis (more than 50 percent of the dry weight of brain tissue is protein). When protein is not available in the diet to supply the amino acids from which brain proteins are synthesized, the brain stops growing. Apparently it can never regain the lost time. Not only is head size reduced in a malnourished youngster, but the brain does not fill the cranium.

Studies in Central and South America have established a strong correlation between nutritional levels and physical and mental development in preschool and school age children. Among underprivileged youngsters studied in rural Mexico, height and mental achievement were positively correlated; all these children were near the lower end of the height and mental-achievement scales for their ages, indicating that their development was affected by their nutrition. Among well-fed, middle-class children in the same society, height and mental development showed no relationship.

In another study in Chile, comparisons were made among Santiago slum children on inadequate diets, other slum children receiving supplemented diets and medical care, and middle-class children. The slum children on supplemented diets more closely resembled the middle-class youngsters in physcial and mental development than they did their neighbors with poor diets, although the two groups of slum children came from otherwise very similar environments. Of the malnourished children only 51 percent reached the normal range of development, compared with 95 percent of the supplemented group and 97 percent of the middle-class group. Another group of children who had had marasmus as infants and had subsequently been given medical care and supplemental food were all found to have considerably below normal intelligence 3 to 6 years later. Although human implications must be inferred with care, studies on rats suggest that malnourished pregnant mothers may also produce children with impaired brain development; at the very least, the stress of the pregnancy represents a threat to the mother's health and her ability to care for the child.

There is some evidence that even adults do not fully recover from episodes of severe deprivation. After apparent recovery, former prisoners of Nazi concentration camps (living in Norway 20 years later) exhibited reduced brain sizes and a variety of emotional and mental problems. How much of this was due to the starvation they endured and how much to other factors such as torture and severe emotional stress is impossible to say.

Governments must be made aware of nutritional levels in their populations and of what these can allow them to expect and demand of people. Undernutrition, together with parasitism and disease, typically produces apathy, listlessness, and low productivity. Well-fed Europeans and North Americans, seeing these symptoms but neither recognizing them as such nor understanding their cause, often conclude that natives of underdeveloped areas are "lazy." By contrast, the improvement of inadequate diets may lead to rebelliousness and aggressiveness—characteristic of the behavior of humans during the recovery period following starvation experiments with volunteers. The implications of the prevalence of malnutrition for the undeveloped countries in the future, when it is more likely than not to be even more widespread and severe, are frightening to say the least. All proposals to increase food production in the UDCs are inevitably attached to elaborate plans for economic development. Can they possibly achieve either with a weakened, malnourished populace and with the prospects of physical and mental impairment in a large portion of the coming generation?

The Picture in America

Americans were shocked in 1968 when the extent of malnutrition and clinical deficiency diseases in the U.S. was made public. Although it was not the first report, a CBS television special program was the first to reach a substantial number of Americans. As in UDCs, this malnutrition appears to be related to poverty and an accompanying syndrome of unemployment, displacement from the land, and appalling sanitary conditions, often accompanied by a high incidence of parasitism. A U.S. Public Health Service doctor testified before the Senate Select Committee on Nutrition and Human Needs that the nutritional level of the segment of the population examined in a government survey conducted by the Public Health Service was as low as those found in many underdeveloped countries.

Among a random sample of 12,000 American men, women and children from low-income areas in Texas, New York, Louisiana and Kentucky, the survey found seven extremely severe cases of marasmus and kwashiorkor, eighteen of rickets, and evidence of widespread goiter. Four percent showed milder symptoms of kwashiorkor and a similar proportion had mild cases of rickets. About 17 percent of these 12,000 people were described as "real risks" nutritionally. Among the children, most were below average size for their ages, and 3.5 percent were definitely stunted. One-third of those less than 6 years of age were anemic, and nearly as many showed signs of being vitamin A deficient, many of them seriously so.

The underlying causes of this level of malnutrition and hunger in a country as rich as the U.S. resemble in some respects those in UDCs, including inadequate food distribution, poverty, and ignorance. Government food-aid programs have clearly failed to achieve their supposed aims. Free surplus foods have indeed been distributed to the poor by the U.S. Department of Agriculture, whose primary interest, unfortunately, seems to have been in the expeditious elimination of the surpluses rather than in the nutritional needs of the recipients. Food stamps have been used in some places to enable the poor to buy food at lower prices, but for the lowest income groups, families with less than $1,000 per year, even the stamps are too expensive. In addition, participation in the government programs was optional, and city and county governments administered them. Many local governments declined to participate, even when they had large eligible populations. Poor administration probably accounts for some of the failure as well.

A courageous Southern Senator, Ernest F. Hollings of South Carolina, made a major contribution toward forcing the Federal government and the public to recognize and attack the problem of hunger in America. In early 1969 he testified to the Senate Select Committee on Nutrition that when he was Governor of South Carolina from 1959 to 1963, he and other state officials deliberately concealed their state's hunger problem in an attempt to boost its industrial development. They feared that knowledge of South Carolina's difficulties would discourage industry from locating there.

The high incidence of deficiencies of vitamins A and D and iodine found by the Public Health Survey is embarassing, since they are easily preventable. Nonfat dry milk, which is now fortified with vitamin A for overseas food aid, is still not fortified for domestic programs; nor is vitamin D added, as it clearly should and easily could be by irradiation. The need for the use of iodized salt may be forgotten or unknown among some of the poor, yet the government survey found that it was not even available in the markets in parts of Texas, a goiter area.

The Public Health Service is now conducting further surveys on the extent of malnutrition in the U.S., and the food programs for the poor are being reorganized. An experimental program with free food stamps for the destitute has begun. Hopefully, public awareness and congressional interest will result in some alleviation of the nutritional problems and some effort will be made toward improving the conditions that produced them. Indeed, it might lead to a more general recognition of nutritional problems by *affluent* Americans, many of whom suffer from *over*nourishment, or malnutrition, or both. It could also help bring about a general improvement in our domestic food industries, which sometimes sacrifice nutrition and quality for flavor, eye-appeal, and economy in production.

Bibliography

Altman, Philip L., and Dorothy S. Dittmer (eds.), 1968. *Metabolism.* Federation of American Societies for Experimental Biology. Bethesda, Md. Good source of detailed information on nutrition.

Barnett, H. J., and Chandler Morse, 1963. *Scarcity and Growth.* Johns Hopkins Press. This book presents the views of the Cornucopian economists.

Borgstrom, Georg, 1967. *Too Many.* Macmillan, New York.

Brown, Harrison, James Bonner, and John Weir, 1957. *The Next Hundred Years.* Viking Press, New York. A classic of futurism, this work is updated in *The Next Ninety Years,* published in 1967 by the California Institute of Technology. *The Next Hundred Years* has a discussion of the theoretical possibility of extracting needed minerals from granite, sea, and air.

Cloud, Preston E., Jr., 1968. Realities of mineral distribution. *Texas Quarterly,* vol. 11, pp. 103–126. A fine brief summary of the nonrenewable resource situation, with commentary on some of the premises of technological optimists.

Cloud, Preston, E., Jr. (ed.), 1969. *Resources and Man.* W. H. Freeman and Company, San Francisco. See especially Chapter 8 by M. King Hubbert on energy resources, Chapter 6 by T. S. Lovering on mineral resources from the land, and Chapter 7 by P. E. Cloud on the mineral resources of the sea.

Cravioto, Joaquin, E. R. DeLicardie, and H. B. Birch, 1966. Nutrition, growth and neurointegrative development: an experimental and ecological study. *Pediatrics* (supplement), vol. 38, no. 2, part II (Aug.).

Dumont, René, and Bernard Rosier. 1969. *The Hungry Future.* Praeger, New York. These authors estimate that in 1969, 300–500 million human beings were undernourished, and 1,600 million people malnourished.

Food and Agriculture Organization of the United Nations, 1968. *Production Yearbook 1967*. FAO-UN, Rome.

Gilluly, James, Aaron C. Waters, and A. O. Woodford. 1968. *Principles of Geology,* 3rd ed. W. H. Freeman and Company, San Francisco. See especially Chapter 12 on mineral resources.

Lessing, Lawrence, 1969. Power from the earth's own heat. *Fortune* (June). This article paints an optimistic picture of the future of the generation of electricity from geothermal power.

Lovering, T. S., 1968. New fuel mineral resources in the next century. *Texas Quarterly,* vol. 11, pp. 127–147. A critical discussion of the views of the Cornucopian economists, and of the practical problems of extracting minerals from common rock.

Paddock, William, and Paul Paddock, 1964. *Hungry Nations.* Little, Brown & Company, Boston. Good descriptions of conditions relating to UDC food production.

Park, Charles F., Jr., 1968. *Affluence in Jeopardy.* Freeman, Cooper & Co., San Francisco. An important discussion of mineral resource problems in a world with an exploding population. There are a few rather minor technical errors, but the book generally gives an accurate picture of resource depletion. The discussion of mineral policy is, in contrast, disappointing.

President's Science Advisory Committee Panel on the World Food Supply, 1967. *The World Food Problem* (3 vols.). Washington, D.C. A very detailed, basic source.

Robinson, H. F., 1969. Dimensions of the world food crisis. *BioScience,* vol. 19, no. 1 (Jan.), pp. 24–29.

Sebrell, William H., Jr., and James J. Haggerty, 1967. *Food and Nutrition.* Time Inc., New York.

Simpson, David, 1968. The dimensions of world poverty. *Scientific American,* vol. 219, no. 5 (Nov.). Includes a somewhat understated discussion of the food problem.

The Rotarian (magazine), 1969. The hungry world (special issue, June).

Watt, K. E. F., 1969. *Ecology and Resource Management.* McGraw-Hill, New York.

Williams, Roger J., 1962. *Nutrition in a Nutshell.* Dolphin Books. Garden City, N.Y.

CHAPTER 5

Food Production

*"The human brain, so frail, so perishable, so full of inexhaustible
dreams and hungers, burns by the power of the leaf."*

Loren Eiseley, *The Unexpected Universe*, 1969

All flesh is grass. This simple phrase summarizes a basic principle of biology
that is essential to an understanding of the world food problem. The basic
source of food for all animal populations is green plants—"grass." Human
beings and all other animals with which we share this planet obtain the
energy and nutrients for growth, development, and sustenance by eating
plants directly, by eating other animals that have eaten plants, or by eating
animals that have eaten animals that have eaten plants, and so forth.

Solar Energy and Food

One may think of the plants and animals in an area, together with their
physical surroundings, as comprising a system through which energy passes,
and within which materials move in cycles. Energy enters the system in the
form of radiation from the sun. Through the process of photosynthesis, green
plants are able to "capture" some of the incoming solar energy and use it to
bond together small molecules into the large (organic) molecules that are
characteristic of living organisms. Animals that eat plants are able to break
down these large organic molecules and put to their own use the energy that
once bound the molecules together. The animal expends some of this energy
in its daily activities and uses some of it to build large molecules of animal

substance (for growth or repair of tissue). Animals that eat other animals once again break down the large molecules and put the energy from them—energy that originally arrived in the form of solar energy—to their own uses. According to the first law of thermodynamics (see Box 4-1), energy can be neither created nor destroyed, although it may be changed from one form to another (as in the change from light energy to the energy of chemical bonds in photosynthesis). The second law of thermodynamics says, in essence, that in any transfer of energy there will be a loss of usable energy; that is, a certain amount of the energy will be degraded from an available, concentrated form to an unavailable, dispersed form. The practical consequence of this law as it applies to food production is that no transfer of energy in a biological system may be 100 percent efficient; there is always some loss of usable energy at each transfer. In the photosynthetic system, usually one percent or less of the sunlight falling on green plants is actually converted to the kind of chemical bond energy that is available to animals eating the plants. Roughly 10 percent of that store of energy in the plants may turn up as available energy in the chemical bonds of animals that have eaten plants. And roughly ten percent of that energy may in turn be incorporated into the chemical bonds of other animals that eat the animals that ate the plants.

Thus, one may picture the flow of energy through this system as a step-wise progression along what is known as a food chain. A food chain starts with the green plants, which are known as the producers. They are the first *trophic* (feeding) *level*. Then, at the second trophic level, come the herbivores (plant-eating animals), the primary consumers. Secondary consumers are the carnivores (or meat-eaters), which eat herbivores. They are at the third trophic level. Tertiary consumers are the carnivores that eat other carnivores, and so forth. Man plays many roles in food chains, but his commonest is that of a herbivore, since grains and other plant materials make up a very great proportion of the diet of most human beings. Man may also be a secondary consumer, as when he eats beefsteak (or the meat of any other herbivorous animal). When he consumes fishes, he often occupies positions even further along the food chain, because many fishes are tertiary or even quaternary consumers themselves. A food chain including man is shown in Figure 5-1.

At each transfer of energy in a food chain, perhaps 90 percent of the chemical energy stored in organisms of the lower level becomes unavailable to those of the higher level (in certain situations the percentage loss may be much higher or lower than this). Since the total amount of energy entering the food chain is fixed by the photosynthetic activity of the plants, obviously more usable energy is available to organisms occupying lower positions in the food chain than is available to those in higher positions. For instance, as an oversimplification, it might take roughly ten thousand pounds of wheat to produce one thousand pounds of cattle, which in turn could be used to produce one hundred pounds of human being. By moving man one step down the food chain, ten times as much energy would be directly available—that is, the ten thousand pounds of wheat used to produce one thousand pounds of cattle could be used instead to produce one thousand pounds of human beings.

It follows from this application of the second law of thermodynamics that in most biological systems the biomass (living weight) of producers will be greater than that of primary consumers; the biomass of primary consumers in turn will be greater than that of secondary consumers; and so forth. The weight of organisms possible at any trophic level is dependent upon the energy supplied by the organisms at the next lowest trophic level; and some energy becomes unavailable at each transfer.

Mankind has always been dependent on the process of photosynthesis for

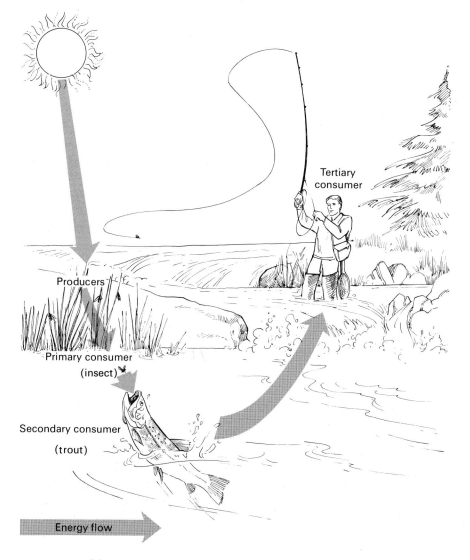

Tertiary
consumer

Producers

Primary consumer
(insect)

Secondary consumer
(trout)

Energy flow

FIGURE 5-1

A food chain including man. A mosquito feeding on the man would be a quaternary consumer.

his food. Whether primitive man ate berries, roots, fishes, reindeer, or whatever, the energy he derived from his food had the same ultimate source: the radiant energy of the sun. Not, however, until the agricultural revolution did man begin to exercise some control over plant growth, and attempt to concentrate and increase the yield from desirable food plants. His earliest attempts at agriculture doubtless were based on the astute observation that certain accidental disturbances of the land by human activities increased the growth of some useful plants. Indeed, today in some tropical areas so-called "slash-and-burn" agriculture consists of little more than cutting and burning clearings in which seeds of various desirable plants are then scattered. It would have been a small step from such practices to the reduction of competition for the desired plants by simple hoeing of weeds and to the utilization of the fertilizing effects of excreta and other organic wastes from human activities.

Modern agriculture, of course, differs completely from primitive slash-and-burn agriculture. The science of plant breeding has produced a vast diversity of crop varieties that are adapted to various growing conditions, high in yield, resistant to diseases, and so forth. Mechanical cultivation and harvesting, improved methods of fertilization and irrigation, the use of chemical and biological controls against plant and insect pests, weather forecasting (and, to a small degree, weather control), and many other technological advances have greatly increased the quantity of food that can be produced on a given area of land. Technology has also increased the quality of some crops, but not of all crops. For instance, high yields in grains are sometimes gained at the expense of lowered protein content.

Although man is able to modify many of the conditions of plant growth, limits are imposed upon agricultural production by geographic variation in the amount of solar energy reaching the surface of the Earth, temperatures of both soil and air, amount of soil moisture available, and so forth. And, because of the key role played by photosynthesis in agriculture, it is inevitable that farming will remain a highly dispersed human activity. Agriculture must remain spread over the face of the Earth, because the energy of sunlight can only be utilized in photosynthesis at its point of arrival. Furthermore, when populations are large, agricultural production and the transport of agricultural goods will always remain intimately intertwined: food production cannot be considered in isolation from food distribution. It is not possible to concentrate agriculture in regions of need, as it is so often possible to concentrate production of other substances required by human beings. Indeed, the existence of high concentrations of human beings tends to be inimical to agriculture. For instance, as anyone knows who has lived in the country around such cities as Philadelphia, Chicago, or Los Angeles, much farmland is taken out of production each year; prime agricultural land is "developed" into subdivisions and highways. For each additional 1,000 people in California, an average of 238 acres of arable land has been covered by buildings and pavement. By 1960 some 3 million acres of California farmland had been converted to nonagricultural use. By the year 2020 that figure is projected to increase to 13 million acres—half of the state's arable land. In addition, smog kills crops. If current trends continue, California will not be able to feed herself much longer, let alone export food.

Man has domesticated many species of food plants. In addition he has improved most of them by selective breeding and/or hybridization. In prehistoric times some 80 kinds of food plants of major importance were domesticated, as opposed to only about two dozen kinds of animals. But in spite of this diversity of food plants, a relatively small number of crop plants supplies the vast majority of the world's food. If one had to pick the three most important food plants in the world, the almost inevitable choice would be three species of grasses: rice, wheat, and corn. So important are these cereal grains that slightly more than one-half of the harvested land of the world is used to grow them.

Rice is probably the most important of all; it is the staple food for an estimated 2 billion people. Mainland China grows about 35 percent of the world's rice, India and Pakistan 27 percent, Japan 7 percent, and Indonesia 6 percent. Other countries, largely in southeast Asia and Latin America, grow about 25 percent. New strains of rice that produce very high yields per acre when properly cultivated have been developed at the International Rice Research Institute (IRRI) in the Philippines. The IRRI strains are now being introduced to farmers in southeast Asia. They may have dramatic effects on rice production in that area and eventually in others.

Close behind rice in importance in the diet of human beings comes wheat, with a total production as large as that of rice, or even slightly larger. Unlike rice, wheat does not grow well in the tropics, in part because one of its major diseases, wheat rust fungus, thrives in warm, humid climates. Wheat is grown mostly where winters are cold and wet, and summers hot and rather dry. The United States produces some 15 percent of the world's wheat, the Soviet Union 24 percent, Canada, France, and India 5 percent each, Italy 4 percent, Turkey 3 percent, Argentina and Australia 2.5 percent each, and all the rest of the world about 34 percent.

Corn, or maize, is the third great cereal crop, its production being about 90 percent that of wheat. The long, warm, moist summers of the eastern half of the United States are ideal for corn production, and more than one-half of the world supply is grown there. Russia ranks number two in corn production, growing a little more than 5 percent of the world total, and Brazil is right behind Russia with almost 5 percent. Slightly more than 13 percent is accounted for by Yugoslavia, Mexico, Argentina, Rumania, and South Africa combined, and the other countries of the world grow 25 percent jointly.

Rice, wheat, and corn together account for somewhat more than ¾ billion metric tons of grain annually. The rest of the world's crop of about one billion metric tons is made up by other grains: barley, oats, rye, millet, and sorghum. Somewhat more than half of the world's production of these grains comes from the United States, Russia, and western Europe.

The protein content of modern high-yield grains tends to be about 5–13 percent and is not complete protein (protein with the proper balance of amino acids for human nutrition), being too low in content of some essential amino acids, especially tryptophan and lysine. Grains are all rich in protein, however, in comparison with the only other staple crop that approaches them in global significance: potatoes. Roughly a third of a billion metric tons of potatoes are grown annually, but the water content of the potato is so high (75 percent) and its protein content so low (1–4 percent wet weight) that the food value of the crop is considerably less than that of any of the "big three" grains. The potato is well adapted to cool climates. Of potato production outside of mainland China (from which information is not available), fully 30 percent comes from the Soviet Union. Poland comes second with 13 percent and West Germany third with a little over 8 percent. France produces 6 percent and the United States and East Germany about 4 percent each. The rest of the world accounts for some 35 percent, mostly produced by European and Latin American countries.

Although legumes cannot compete with grasses in volume in world food production, they have two to four times the protein content, and are thus critically important in human nutrition. They are not only an important source of protein for man but are also the ultimate source of much of the protein in domestic animals. Bacteria associated with the roots of legumes have the ability to fix gaseous nitrogen from the atmosphere and convert it to a form that may be directly used by plants. As a result legumes also serve man as fertilizer, "green manure," and thus contribute indirectly to the protein he derives from other plants.

Two legumes, soybeans and peanuts, are grown primarily as oil sources. They account for about half of the world's legume production of some 80 million metric tons. Soybean and peanut oil are used for making margarine, salad dressings, and shortenings, and are used in various industrial processes. The material remaining after the oils are pressed out (press cake) is valued as a feed for livestock. Little of the soybean crop is directly consumed by man, whereas a significant portion of the peanut crop is eaten in the nut form or in candy or peanut butter. The remaining legumes—beans and peas —are known collectively as pulses. There is a wide variety of these, including lima beans, string beans, white beans, kidney beans, scotch beans, peas, cowpeas, garbanzos, lentils, and so forth. Legumes are grown all over the world; production of soybeans is concentrated in the United States and mainland China, that of peanuts in India and Africa, and of pulses in the Far East and Latin America.

Grains and legumes are the mainstays of man's vegetable diet on a global basis, but a vast variety of other plants are cultivated and consumed. Cassava, sweet potatoes, and yams (all root crops), supply starch to many people in the world, especially the poor. The roots of the sugar beet plant and the stem of the cane sugar plant (a grass) supply us with our sugar. The roots, stems, and leaves of many plants are eaten as vegetables: cabbage, lettuce, celery, carrots, cauliflower, spinach, and rhubarb to name a few. Fruits and berries are also widely eaten: apples, peaches, pears, citrus fruits, tomatoes, eggplants, peppers, pineapples, bananas, passion fruits, papayas, mangoes, apricots, dates, grapes, strawberries and many dozens more.

Many plants are also used as forages—food for domestic animals. Although domestic animals are often just turned loose to graze and fend for themselves, many crops are grown specifically as feed for animals. For instance, some 60 million acres of the world are planted to the most nutritious of all forage crops, the legume alfalfa (called lucerne in Europe), which is especially rich in protein. Clovers and other legumes are also grown as forage, as are various grasses.

The primary importance of domesticated animals today is as a source of high-quality protein. As noted previously, the selection of animals to domesticate for food has been more limited than the selection of plants. Only nine species—cattle, pigs, sheep, goats, waterbuffalo, chickens, ducks, geese, and turkeys—account for virtually 100 percent of the world's production of protein from domesticated animals. Beef and pork together, in roughly equal amounts, account for some 90 percent of the nonpoultry meat production. Cows produce more than 90 percent of the milk consumed, waterbuffalo about 4 percent, and goats and sheep the remainder (ignoring tiny amounts from reindeer and some other minor domestic mammals).

Although certain breeds of domestic animals are adapted to the tropics, one can say that animal husbandry is generally easier and more productive in temperate areas than in the tropics. It is primarily in the temperate zones that geneticists have produced animals capable of extraordinary yields of meat, milk, and eggs. The year-round high temperatures and possibly the high humidity of the tropics tend to slow growth and, in milk-producing animals, lower the production of milk and milk solids. High temperature and humidity also often provide ideal conditions for parasites and carriers of disease. For instance, in parts of Africa where rainfall and other conditions are suitable, tsetse flies carry a serious disease, nagana (caused by single-celled animals called trypanosomes), which makes cattle herding impossible. Furthermore, although forage may grow luxuriantly in many tropical areas, it is often low in nutrient value.

Domestic animals, especially cattle, are often more than mere meat or milk producers in the UDCs. In the semiarid zones of East and West Africa, cattle are the basis of entire cultures. They are regularly tapped for blood as well as milk, and are intimately related to the social and economic life of certain groups. Cattle provide their owners with wealth and prestige, are used ceremonially, and have aesthetic value. In India there is a large population of "sacred cattle," so called because of the Hindu taboo against slaughter. Visitors to India rather commonly conclude that the Indian food situation could be ameliorated by slaughtering these "useless" animals. This judgment is based on a fundamental misunderstanding of the situation. Like so many folkways and taboos, the Indian taboo has a vital influence on the local ecology. Most of the cattle feed on forage and wastes that are not human foods: they do not compete with man. The cattle *do* supply milk, and above all they supply power. Bullocks (castrated bulls) are the tractors of India; they are absolutely essential to her agricultural economy. Finally, the cattle also supply dung, which is the main cooking fuel of India, and which is also used as plaster in houses and as fertilizer. Of an estimated 800 million tons of dung produced each year some 300 million are used as fuel. This fuel produces heat equivalent to that obtained from burning 35 million tons of coal (about half of India's coal production).

Recent History of Agricultural Production

Following the Second World War there was a steady worldwide upward trend in food production per capita. This trend has generally continued in the DCs, with some exceptions, to the present day. In the UDCs, however, this steady increase was halted between 1956 and 1958, depending on the country, and things have been nip and tuck ever since. Table 5-1 shows the United Nations

TABLE 5–1
Index Numbers of Per Capita Food Production, by Regions (1963 = 100)

Region	1956	1957	1958	1959	1960	1961	1962	1964	1965	1966
World*	95	94	98	98	99	99	100	101	100	102
Africa	98	96	96	98	100	96	99	99	97	94
America, North	97	92	98	97	97	94	95	97	98	101
America, Latin	101	100	103	99	98	101	99	101	100	98
Asia										
Near East	95	97	98	98	96	95	99	98	97	97
Far East*	95	93	96	98	100	101	100	101	97	95
Europe										
Eastern and U.S.S.R.	94	96	103	104	104	105	106	108	109	120
Western	86	88	90	91	96	94	100	100	100	101
Oceania	86	82	95	91	95	93	100	102	95	108

SOURCE: Food and Agriculture Organization of the United Nations (FAO).
NOTE: The indexes are calculated as a ratio between the index numbers of food production and the corresponding index numbers of population. For further information see the *Production Yearbook* published by the FAO and the *1967 Supplement to the United Nations Statistical Yearbook and Monthly Bulletin of Statistics.*
* Excluding China (mainland).

index numbers of per capita food production for the years 1956–1966. In 1966 the average country in Africa and Latin America grew less food per person than it did 10 years before, and the average country in the Far East had about held its own. This situation obtained in spite of substantial increases (roughly 25 percent) in absolute food supplies in these areas during that period; population growth more than offset the gains. One cannot judge directly from per capita food production figures exactly what happened to the average diet of individuals in these areas, since consumption equals production plus or minus trade. The trade position of many of these countries changed markedly between 1956 and 1966. Many of them became heavy grain importers.

Local weather conditions are extremely important to food production. Bad weather affected the growing seasons of 1965–1966 and 1966–1967 in many parts of the world. As a result, per capita index numbers for 1965 and 1966 were very low. Good weather in 1967–1968 brought per capita production in the UDCs almost back to the 1964 level. Weather was less favorable in 1968–1969, according to preliminary estimates, and as a result there was no worldwide per capita rise in food production during that period. In many UDCs there was a per capita drop. For instance, 23 Latin American countries and Africa had the following pattern of per capita agricultural production index numbers over this period (1957–1959 = 100):

	1964	*1965*	*1966*	*1967*	*1968* (estimate)
Latin America	97	105	97	98	97
Africa	103	101	99	103	100

India is often considered to be the indicator for the UDCs. Agricultural expert Raymond Ewell made an interesting analysis of India's food-grain production from the 1949–1950 growing season to the 1968–1969 season. Figure 5-2 presents his data. The trend line is fitted by the statistical method of least squares, a method of plotting the line through the data points so

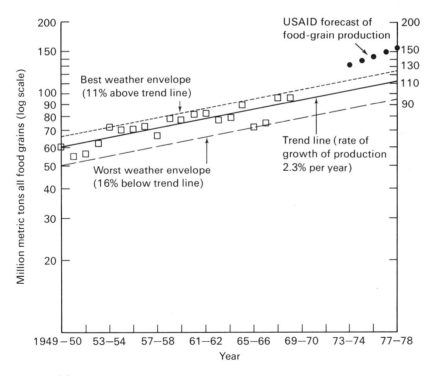

FIGURE 5-2

Trends in Indian food-grain production from 1949–1950 to 1968–1969. Solid circles indicate USAID forecasts of production. If they are achieved India will have made a substantial breakthrough in agricultural production. [Courtesy of Dr. Raymond Ewell.]

that the sum of the squared deviations of the points from the line is minimized. The trend line shows a growth rate of 2.3 percent per year; India's current population growth rate is 2.5 percent per year. Although there are optimistic forecasts that India can reach and sustain a grain production growth of 3 percent a year or better, Dr. Ewell, who is more pessimistic, said in 1969 that it would probably take 3 to 4 years before sufficient data for reaching a conclusion will be available.

Of course index numbers are at best a crude indicator of the food situation. Even within a single country conditions may vary tremendously from area to area. For instance, by mid-1968 most of Northern India was completely out of the famine conditions that had held sway for several years before. In most parts of the provinces of Bihar, Punjab, Uttar Pradesh, Bengal, and Orissa, wheat and rice were superabundant, and as a result prices were dropping steadily. But in spite of this surplus of food, 7 million people were in danger of starvation in Orissa alone. Within Northern India as a whole, some 20 million people were in "acute distress," due largely to local droughts in areas adjacent to those producing surpluses. The people are so poor that they cannot create effective demand for food, producing the spectacle of surpluses and dropping prices in close proximity to starvation. This local situation is a microcosm of the story of food distribution throughout the world.

To picture the UDCs simply as net food importers would be an error. Although the DCs annually deliver some 2.5 million tons of gross protein to the UDCs, the latter send to the DCs about 3.5 million tons of higher quality protein in fish meal, presscakes of oilseeds, and soybeans. Peru exports to the DCs large catches of various fishes that could greatly alleviate severe protein deficiencies at home. More than sixty countries, including Mexico, Panama, Hong Kong, and India, supply the United States with shrimp, which could otherwise be a life saver for the protein-starved children of these countries. Georg Borgstrom describes the advantage held by the rich countries of the world in the present pattern of protein flow as a "treacherous exchange." That it is based primarily on the present world economic system is an indictment of that system and its values.

The food supply in the UDCs is at best marginal. *Large-scale efforts are required simply to avoid drops in per capita food production.* In order to *improve* the lot of the Earth's one to two billion hungry people, food production will have to increase at an unprecedented rate. What are the prospects for continuing to increase the food production of the world? Within the framework of any system of technology or any economic system, the environment imposes limits on agricultural production. As noted earlier, for the foreseeable future terrestrial food production will depend on the availability of sunlight, fertile soil, water, and a growing season long enough for crops to mature. Unfortunately these conditions are unevenly distributed over the Earth. For example, although many tropical forest areas have a year-round growing season and abundant rainfall, their soils are often extremely poor, making large scale agriculture there virtually impossible at present.

Amount of Land Under Cultivation

In 1967 the report of the President's Scientific Advisory Committee estimated the amount of potentially arable (farmable) land on the Earth to be 7.86 billion acres. This amounts to only 24 percent of the total ice-free land area, but is more than triple the area actually planted and harvested in any given year. About 4.13 billion acres, more than half of the estimated total, lies in the tropical areas. Warm-temperate and subtropical areas account for another 1.37 billion potentially arable acres, and cool-temperate areas ac-

TABLE 5–2

Present Population and Cultivated Land on Each Continent,
Compared with Potentially Arable Land

Continent	Population in 1965 (millions of persons) (1)	Area in billions of acres			Acres of cultivated* land per person (5)	Ratio of cultivated* to potentially arable land (percent) (6)
		Total (2)	Potentially arable (3)	Cultivated* (4)		
Africa	310	7.46	1.81	0.39	1.3	22
Asia	1,855	6.76	1.55	1.28	.7	83
Australia and New Zealand	14	2.03	.38	.04	2.9	2
Europe	445	1.18	.43	.38	.9	88
North America	255	5.21	1.15	.59	2.3	51
South America	197	4.33	1.68	.19	1.0	11
U.S.S.R	234	5.52	.88	.56	2.4	64
Total	3,310	32.49	7.88	3.43	1.0	44

SOURCE: President's Science Advisory Committee, *The World Food Problem* (1967).

* Our cultivated area is called by FAO "Arable land and land under permanent crops." It includes land under crops, temporary fallow, temporary meadows, for mowing or pasture, market and kitchen gardens, fruit trees, vines, shrubs, and rubber plantations. Within this definition there are said to be wide variations among reporting countries. The land actually harvested during any particular year is about one-half to two-thirds of the total cultivated land.

count for most of the rest, 2.24 billion acres. The distribution of cultivated and potentially arable land in relation to population and area of continents in 1965 is shown in Table 5-2. As you can see, the majority of potentially arable land is in Africa and South America, with Asia close behind.

But the term "potentially arable" can be misleading. Actually, almost all the land that can be cultivated under today's economic circumstances is now under cultivation. Most of the "potentially arable" land in Asia could not support one four-month growing season without irrigation; subtracting this land leaves very little additional arable land available in Asia. Irrigation is just one factor among many that will have to be considered if the potential of this land is to be realized. Technical expertise must be available to evaluate the fertility of soils, the feasibility of irrigation, the availability of capital and labor for both farming and support activities (such as constructing farm roads), and so forth. Such surveys cost money. So do farm roads, which account for 10 to 30 percent of the cost of developing new agricultural land. Clearing land, removing stones, improving drainage, and other necessary improvements also cost money, and these costs are extremely variable from area to area. Other costs that must be considered include the expense of irrigation when irrigation is necessary, the costs of administering new developments resettling people, supplying them with homes, schools, services, and so on. The per-acre costs of seven sample projects in UDCs ranged from $32 to $973, with a median of $218.

How much time could we buy in the population-food crisis by concentrating on the development of new lands? Under the optimistic assumption that one acre of land will support one person, and the even more optimistic assumption that development costs will be only $400 per acre (the cost of irrigating alone now averages almost $400 per acre), the world would have to invest *$28 billion per year* simply to open new lands to feed the people now being added to the population annually. And, since there is an inevitable "lag time" in opening up new lands, it would seem reasonable to start immediately with the financing of at least a 10-year program costing at least $280 billion.

The chances are, however, that such a program would be as unsuccessful as previous attempts have been at opening "potentially arable" lands. In 1954 large sections of the dry plains of Kazakhstan in the U.S.S.R. were put into grain production. Premier Khrushchev had great hopes for this highly promoted "virgin lands" program, but unfortunately the virgin turned out to be a harlot in disguise. Rainfall there is marginal, roughly 12 inches per year, and drought has afflicted the area. In the 1950's Turkey also expanded grain plantings into grassland areas that subsequently had to be allowed to revert to grass because of inadequate rainfall.

A classic example of lack of attention to the agricultural limits imposed by local conditions was the ill-fated British groundnut (peanut) project started in Tanganyika (now Tanzania) after World War II. Although agricultural experts predicted that weather conditions would be satisfactory in only 8 years out of 19, millions of dollars were spent on the program. All the expertise of the British was to no avail; the program was a catastrophic failure.

Brazil's attempts to set up an agricultural colony in the Amazon basin have been utterly defeated by poor tropical soils. A most poignant account of the realities of agricultural development of virgin lands is "The Myth of Fertility Dooms Development Plans," by Darryl G. Cole, which appeared in the *National Observer,* April 22, 1968. Thirteen years earlier Cole took his family to Cañas Gordas, Costa Rica, where they attempted to clear a piece of highland rain forest and set up a diversified farm. They failed from the beginning, in spite of their farming experience in the United States, extensive consultation with experts, and considerable experimentation with fertilizers, insecticides, fungicides, various cover crops and methods of tillage. The basic reason for failure was the thin soil, whose fertility quickly vanished in the heavy rain when the forest was removed. The Coles were reduced to dependence on a monoculture of coffee, a bush crop grown in the shade of trees. Cole wrote, "I would like to submit that such hopes [of prosperity for farmers on virgin lands] have not been realized in the Cañas Gordas–San Vita area, that they are not being realized in other areas of Costa Rica, and that, on the basis of our present knowledge of tropical agriculture, they will not be realized in similar new lands in underdeveloped nations. The myth of the fertility of these virgin lands has been too long in dying."

Perhaps the most discussed approach to bringing substantial amounts of new land under cultivation lies in the irrigation of arid (but otherwise arable) lands. Such attempts are mainly limited to large-scale water projects that would include dams and canals or the removal of salt from ocean and brackish water (desalination). Supplies of usable groundwater are already badly depleted in most areas where they are accessible, and natural recharge is so low in most arid regions that such supplies do not offer a solution in any case.

Some recent statistics will give perspective to the following discussion of water projects and desalting. The United States in 1966 was using about 300 billion gallons of water per day, of which 135 billion gallons were consumed by agriculture and 165 billion gallons by municipal and industrial users. The bulk of the agricultural water cost the farmer from 5 to 10 cents per 1,000 gallons; the highest price paid in 1966 for agricultural water was 15 cents per 1,000 gallons. For small industrial and municipal supplies prices as high as 50 to 70 cents per 1,000 gallons were paid in arid regions of the United States. Some communities in the Southwest were paying about $1.00 per 1,000 gallons for "project" water, the extremely high cost of which was due largely to transportation costs, which have been estimated at 5 to 15 cents per 1,000 gallons per 100 miles.

What are the implications of such numbers with reference to the irrigation of arid lands? The most ambitious water project yet conceived in this country is the North American Water and Power Alliance, which proposes to distribute water from the great rivers of Canada to thirsty locations all over the United States. Formidable political problems aside (some based on the certainty that in the face of expanding populations, demands for water will certainly rise in Canada), this project would require the expenditure of $100 billion in construction costs over a 20-year completion period. At the end of this time, the yield to the United States would be 69 million acre-feet of water per year, or 63 billion gallons per day. If past experience with massive water projects is any guide, these cost and water figures are overly optimistic. Such projects virtually always have cost more than the estimates of the original promoters. But even if the figures are assumed to be accurate, it is instructive to note that this monumental undertaking would provide for an increase of only 21 percent in the water consumption of the United States, during a period in which the population is expected to increase by between 25 and 43 percent. For the sake of argument, it may be assumed that *all* of the additional water could be devoted to agriculture, although extrapolation of present consumption patterns indicates that only about half would be. Using the rather conservative figure of 500 gallons per day to grow enough food for one person, it is found that this project could feed 126 million additional people. Since this is somewhat less than the number of people expected to be added to the North American population between 1970 and 2000, it should be clear that even the most massive water projects can make but a token contribution to the long-term solution of the world food problem. And in the crucial short term, the years preceding 1980, *no* additional people will be fed by projects that exist only on the drawing board today.

The costs of such projects are staggering, the scale insufficient, and the lead time too long. And we need not merely speculate about the future of such projects to produce evidence of the failure of such technological "solutions" in the absence of population control. The highly publicized and expensive Aswan Dam project will ultimately supply food (at the present miserable diet level) for much less than Egypt's population growth during the time of its construction. In addition, as is discussed in Chapter 12, it is creating a series of ecological disasters. Moreover, as is true of all water projects of this nature, before long (perhaps in 100 years) silting of the reservoir will eliminate all of the temporary gains.

Desalting water for irrigation also has serious economic limitations. The desalting plants operational in the world today produce water at individual rates of 7.5 million gallons per day and less at a cost of 75 cents per 1,000 gallons and up, the cost increasing as the plant size decreases. The most optimistic proposal that anyone seems to have made for desalting with present or soon-to-be-available technology is for a 150-million-gallon-per-day nuclear-powered installation under study by the Bechtel Corporation for the Los Angeles Metropolitan Water District. Bechtel's original figures indicated that water from this proposed complex would be available at the site for 27–28 cents per 1,000 gallons, or $88–90 per acre-foot. Spiralling construction cost estimates caused the project to be shelved after the anticipated water cost had reached 40–50 cents per 1,000 gallons. But even using the earlier low figures does not alter the verdict. At those figures the water that would be supplied by the largest and most economical municipal desalting facility yet proposed in the United States would cost approximately twice the highest price that farmers have hitherto been willing to pay for irrigation water. The transportation costs for farmers a few hundred miles from the sea might easily double the on-site cost. Moreover, studies have shown that at present and short-term future energy costs, no further economies are to be gained by building desalination facilities with a greater capacity than that of the proposed plant, whether conventional or nuclear. On purely economic grounds, then, it is unlikely that desalting will revolutionize food production. Technology may improve this outlook with the passage of time, especially if new strains of crop plants that are more tolerant to slightly brackish water can be produced. Indeed, it may eventually be possible to select high-yield strains of salt-tolerant grasses (such as *Zostura* and *Phyllospadix*), and raise grains with salt-water irrigation. This would pose many difficult problems, and any eventual success can be expected to come, at best, in the distant future. Unfortunately, world population growth will not wait.

Desalting becomes more promising if the high cost of the water can be offset by increased agricultural yields per gallon and, perhaps, by the use of a single nuclear installation to provide power for both the desalting process and a profitable on-site industrial process. This prospect has been investigated in a thorough and well-documented study headed by nuclear engineer E. A. Mason at Oak Ridge National Laboratory. The result is a set of preliminary figures and recommendations regarding nuclear-powered "agro-industrial complexes" for arid and semiarid regions, in which desalted water and fertilizer would be produced for use on an adjacent, highly efficient farm. In underdeveloped countries incapable of using the full excess power output of the reactor, this energy would be consumed in on-site production of industrial materials for sale on the world market. Technologies for both near-term (10 years hence) and far-term (20 years hence) projects are considered, as are various combinations of farm and industrial products. The representative near-term project for which a detailed cost breakdown is given consists of a seaside facility with a desalting capacity of a billion gallons per day, a farm size of 320,000 acres, and an industrial electric power consumption of 1585 megawatts. The initial investment for this complex is estimated at $1.8 billion, and annual operating costs at $236 million. If both the food and the industrial materials produced were sold (as opposed to giving the food to those who could not pay) the estimated profit for such a complex, before subtracting financing costs, would be 14.6 percent.

Mason and the co-authors of the study are commendably cautious in outlining the assumptions and uncertainties upon which these figures rest. The key assumption is that 200 gallons of water per day will grow the 2,500 calories required to feed one person. Water to calorie ratios of this order or less have been achieved by the top 20 percent of farmers specializing in such crops as wheat, potatoes, and tomatoes, but more water is required for urgently needed protein-rich crops such as peanuts and soybeans. The authors recognize the uncertainty that crops usually raised separately can be grown together in tight rotation on the same piece of land. Also mentioned are problems of water storage between periods of peak irrigation demand, optimal patterns of crop rotation, and seasonal acreage variations. These important "ifs" and assumptions, and those associated with the other technologies involved, are unfortunately often omitted when the results of such painstaking studies are put forth in oversimplified terms for popular consumption. As a result, the general public tends to assume there are easy solutions where none exist and to foresee panaceas where, in fact, scientists in the field concerned see only potential palliatives that would require much time and huge sums of money.

It is instructive, nevertheless, to examine the impact that the complexes proposed by the Oak Ridge group might have on the world food problem if construction were to begin today, and if all their assumptions about technology 10 years hence were valid *now*. The food produced at an industrial-agricultural establishment of the sort described above would be adequate for just less than 3 million people. This means that 23 such plants per year, at a cost of $41 billion, would have to be put into operation merely to keep pace with world population growth, without even trying to improve the substandard diets of between one and two billion members of the present population. Fertilizer production beyond that required for the on-site farm might conceivably be used to raise food production elsewhere, but the substantial additional costs of transporting the fertilizer to where it is needed would have to be accounted for. From the start of construction, approximately 5 years would be required to put such a complex into operation, so we should commence work on at least 125 units at once, and plan to begin at least another 25 per year thereafter. If the technology *were* available now, the investment in construction during the five-year construction period would be $315 billion—about 20 times the United States foreign aid expenditure during the past 5 years. By the time the technology is available, the cost will be even greater. This example, too, illustrates that scale, time, and cost are all working against technology.

Improving Yields on Land

A great deal of publicity has been given lately to the so-called Green Revolution, an agricultural transformation that some claim has the potential for keeping agricultural production in the UDCs well ahead of population growth. There are two general components in this revolution: increased use of fertilizers and, especially, increased use of the new "high-yield" varieties of grain.

Probably the most widely recommended means of increasing agricultural yields is through more intensive use of fertilizers. Their production is straightforward, and a good deal is known about their effective application. But the environmental consequences of heavy fertilizer use are ill-understood and dangerous (Chapter 7). Even if we could ignore such problems, we find staggering difficulties barring the implementation of fertilizer technology on the scale required. The accomplishments of Japan and the Netherlands are often cited as offering hope to the underdeveloped world. Some perspective on this point is afforded by noting that if India were to apply fertilizer at the per capita level employed by the Netherlands, Indian fertilizer needs alone would amount to nearly half the present world output. Per capita use in the Netherlands is more than 100 times that of India.

Although the goal for nitrogen fertilizer production in 1971 under India's fourth five-year plan is 2.4 million metric tons, Raymond Ewell (who has served as fertilizer production adviser to the Indian government for the past 12 years) suggests that less than 1.1 million metric tons is a more realistic figure for that date. Ewell cites poor maintenance, shortages of raw materials, and power and transportation breakdowns as factors that contribute to continuing low production by Indian factories. Moreover, even when fertilizer is available, increases in productivity do not necessarily follow. In parts of the underdeveloped world the lack of farm credit limits fertilizer distribution; elsewhere, internal transportation systems are inadequate to the task. Nor can the difficulties of educating farmers on the advantages and techniques of fertilizer use be ignored. A recent study of the Intensive Agriculture District Program in the Surat district of Gujarat, India (in which scientific fertilizer use was to have been a major feature) notes that "on the whole the performance of adjoining districts which have similar climate but did not enjoy the relative preference of input supply was as good as, if not better than, the programme district. . . . A particularly disheartening feature is that the farm production plans, as yet, do not carry any educative value and have largely failed to convince farmers to use improved practices in their proper combinations." Obviously, increasing agricultural production requires much more than just supplying more fertilizer.

A main area of hope in conventional agriculture is the development and distribution of new high-yield or high-protein strains of food crops. That such strains can potentially make a major contribution to the food supply of the world is beyond doubt. Unfortunately, this potential seems small in contrast to the potential for population growth, and it seems inevitable that it will be

TABLE 5-3
Estimated Asian Acreage
in New Grain Varieties

Year	Acres
1964–1965	200
1965–1966	37,000
1966–1967	4,800,000
1967–1968	20,000,000
1968–1969	34,000,000*

SOURCE: Dalrymple, *International Agric. Devel. Service,* USDA, Nov. 1968.
* Projected acreage.

realized too slowly to have anything but a small impact on the immediate crisis. Nonetheless, according to some observers, there are some heartening indications that fundamental changes are occurring in UDC agriculture, especially in Asia. There has been a rapid increase in the estimated acreage planted to new high-yielding grain varieties in Asia (Table 5-3).

In 1968 the Indian wheat harvest was 35 percent above the previous record, and the Pakistani crop was 37 percent higher than any other year. There were also large gains in rice production in the Philippines and Ceylon in 1966–1968. These gains were in part due to superb weather, but agricultural experts, such as Lester Brown (who during that period served as administrator for the International Agricultural Development Service of the USDA), feel that a highly significant contribution was made by the new grain varieties. These grains have several advantages over traditional varieties. Not only do they tend to mature early, but unlike traditional varieties they are relatively insensitive to day length; these two characteristics make multiple cropping (growing two or three crops a year) more practical. In Mysore State in India, farmers are growing three corn crops every 14 months. When adequate water is available, Indian, Indonesian, and Philippine farmers can grow two and even three rice crops each year. Where there is a dry season with inadequate water available for growing rice, some farmers are growing new high-yielding grain sorghums (which require less water). In some areas of Northern India and Western Pakistan, farmers are alternately planting rice in the summer and wheat in the winter.

Such advances do indicate that significant increases in yields are *possible* in some UDCs. There are, however, many unanswered questions about the ulti- mate scale and duration of the Green Revolution. Typically the new grain varieties *must* have high fertilizer inputs in order to realize their potential. This means that the problems mentioned above must be dealt with: fertilizer must be produced within the UDC or purchased from outside, and it must then be transported to the fields. Capital is required for fertilizer plants, fertilizer purchases, road construction, railroad construction, trucks, and so forth. Abundant water is also essential for most of the grains, requiring investment in tubewells, pumps, and irrigation ditches. Similarly pesticides and mechanized planting and harvesting are necessary to get the most out of the new varieties. These too are expensive, and capital is in short supply in most UDCs.

There are other economic problems. For instance, in some areas farmers' crops are increased by the new grains to the point where their marketable surplus is doubled. This produces a grain glut that the marketing system can- not handle. Transport facilities are inadequate for distribution, and there is not sufficient "demand" for the food. After all, demand is purchasing power, and starving people may create no demand at all. It is common for agri- cultural economists to speak of helping hungry peoples by increasing the *demand* for food in a country. High grain production all too often means low grain prices. Governments in UDCs are forced into grain price support programs that they can ill afford. The Mexican government, for instance, supports local wheat prices at about double the world market price. Finally, in some countries progress is hindered by a lack of farm credit. New grains are first introduced to "progressive" farmers, usually those with the largest, richest farms. They are in the best position to pay for the inputs of fertilizer, pesticides, irrigation water, and so forth. As attempts are made to spread the Green Revolution to smaller farmers, the need for credit becomes acute.

Another serious problem in spreading new agricultural technology is a critical shortage of agricultural research workers and technicians in the UDCs. Table 5-4 summarizes the number of such workers in various countries in 1960. Many more research organizations like the International Maize and Wheat Improvement Center (CIMMYT) in Mexico and the International Rice Research Institute (IRRI) in the Philippines are needed. Two units with broader missions in tropical agriculture were being organized in the late 1960's: the International Center for Tropical Agriculture (CIAT) in Colom- bia, and the International Institute for Tropical Agriculture (IITA) in Nigeria. The IRRI and the CIMMYT were set up and supported by private

TABLE 5-4

Agricultural Research Workers per 100,000 People Active in Agriculture, 1960

India	1.2	Iran	10.0
Philippines	1.6	Argentina	14.0
Mexico	3.8	Japan	60.0
Pakistan	4.5	Taiwan	79.0
Thailand	4.7	Netherlands	133.0
Colombia	9.0		

SOURCE: USDA, *Changes in Agriculture in 26 Developing Nations, 1948–1963.*

foundations (Ford and Rockefeller); the CIAT and IITA also will be supported by foundations. Many more institutions such as these, supported where necessary by government funds from the DCs, should be established all over the tropical world as trained researchers become available to staff them.

In many ways the problem of revolutionizing UDC agriculture is inextricably tied up with the general problem of UDC "development." Shortages of capital, demand, resources, and trained technicians, lack of effective planning, and the absence of adequate transport and marketing systems all tend to combine with extremely high rates of population growth, malnutrition, and disease to make any kind of development extremely difficult, and thus retard agricultural development. It is a vicious cycle—one that the Green Revolution may not be able to break.

Perhaps even more important than the effects of these economic problems on agricultural development are those of potential biological problems. For instance, the new grain varieties are being rushed into production in places like West Pakistan, where the climate is most favorable. How they will fare in less favorable climates remains to be seen. They are also going into production without adequate field testing, so that we are unsure of how resistant they will be to the attacks of insects and plant diseases. In general, when crops are selected for high yield, something is sacrificed, such as protein content or resistance to bacteria or insects. We suspect that in the next few years escalating pest problems will cut heavily into "miracle yields." William Paddock has presented a plant pathologist's view of crash programs designed to shift agriculture in the UDCs to the new varieties. With reference to India's dramatic program of planting improved Mexican wheat, he writes: "Such a rapid switch to a new variety is clearly understandable in a country that tottered on the brink of famine. Yet with such limited testing, one wonders what unknown pathogens await a climatic change which will give the environmental conditions needed for their growth." Introduction of the new varieties creates enlarged monocultures of plants with unknown levels of resistance to diseases and pests. Clearly, one of the prices that is paid for higher yield is a higher risk of widespread catastrophe.

Another may be acceleration of the loss of reserves of genetic variability in crop plants, variability badly needed for continuing development of new strains. This process is already well under way as old varieties, reservoirs of variability, are replaced by high yielding varieties over large areas. FAO agronomists estimate that seed stock reserves must be collected within the next five years, or "mankind will have lost them for good and ever."

Since the new varieties may require more input of pesticides, with all of their deleterious ecological side-effects, part of the price of agricultural development may be increased pollution of the environment and a decrease in the harvest of food from the sea. (These and similar biological problems are discussed in detail in Chapter 7). Because biological problems usually develop over considerable periods of time, it is possible that early successes in the Green Revolution may have given the world a false impression of what rates of improvement in yield can be sustained. The new grain varieties were adopted primarily by progressive farmers in the most suitable areas; it remains questionable whether their success will be duplicated by less progressive farmers who may not do as well with the new strains, or may not even be willing or able to try them. On the other side of the coin it can be argued that the Green Revolution may break the crust of tradition and become self-accelerating. Only time will tell.

A final problem must be mentioned in connection with these strains of food crops. In general, the hungriest people in the world are also those with the most conservative food habits. In South China a local vitamin B deficiency was caused because people refused to eat their rice unmilled. They objected to the additional cooking time required, they did not like the flavor, and it gave them upset stomachs. Even rather minor changes, such as from a rice variety in which the cooked grains stick together to one in which the grains fall apart, may make food unacceptable. It seems to be an unhappy problem of human nutrition that people would sometimes rather go hungry than eat a nutritious substance that they do not recognize or accept as food.

Beyond the economic, ecological, and cultural problems already mentioned in connection with high-yield agriculture, there is the overall problem of time. We need the time to breed the desired characteristics of yield and hardiness into a vast array of new strains (a tedious process indeed), time to convince farmers that it is necessary to change their traditional ways of cultivation, and time to convince even hungry people to change the staples of their diet. Agricultural experts William and Paul Paddock give twenty years as the rule-of-thumb for a new technique or plant variety to progress from conception to substantial impact on farming. They state (writing as a single person): "It is true that a *massive* research attack on the problem could bring some striking results in less than twenty years. But I do not find such an attack remotely contemplated in the thinking of those officials capable of initiating it." The International Rice Research Institute did produce and introduce a high-yield strain of rice, IR–8, in just six years, which shows that under ideal circumstances the lead time can be reduced, as the Paddocks noted. But there are signs that IR–8 was introduced prematurely. The report in late 1969 was that the new rice varieties were proving to be of poorer quality than the traditional rice varieties, being less palatable and having poor milling qualities. In addition, they are very susceptible to pests. It would seem that a decade would be an *optimistic* average for lead time in properly developing plant varieties. As promising as high-yield agriculture may be, the funds, the personnel, the ecological expertise, and the necessary time are unfortunately not at our disposal. Fulfillment of the promise will come too late for many of the world's billions, if it comes at all. Even the most enthusiastic boosters of the Green Revolution admit that it cannot possibly keep food production abreast of population growth for more than two decades or so. Since a birth control solution to the population explosion will inevitably take longer than that, the prospects for avoiding massive increases in the death rate from starvation are dim indeed.

Food From the Sea

Perhaps the most pervasive myth of the population-food crisis is that mankind will be saved by harvesting the "immeasurable riches" of the sea. Unfortunately, the notion that we can extract vastly greater amounts of food from the sea in the near future is just an illusion promoted by the uninformed. Biologists have carefully measured the riches of the sea, considered the means of harvesting them, and have found them wanting as a solution to the food problem.

The basis of the food-from-the-sea myth seems to be theoretical estimates that fisheries productivity might be increased to many times current yields. However, the most recent analysis by J. H. Ryther of the Woods Hole Oceanographic Institution (Box 5-1), puts the maximum sustainable fish yield in the vicinity of 100 million metric tons, somewhat less than twice the 1967 harvest of some 60 million metric tons. Some other marine biologists think a yield of 150 million metric tons is conceivable. To surpass 100–150 million metric tons would require moving down the food chain from the big fish ordinarily found in fish markets to the harvesting of plankton. All signs at the moment indicate that this will not be feasible or profitable in the foreseeable future, if ever. More calories of fuel and human energy would be spent on harvesting the plankton than could be gained, the expenditure of money would be colossal in relation to the yield, and the product would require considerable processing to be made palatable as human food. In addition, harvesting plankton would result in the depletion of desirable stocks of larger fish living further up the food chain. The most careful analysis indicates that the world harvest might be increased to 70 million tons or so by 1980. On a per capita basis, however, an increase of this amount would actually constitute a small *decline*—unless the human population growth rate were to decrease in the next decade.

But two things stand between man and the future achievement of that 70 million or more tons of yield. The first is overexploitation, the second is oceanic pollution (which is discussed in Chapter 7). The story of the whale fisheries* serves as a model of overexploitation. In 1933, 28,907 whales were caught, and they produced 2,606,201 barrels of whale oil. In 1966, a third

---

* Although whales are mammals, not fishes, the hunting of them is arbitrarily called a "fishery."

BOX 5-1 PRODUCTIVITY OF THE SEA

It is common for laymen to consider the oceans of the world a virtually limitless source of food. They would do well to heed the words of marine biologist J. H. Ryther, "The open sea—90 percent of the ocean and nearly three-fourths of the earth's surface—is essentially a biological desert. It produces a negligible fraction of the world's fish catch at present and has little or no potential for yielding more in the future." The upper layer of open sea, where there is enough light for photosynthesis, lacks the nutrients necessary for high productivity. The photosynthetic producer-organisms (phytoplankton) that live in this layer are extremely small in size. As a result very small herbivores and lower order carnivores are able to function in food chains, and roughly five steps in the chains are interposed between the producers and man. Thus not only are the basic mineral resources for the producers in short supply, but the energy losses in repeated transfers up the long food chains result in further reductions in the potential harvest.

Close to shore, in certain offshore areas, and in a few coastal areas where powerful upwelling currents bring nutrients to the surface, productivity is 2–6 times higher; phytoplankton are larger, and food chains thus tend to be shorter. It is these areas that supply man with virtually all of his fishes. These are also the areas where pollution is the most serious. Indeed, in many areas one-quarter to one-half of fishing production is dependent on estuaries, directly or indirectly, and mankind is busily destroying many of the world's estuaries.

The fisheries situation is summarized in the following table.

Area	Percent of ocean	Area (square kilometers)	Average productivity (grams of carbon per square meter per year)	Average number of trophic levels (approximate)	Annual fish production (metric tons)
Open ocean	90	326,000,000	50	5	160,000
Coastal zone[a]	9.9	36,000,000	100	3	120,000,000
Coastal up-welling areas	0.1	360,000	300	1.5	120,000,000
		Total annual fish production			240,160,000
		Amount available for sustained harvesting[b]			100,000,000

SOURCE: After Ryther, *Science*, 1969.
[a] Including certain offshore areas where hydrographic features bring nutrients to the suface.
[b] Not all the fishes can be taken; many must be left to reproduce or the fishery will be overexploited. Other predators, such as sea birds, also compete with us for the yield.

of a century later, 57,891 whales were killed; almost exactly twice as many as in 1933. But twice as many whales yielded only 1,546,904 barrels of oil, just about 60 percent of the 1933 yield. The reason can be seen in the charts of Figure 5-3. As the larger kinds of whales were driven toward extinction, the industry shifted to harvesting not only the young individuals of large species, but, with time, smaller and smaller species.

After the Second World War, the 17 countries interested in whaling established the International Whaling Commission (IWC). This commission was charged with regulating the annual harvest, setting limits to the catch and protecting whale species from extinction. In theory, commissioners from the various nations were to be responsible for ensuring the compliance of their nation's whalers with IWC decisions, but in fact their powers of inspection and enforcement were nonexistent. Instead of setting quotas on individual whale species, the IWC unfortunately established quotas on the basis of "blue whale units." A blue whale unit (bwu) is one blue whale or the equivalent in terms of other species: two fin whales, two-and-a-half humpback whales, or six sei whales. The nations engaged in whaling in the antarctic fishery were allowed a combined quota of 16,000 blue whale units. Since the blue whales were the largest, they were the most sought after. Up until about 1950, although blues continued to be taken, their numbers declined sharply, which meant that the next largest, the fin whales, were hunted more vigorously.

In 1960 the Commission appointed a committee of biologists to investigate the stocks of antarctic whales. Catches of blues and fins continued to decrease in the interval between establishment of the committee in 1960 and its report in 1963. The report detailed the overexploitation of the fisheries and warned that blues and humpbacks were in serious danger of extinction. It recommended that blues and humpbacks be totally protected, and that the take of fins be strictly limited. It also urged abandonment of the system of blue whale units in favor of limits on individual species.

The committee also made some predictions. Their report stated that if unrestricted whaling continued in 1963–1964, no more than 8,500 blue whale units would be taken, and that 14,000 fins would be killed. Predictably, the warnings were ignored, and the limits were set at 10,000 bwu. The whalers killed 8,429 bwu that season, and 13,870 fins were taken: the biologists' predictions proved uncannily accurate. An ominous note in these figures is that the catch of fin whales was about 35 percent of the estimated total fin population—probably three times the estimated *sustainable* yield.

When the results for 1963–1964 were in, the biologists recommended a bwu total for 1964–1965 of 4,000, 3,000 bwu in 1965–1966, and 2,000 bwu in 1966–1967, in order to allow for recovery of the whale stocks. Again their advice was ignored. All four countries then engaged in antarctic whaling— Japan, the Netherlands, Norway, and Russia—voted against accepting the recommendation, and instead agreed only to limit the 1964–1965 seasons's catch to 8,000 bwu, double the recommended number of units.

What happened in 1964–1965? Only 7,052 blue whale units were taken, well short of the 8,000 quota. Furthermore, only 7,308 fins were taken, and the majority of the remaining bwu consisted of almost 20,000 seis, well over

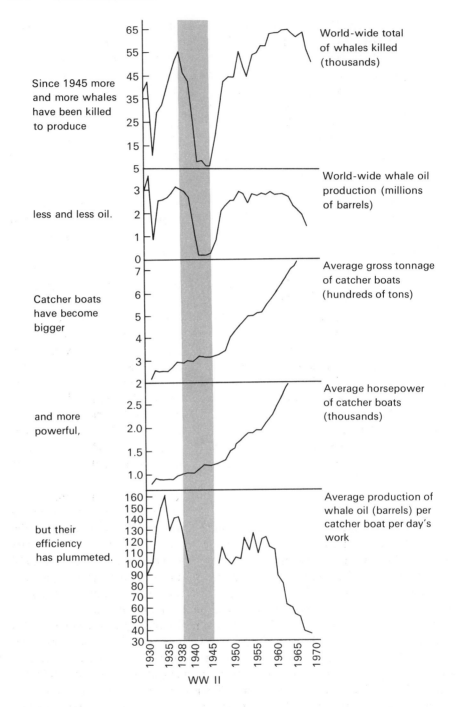

FIGURE 5-3
Overexploitation of whale fisheries. [After N.Y. Zoological Society Newsletter, Nov. 1968.]

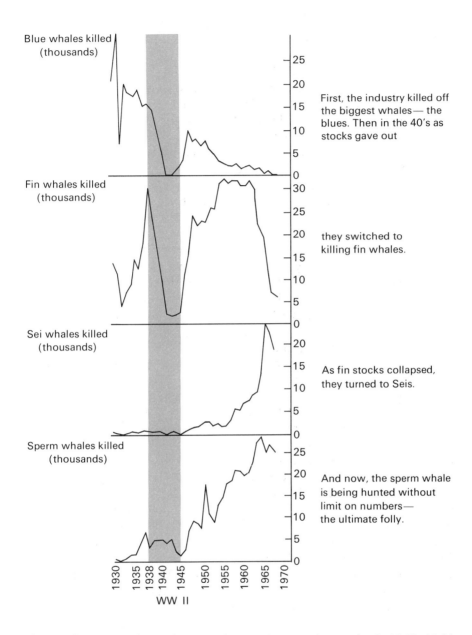

Blue whales killed
(thousands)

First, the industry killed off
the biggest whales— the
blues. Then in the 40's as
stocks gave out

Fin whales killed
(thousands)

they switched to
killing fin whales.

Sei whales killed
(thousands)

As fin stocks collapsed,
they turned to Seis.

Sperm whales killed
(thousands)

And now, the sperm whale
is being hunted without
limit on numbers—
the ultimate folly.

WW II

a third of the total estimated population of that species. In both 1963–1964 and 1964–1965 the total antarctic catch of whales was less than that from other areas of the world—an unprecedented situation. Meanwhile, the Netherlands had given up whaling and sold her fleet to Japan.

In an emergency session in May of 1965, the IWC decided to limit the 1965–1966 catch to 4,500 bwu, which again exceeded the biologists' recommendation. The IWC also tried unsuccessfully to give the now heavily fished sperm whales some protection. The whaling industry did not catch the 4,500-bwu limit in 1965–1966; the total was only 4,089 units, and sei whales made up the majority. Meanwhile, whaling stations in Peru and Chile (not members of the IWC) killed 449 more blue whales, which were already dangerously near extinction.

Subsequent attempts to reach agreements to limit the take of fin, sei, and sperm whales in antarctic and other waters have failed. In 1966–1967 there were four Japanese, two Norwegian, and three Russian antarctic whaling expeditions; the take was 3,511 bwu (4 blues, 2,893 fins, and 12,893 seis). Outside of the Antarctic, seven factory ships and 24 land stations processed 29,536 whales, many of them sperms. In the calendar year 1967 a grand total of 52,046 whales were slaughtered, 25,911 of them sperm whales. In addition, Japan, desperate for protein, killed 20,000 porpoises. In 1968 Norway was forced out of the whaling industry, leaving the field to Japan and Russia.

Setting aside any consideration of the aesthetics of such unrestricted slaughtering of these magnificent and intelligent animals, what can be said about the whaling industry's performance? For one thing, of course, their drive toward self-destruction tends to contradict the commonly held notion that people would change their behavior if they realized that it was against their own self-interest. The whaling industry has operated against its own long-term self-interest continually since 1963, in full knowledge of what it was doing. Short-term self-interest, the lure of the "quick buck," clearly is too strong to allow the long-range best interest of everyone to prevail. This is just one example of a cost-benefit analysis done over too short a term (see Chapter 12).

Cetologist Roger Payne of Rockefeller University has pointed out the ultimate absurdity of the whaling industry's behavior. It is now in such difficulties that the Soviet Union has moved into the business of harvesting krill, the abundant antarctic shrimp that is the primary source of food for the baleen whales. All of the species mentioned above except the sperm whale belong to a group called baleen whales—those that sieve their food out of vast amounts of sea water by means of a hairlike mesh of whalebone in their mouths (they do not have functional teeth). The best krill-catch rates achieved thus far by large ships in the densest clouds of krill have been about 12 tons per day. Even if this rate could be maintained for 24 hours a day, and if oil and protein could be extracted at 80 percent efficiency (an extremely high efficiency), the catch would still be less than the krill equivalent of the whale catch (krill is 6 percent oil and 20 percent protein). As Dr. Payne says, killing whales and harvesting krill "is like wiping out beef cattle in order to have the pleasure of eating grass-protein-concentrate." What the whalers do not seem to recognize is that the most efficient way to utilize the krill is not by harvesting it, but by leaving it unexploited so that the catch of whales could be sustained.

Technological "space-age" advances have greatly aided the whalers in their overexploitation. Ship-based helicopters locate whales and then guide killer boats to the quarry. The killer boats hunt by sonar, killing the quarry with an explosive harpoon head attached to a nylon line with an 18-ton test strength. The dead whale is inflated with compressed air so it will not sink, and a radio beacon is attached to the catch so that the towboat can find it and tow it to the factory ship, where it is rapidly processed.

Similar technological advances are already being applied to other major fisheries around the world. The Soviet Union and other eastern European nations have moved into big-time fishing with a vengeance. A single Rumanian factory ship equipped with modern devices caught in one day in New Zealand waters as many tons of fish as the whole New Zealand fleet of some 1,500 vessels. *Simrad Echo,* a Norwegian periodical published by a manufacturer of sonar fishing equipment, boasted in 1966 that industrialized herring fishing had come to the Shetland Islands, where 300 sonar-equipped Norwegian and Icelandic purse-seiners had landed undreamed-of quantities of herring. An editorial in the magazine queried, "Will the British fishing industry turn . . . to purse-seining as a means of reversing the decline in the herring catch?" Another quotation from the same magazine gives further insight: "What then are the Shetlands going to do in the immediate future? Are they going to join and gather the bonanza while the going is good—or are they going to continue drifting and if seining is found to have an adverse effect on the herring stocks find their catches dwindling?" The answer is now clear. In January 1969, British newspapers announced that the country's east coast herring industry had been wiped out. The purse-seiners took the immature herring that had escaped the British drifter's nets, which are of larger mesh, and the potential breeding stock was destroyed.

The April 1967 issue of *Simrad Echo* contains another example of activities in the modern fishing industry. In an article discussing a newspaper item about a purse-seiner that was being built by a Norwegian shipyard for Peru, which has one of the world's major anchovy fisheries in the rich Humboldt Current, *Simrad Echo* says:

> Fish-rich Peru nurses an ever-growing apprehension. Increasingly it is asked: surely the anchovy stocks off the coast—seemingly limitless at present—cannot sustain catch losses running into millions of tons year after year?
>
> Behind the news item lies what many people consider to be the answer to the Peruvian question—bigger and better equipped boats to augment the hundreds of small 'day trip' purse-seiners engaged in the stupendous coastal fishery.
>
> They theorize that if the present abundant stocks *do* start to get scarce there will be boats on the scene able to go much further afield and be suitably equipped to track fish down.
>
> They theorize further that *now* is the time for action, while things are still relatively good, not at the last moment of truth. In the meantime valuable experience can be gained in operating the latest fish-finding devices, such as echo sounders and sonars.

One wonders whether the author of these words (and the captains of industry who promote these electronic marvels) ever heard of the fable of the goose that laid the golden eggs.

Other examples of overexploited stocks are East Asian and California sardines; Northwest Pacific salmon; cod in many areas; menhaden; tunas in the Atlantic, Pacific, and Indian Oceans; flat-fish in the Bering Sea; plaice in the North Sea; hake in the North Atlantic; and bottom fish in the West Pacific and East Atlantic oceans. Some fish stocks, such as Pacific hake, South Atlantic herring, Yellow Sea bottom fish, anchovy off California, and clupeids in the Atlantic and Indian oceans, are at present underexploited. It seems unlikely they will remain so for long, at least wherever their numbers are not too dispersed for efficient fishing.

Unfortunately, as biologist Garrett Hardin of the University of California at Santa Barbara has pointed out, the sea is a "commons," analogous to a communal pasture open to all. From the point of view of an individual herder exploiting such a pasture commons, there seems to be every reason to keep adding to his herd. Although the grass is limited he will get a larger share if he has a larger herd. If his animals do not eat the grass, someone else's will. Such reasoning is, of course, followed by each user of the commons. Individuals struggle to increase their herds until, at some point, the carrying capacity of the pasture is exceeded and it is destroyed by overgrazing. Similarly, in the sea each individual, company, or country exploiting a fish stock (equivalent to the grass of the pasture) strives to get a maximum share of the catch because each increment represents further immediate profit. Unless some strict agreement is reached about the degree of utilization of the fishery commons, maximum utilization seems the best short-range strategy from the point of view of each user. After all, the Japanese reason, if we don't get the fish, the Russians will. The Russians take a similar view, as do the Peruvians and all the others. Unhappily, the end result of all these individual optimum strategies for dealing with the commons is disaster for all.

The race to loot the sea of its protein is now in full swing. Fish catches more than doubled between 1953 and 1967. Peru, Japan, and Russia took the lion's share in 1966, jointly landing almost 40 percent of the catch (the catch of mainland China, not included in UN statistics since 1961, is not included here: it may amount to some 6–8 metric tons). The United States and Norway, who came next, landed not quite 10 percent between them. The pressures of competition are beginning to show. Russian fishing ships make headlines by penetrating waters off both coasts of the United States. Between 1961 and 1969 the Peruvian government seized 24 United States fishing boats, and other Latin American countries have taken 50 others in disputes over the limits of territorial waters. The activities of far-ranging Japanese fishing fleets have aroused the antagonism of the Mexicans. The list of conflicts grows, and will undoubtedly continue to do so unless competition is regulated.

Yet, since only a few percent of the world's calories come from the sea, one might easily draw the conclusion that the impending reduction of per capita yield is not particularly important. Unhappily, it will be extremely serious. Although food from the sea provides comparatively few calories, it supplies almost one-fifth of the world's animal protein, and two-fifths of it exclusive of milk and eggs (see Fig. 4-4). For some countries the loss of this protein would be catastrophic. Japan's fisheries, for instance, supply her with more than one-and-one-half times as much protein as is provided by her agriculture.

What about "farming" the sea? Unfortunately, the impression that sea farming is here today, or just around the corner, is illusory. For the most part we still hunt the sea today, or in a relatively few cases herd it (for example, we herd oysters). It is certainly true that we can increase our yields from sea-herding. In 1965 some 66 thousand metric tons of yellowtail were produced in Japan's Inland Sea, more than 80 percent from fishes raised in net cages, and yields since then show an upward trend. The potential of both fresh- and salt-water herding (fish culture or aquaculture) is considerable, although it must be emphasized that the potential is small compared to the scale of the world food problem, and increasing pollution now threatens our hope of even realizing this potential.

Farming the sea presents an array of formidable problems, especially of of fertilizing and harvesting. About the only planting and harvesting of marine plant crops done today is some seaweed culture in Japan, and this is really best viewed as an extension of land agriculture into shallow water. Perhaps if the sea is finally emptied of its fishes and shellfishes, some kind of phytoplankton farming could be attempted (if the sea is not by then too badly poisoned by pollution). The crop would be extremely costly at best, and it would not be very tasty, but in desperation we might give it a try. For the immediate future, however, sea-farming offers no hope at all.

Most of the plans for increasing the yield of fishes from the sea disregard the effects of pollution and are based on the premise that the fish stocks will be harvested rationally. The history of fisheries so far gives little hope that rationality will prevail. One can, for instance, expect continuation of attempts to harvest simultaneously young and old of the same species, and both the big fishes and the little fishes that big fishes must eat to live. And one can expect pollution to help reduce the size of many or all fish populations.

Thus, far from being a food panacea, the sea may not even be able to continue to support the limited yield we now extract from it. There is a real possibility that the total yield will decline rather than grow, and we will be extremely fortunate if by 1980 the yield per capita is as high as today's. Judging from the fishing industry's behavior toward the sea, one might conclude that if they were to go into the chicken-farming business they would plan to eat up all the feed, all the eggs, all the chicks, and all the chickens simultaneously, while burning down the henhouses to keep themselves warm.

Novel Sources of Food

What about some of the other proposed solutions to the world food problem that we often see in the public press? Certain food novelties do have potential for helping to alleviate the protein shortage. For instance, protein-rich material can be produced by culturing single-celled organisms on petroleum or other substrates. Theoretically, much, if not all, of the world's protein deficit in the last two decades of this century *could* be made up with protein from such sources. Knowledgeable people think it conceivable that single-cell protein (SCP) could be made sufficiently pure for human consumption by 1980, although whether the purification costs would make it uneconomical is another question. After that the problem would be one of building the requisite plants, arranging for distribution, and solving local political and economic problems relative to SCP use. Perhaps most important of all, people will then have to be convinced that SCP is food. As has been mentioned before, people tend to be extremely conservative in their food habits. The hungriest people are precisely those who recognize the fewest items as food. They have always existed on a limited diet. Even though most Americans are used to an extremely varied diet, many would choose to starve to death rather than eat grasshoppers and snakes—which are perfectly nutritious, but are not generally acceptable as food in our culture.

British Petroleum is building an SCP plant in France that will start production in 1970 with a capacity of 17,000 tons yearly. The yield, however, will be suitable only for livestock feed, not for human consumption. In any case, SCP will not be available in quantity in time to help ameliorate the current crisis. Since the most frequently mentioned substrate is petroleum, we cannot look to SCP as a long-term cure either, because the supply of that substrate is limited and in demand for other uses.

Other ways of reducing the protein deficit are being actively promoted. Work is going ahead on the production of grains with higher quality proteins, those which contain a better balance of the protein building-blocks (amino acids) that are necessary for human nutrition. This is being done both by breeding new varieties and by fortifying grain grown from traditional varieties. This is critically important work, and, if successful, it could make a substantial contribution to the improvement of the human diet. Lysine-enrichment of wheat has been shown to be beneficial to rats and human babies under rigidly controlled conditions. Whether its benefits are well enough demonstrated to warrant large-scale introduction is still a matter of debate.

New protein foods are being produced by adding oilseed protein concentrates to foods made from cereals. The best known of these is Incaparina, developed by INCAP (Institute of Nutrition for Central America and Panama). It is a mixture of corn and cottonseed meal enriched with vitamins A and B. Another is CSM formula (corn, soya, milk), a mixture of 70 percent processed corn, 25 percent soy protein concentrate, and 5 percent milk solids. A third is Vita-Soy, a high-protein beverage now being marketed very successfully in Hong Kong. These and all similar products should be viewed more as "future hopes" than as current cures. As valuable protein and vitamin supplements, they hold considerable promise, but the economics of their production and distribution are not well worked out. More important, the question of their general acceptability remains open. Incaparina has been available in Central America for more than a decade, but its impact, to quote the Paddock brothers, "remains insignificant." It remains insignificant in the face of determined efforts by private and commercial organizations to push its acceptance, and in spite of tremendous worldwide publicity. The Paddocks consider the principal problem to be its bland taste and texture.

As they say, "The food tastes of a people are truly puzzling and as difficult to alter as their views on family planning." Efforts should, nonetheless, be continued to promote Incaparina and other protein-rich products made from oilseeds. The press cakes that remain after oil is squeezed out of soybeans, cottonseed, peanuts and sesame seeds are perhaps the most accessible untapped source of protein for human consumption.

Other unorthodox ways of providing more food are presently being discussed or are under preliminary development. These include herding animals not presently being herded, such as the South American capybara (a rodent), and the African eland (an antelope); converting water hyacinths and other aquatic weeds to cattle feed, making cattle feed from wood, extracting protein from leaves and little fishes, and culturing algae in the fecal slime of sewage treatment plants. Some of these hold promise, at least to help local situations. But all are subject to serious problems. For instance, although herding native antelopes instead of cattle might improve meat yields from African plains, local herders often base their culture on an extraordinarily intricate relationship with their cattle. The economy, social structure, indeed their entire lives revolve around their animals. They will not take kindly to antelope herding. And, although water hyacinths are abundant (and pestiferous—they clog waterways) and contain protein that is high in lysine, their dry weight is only 5 percent of their wet weight, which presents tremendous problems in their processing even into cattle feed. Furthermore, an attempt to herd manatees, which eat the hyacinths, has proven unsuccessful.

Much has been written about fish protein concentrate (FPC) as a valuable protein source. It may help, but it is no panacea. Its chief advantage might be that it would exploit fish stocks that are largely unexploited at present; but the corollary disadvantage is that these often supply food for stocks that we do catch at present. FPC harvesting is subject to all the problems of fishing in general, and the processing is relatively complex and demands an expensive factory. The acceptability of FPC involves the same problems as SCP and Incaparina. Extracting leaf protein from forests presents some ecological problems as well as those mentioned for SCP and FPC. Finally, the reaction of people in the UDCs (or in DCs for that matter) to proposals to feed them protein grown on sewage can well be imagined.

We must, of course, press ahead to develop unorthodox foods and, especially, to find ways to make them acceptable to diverse peoples. But it is reasonably clear that few of them will be a major factor in the world food picture during the critical decade or two ahead. Hopefully, if mankind can survive that period, we will be able to reduce our numbers to the point where the most ecologically, economically, nutritionally, and esthetically desirable of these processes will be integrated into normal food supplies.

Reduction of Food Losses

One area in which technology can greatly help to improve the food supply is in reduction of losses in the field, in transit, and in storage. For instance, the Indian Food and Agriculture Ministry estimated that in 1968 rats devoured almost 10 percent of India's grain production, and others think 12 percent is more nearly accurate. It would take a train almost 3,000 miles long to haul the grain India's rats eat in a single year. And yet in 1968 India spent $265 million on importing fertilizers, about *800 times* as much as was spent on rat control. The rats in two Philippine provinces in 1952–1954 devoured 90 percent of the rice, 20–80 percent of the maize, and more than 50 percent of the sugar cane. Since 1960 birds in Africa have destroyed crops worth more than $7 million annually. Insects in UDCs may destroy as much as 50 percent of a stock of grain in a year's storage period. Spoilage from molds, mildews, and bacteria also take a heavy toll, even in the DCs.

The problems of controlling populations of insect pests in fields are discussed in Chapter 7. Reducing these losses requires great care to avoid serious ecological problems. Controlling rats, birds, rusts, and other non-insect pests in fields also presents similar problems. Protection of foods once they are harvested, however, is much more straightforward and ordinarily involves much less ecological risk. Storage facilities may be made rat-proof, be refrigerated, and be fumigated with nonpersistent pesticides which are not released into the environment until they have lost their toxicity. Transport systems may be improved so that more rapid movement, proper handling, refrigeration where necessary, and other measures greatly reduce spoilage en route. Perhaps the safest investment man could make toward improving the quantity and quality of food would be to improve his methods of handling, shipping and storing crops after the harvest.

Should We Be Pessimistic?

As must be apparent by now, we tend not to share the enthusiasm of many for various proposed "solutions" to the world food problem. The most practical solution, that of increasing yield on land already under cultivation (the Green Revolution) presents great difficulties. This and other programs are usually carried out with little consideration for their ecological consequences, and all too often they neglect the critical importance of high-quality protein in the human diet. Still, if we press on with many of these programs simultaneously, we may buy some badly needed time to bring the population explosion to a halt. It is certainly evident that no conceivable increase in food supply can keep up with the current population growth rates for long. We emphatically agree with the report of the President's Science Advisory Committee's Panel on the World Food Supply, which in 1967 stated: "The solution to the problem that will exist after about 1985 *demands* that programs of population control be initiated now."

The basic questions for the next decade or so seem to be:

1. Will the weather tend to be favorable?
2. Can apparent breakthroughs in UDC agriculture be sustained and converted into real revolutions in spite of the substantial problems associated with their achievement?

3. Will the ecological price paid for a Green Revolution be too high?
4. Can we rapidly develop international agreements for rational use of the sea?

Only time will bring the answers. Obviously, the most prudent course is to work for the best but prepare for the worst.

Bibliography

Addison, Herbert, 1961. *Land, Water and Food*. Chapman & Hall, Ltd., London. Describes barrages, tube wells, etc. in a general discussion of irrigation and land reclamation.

Asian Agricultural Survey, 1969. Asian Development Bank. University of Washington Press, Seattle.

Bardach, John, 1968. *Harvest of the Sea*. Harper & Row, New York. An overview of the oceans—reasonably optimistic.

Borgstrom, Georg, 1967. *Hungry Planet*. Collier-Macmillan, Toronto. See especially the discussion of fisheries.

Borgstrom, Georg, 1968. *Principles of Food Science*. Collier-Macmillan, New York. Useful for those interested in food technology.

Borgstrom, Georg, 1969. *Too Many*. Collier-Macmillan, Toronto. An excellent discussion of the limits of food production.

Brown, Lester R., 1968. A new era in world agriculture. Sen. F. Carlson Symposium on World Population and Food Supply, Kansas State University, Manhattan, Kansas. USDA-3773-68. Good summary of the Green Revolution.

Brown, Lester R., *Seeds of Change: The Green Revolution and Development in the 1970's*. Frederick A. Praeger, New York. A current analysis of the green revolution and its impact on the various aspects of development strategy by an author eminently qualified to discuss the topic.

Carefort, G. L., and E. R. Sprott, 1967. *Famine on the Wind*. Rand-McNally, New York. Popular story of the battle against plant diseases.

Chedd, Graham, 1969. Famine or sanity? *New Scientist* (Oct. 23).

Christy, Frances T. Jr., and Anthony Scott. *The Common Wealth in Ocean Fisheries*. Johns Hopkins Press, Baltimore. See especially the discussion of the productivity of the sea.

Clawson, M., H. H. Landsberg, L. T. Alexander, 1969. Desalted seawater for agriculture: is it economic? *Science*, vol. 164, pp. 1141–1148. Detailed critique of desalting procedure.

Cole, Darryl G., 1968. The myth of fertility dooms development plans, *National Observer* (April 22).

Cole, H. H., ed., 1966. *Introduction to Livestock Production, Including Dairy and Poultry,* 2nd ed. W. H. Freeman and Company, San Francisco. A basic source.

Curwen, E. C., and Gudmund Hatt, 1953. *Plough and Pasture.* Henry Schuman, New York. Deals with the early history of farming.

Dumont, René, and Bernard Rosier, 1969. *The Hungry Future.* Frederick A. Praeger, New York. See especially the discussion of agricultural problems in socialist countries.

Food and Agriculture Organization of the United Nations, 1968. *Production Yearbook 1967.* FAO-UN. Rome. A basic source for agricultural data.

The Nutrition Foundation, Inc., 1968. *Food, Science and Society.* The Nutrition Foundation, Inc., Berkeley.

Foreign Agricultural Service. *Foreign Agriculture.* U.S. Department of Agriculture, Washington, D.C. A monthly journal.

Frankel, Sir Otto, W. K. Agble, J. B. Harlan and Erna Bennett, 1969. Genetic dangers in the green revolution. *Ares* (FAO) vol. 2, no. 5, pp. 35–37 (Sept.–Oct.). Describes the loss of genetic variation in crops as new varieties replace diversity of older ones.

Freeman, Orville, 1968. *World Without Hunger.* Frederick A. Praeger, New York. An extremely optimistic appraisal of the world food situation.

Hardin, Garrett, 1968. The tragedy of the commons. *Science,* vol. 162, pp. 1243–1248. Reprinted in *Population, Evolution and Birth Control,* W. H. Freeman and Company, San Francisco.

Hendricks, Sterling B., 1969. Food from the land. *In* P. E. Cloud, Jr. (ed.), *Resources and Man.* W. H. Freeman and Company (Ch. 4). A hard-headed look at the food problem; the last section contains a good summary of what might be possible if an all-out effort to feed the world were undertaken.

Iowa State University Center for Agricultural and Economic Development, 1967. *Alternatives for Balancing World Food Production and Needs.* Iowa State University Press, Ames, Iowa. Somewhat out of date, but contains interesting papers.

Janick, J., R. W. Schery, F. W. Woods, and V. W. Ruttan, 1969. *Plant Science.* W. H. Freeman and Company, San Francisco. A fine survey covering all aspects of man's use of plants.

Leeds, Anthony, and Andrew P. Vayda (eds.), 1965. *Man, Culture and Animals.* American Association for the Advancement of Science, Washington, D.C. See especially chapters of cattle herding in Africa and sacred cows of India.

Meier, Richard L., 1969. The social impact of a nuplex. *Bulletin of the Atomic Scientists,* March, pp. 16–21. Describes the many nontechnical problems of establishing nuclear agro-industrial complexes.

Owen, Dennis F., 1966. *Animal Ecology in Tropical Africa.* W. H. Freeman and Company, San Francisco.

Paddock, William C., 1967. Phytopathology in a hungry world. *Annual Review of Phytopathology,* vol. 5. pp. 375–390.

Paddock, William, and Paul Paddock, 1964. *Hungry Nations*. Little, Brown & Co., Boston. Good descriptions of conditions relating to UDC food production.

Paddock, William, and Paul Paddock, 1967. *Famine 1975!*, Little, Brown & Co., Boston. Discussion of the possibilities for revolutionizing UDC agriculture. Many consider the Paddocks overly pessimistic; "realistic" is a better appraisal.

Patton, S., P. T. Chandler, E. B. Kalan, A. R. Loeblich III, G. Fuller, and A. A. Benson, 1967. Food value of red tide (*Gonyaulax polyedra*). *Science,* vol. 158, pp. 789–798. An example of a possible protein food developed from algae.

Payne, Roger, 1968. Among wild whales. *New York Zoological Newsletter* (Nov.). A good summary of the whaling situation.

Phillips, John, 1961. *The Development of Agriculture and Forestry in the Tropics*. Faber and Faber, London. Introduction to many of the problems faced by the UDCs.

Pirie, N. W., 1969. *Food Resources, Conventional and Novel*. Penguin Books, Baltimore. See especially the material on novel foods.

Ricker, William E., 1969. Food from the sea. *In* P. E. Cloud, Jr. (ed.), *Resources and Man* (Ch. 5). W. H. Freeman and Company, San Francisco. Slightly more optimistic than the most recent estimates by Ryther.

Ryther, John H., 1969. Photosynthesis and fish production in the sea. *Science,* vol. 166, pp. 72–76. An excellent discussion of the potential maximum sustainable fish yield to man.

Sewell, W. R. Derrik, Vincent Ostrom, Jones A. Crutchfield, E. Roy Tinney, and William F. Roger, 1967. Nawapa: a continental water system. *Bulletin of the Atomic Scientists,* Sept., pp. 8–27. A series of articles on the North American Water and Power Alliance.

The Rotarian (magazine), 1969. This hungry world (special issue, June).

The President's Science Advisory Committee Panel on the World Food Supply. 1967. *The World Food Problem* (3 vols.), Washington, D.C. A very detailed and basic source. Summaries and individual papers.

United Nations, *U.N. Statistical Yearbook,* New York. Annual volume full of information.

Watt, K. E. F., 1968. *Ecology and Resource Management*. McGraw Hill, New York. See especially Chapters 4 and 5 of this fine book.

Went, Frits, 1957. Climate and agriculture. *Scientific American,* vol. 196, no. 6 (June).

Wharton, Clifton R., Jr., 1969. The green revolution: cornucopia or Pandora's box? *Foreign Affairs,* vol. 47, pp. 464–476 (April). An excellent summary of economic and social consequences of the Green Revolution.

Williams, G. and W. J. A. Payne, 1959. *An Introduction to Animal Husbandry in the Tropics*. Longmans, Green & Co. Ltd, London.

CHAPTER 6

Environmental Threats to Man

"He will manage the cure best who foresees what is to happen from the present condition of the patient"

Hippocrates (ca. 460–377 B.C.)

"Don't drink the water and don't breathe the air."

Tom Lehrer, *Pollution*, 1965

In many ways man has made his environment much more hospitable in the past few centuries, as was noted in Chapter 2, but in some ways he has made it more hostile. Overpopulation and industrialization have contributed in various ways to the general deterioration of the environment upon which man depends for life. Only relatively recently has man been made somewhat aware of the harmful effects of the ever-increasing number of biologically active substances that he has produced and exposed himself to—substances with which *Homo sapiens* has had no evolutionary experience and against which human cells have evolved no natural defenses.

Direct threats to human health are the most obvious aspect of environmental deterioration, and of these direct threats the phenomena commonly lumped under the term "pollution" are the most widely discussed. Pollutants reach us through the air we breathe, the water we drink, and the food we eat. But these direct threats are not the only ones; they are merely the most obvious. Less obvious are the indirect effects of mankind's activities on the Earth's ecosystems—those complex environmental systems upon which the existence of all human life ultimately depends. Because the problem of environmental deterioration is exceedingly vast and complex, we have chosen to discuss the direct and indirect effects in separate chapters; this chapter considers the direct assaults upon human physical and mental health; Chapter 7 explores the indirect effects upon ecosystems. Actually, many kinds of deterioration have both direct and indirect effects as will be shown in these two chapters.

Air Pollution

"The air nimbly and sweetly recommends itself unto our gentle senses." So wrote William Shakespeare in *Macbeth*. Would a poet of comparable skill living in a modern city be likely to express a similar sentiment? Probably not; the form of pollution that most of us are aware of is air pollution. Those of us who live in or near cities can see it, and we can feel it when it burns our eyes and irritates our lungs. Virtually every major metropolis of the world has serious air-pollution problems. Travelers know how often their first sight of a city can be spoiled by a pall of smog, as our first view of Sydney's magnificent harbor was when we went to Australia in 1965. Pollution at times cuts down the amount of sunlight that reaches New York by nearly 25 percent, and that reaching Chicago by approximately 40 percent, giving a foretaste of what the world can expect if current trends are allowed to continue. Today, however, it is not only the air over our cities that is polluted. The *entire atmosphere* of our planet is now afflicted to some degree. Meteorologists talk about a nebulous veil of air pollution encircling the entire Earth. Smog has been observed over oceans, over the North Pole, and in other unlikely places. Mankind is taxing the capacity of the atmosphere to absorb and to transport away from areas of high population density the enormous amounts of wastes exhausted into it. Air pollution is now recognized not only as an agent that rots nylon stockings and windshield wiper blades, that corrodes paint and steel, blackens skies and the wash on the clothesline, and damages $500 million worth of crops annually; it is recognized as a killer of people. A 1968 UNESCO conference concluded that man had only about 20 more years before the planet started to become uninhabitable because of air pollution alone.

Air pollution comes from many sources. According to the United States Public Health Service, in the late 1960's our 90 million motor vehicles annually spewed into the atmosphere 66 million tons of carbon monoxide, 1 million tons of sulfur oxides, 6 million tons of nitrogen oxides, 12 million tons of hydrocarbons, 1 million tons of particulate matter, and assorted other dangerous substances, such as tetraethyl lead. Translated into daily amounts, the figures mean that each day American cars exhaust into our atmosphere a variety of pollutants weighing more than a bumper-to-bumper line of cars stretching from Chicago to New York.

The principal industrial sources of air pollution, according to the U.S. Public Health Service, are pulp and paper mills, iron and steel mills, petroleum refineries, smelters, and chemical plants. Their annual contribution to the atmosphere includes 2 million tons of carbon monoxide, 9 million tons of sulfur oxides, 3 million tons of nitrogen oxides, nearly 1 million tons of hydrocarbons, and 3 million tons of particulate matter. The fuel burned for heating houses, apartments, and offices sends another 2 million tons of carbon monoxide, 3 million tons of sulfur oxides, 1 million tons of hydrocarbons, and 1 million tons of particulate matter up flues and into the atmosphere each year. And, finally, trash burning adds about 1 million tons of carbon monoxide, nearly 1 million tons each of sulfur oxides and nitrogen oxides, 1 million tons of hydrocarbons, and 1 million tons of particulate matter. In total, more than 140 million tons of these pollutants are added to the atmosphere, almost three-quarters of a ton annually for every man, woman, and child in the United States.

For many human beings air pollution has already proven lethal. Death rates are above normal when and where smog occurs. The demise of the very old, the very young, and those with respiratory ailments is accelerated. Perhaps the most dramatic case thus far recorded was the London smog disaster of 1952 (see Box 6-1). But such disasters have still been of less significance to public health than have the less spectacular but ultimately more far-reaching effects that day-to-day exposure has on people living in seriously polluted localities. In 1969, sixty faculty members of the Medical School of the University of California at Los Angeles made a recommendation to the residents of southern California's smoggy areas. Their statement read, in part: "air pollution has now become a major health hazard to most of this community during much of the year . . . ," and they advised "anyone who does not have compelling reasons to remain to move out of smoggy portions of Los Angeles, San Bernardino, and Riverside counties to avoid chronic respiratory diseases like bronchitis and emphysema." It is estimated that physicians in private practice around Los Angeles recommend to about 10,000 patients a year that they leave the area as part of their treatment.

What are the general effects of individual air pollutants on health? Carbon monoxide combines with the pigment hemoglobin in our blood, displacing the oxygen that hemoglobin normally transports. In fact, carbon monoxide binds to hemoglobin more efficiently and tightly than oxygen does. Carbon monoxide tends to cause suffocation by occupying the high-speed transport system which in the human organism normally guarantees a steady renewal of the supply of oxygen necessary to maintain metabolism in the cells. When oxygen supply to the cells is reduced, the heart must work harder, as must the respiratory mechanism. These effects may produce a critical strain in people with heart and lung diseases. When a person lives for eight hours in an atmosphere containing 80 parts per million (ppm) of carbon monoxide, the oxygen-carrying capacity of the circulatory system is diminished by about 15 percent. This has about the same effect as the loss of more than a pint of blood. When traffic is badly snarled, the carbon monoxide content of the air may approach 400 ppm. Symptoms of acute poisoning, often experienced by people in traffic jams and on freeways, include headache, loss of vision, decreased muscular coordination, nausea, and abdominal pain. In extreme cases unconsciousness, convulsions, and death follow. Cases of chronic carbon monoxide poisoning have also been reported.

Oxides of sulfur are contributors to respiratory disease. Sulfur dioxide has caused attacks of severe respiratory illness in older patients with chronic lung disease. Most sulfur compounds are harshly irritating to respiratory passages, causing coughing and choking. Their effects are thought to be a major cause of the abnormal death tolls that have occurred during smog disasters. A 1968 press release put out by the University of Chicago Toxicity Laboratory stated, "sulfur dioxide produced by coal burning adheres to coal dust particles and spreads through urban air. These particles get into our lungs and create sulfuric acids, which can be highly dangerous."

Sulfur dioxide is without doubt involved in the increased rates of acute and chronic asthma, bronchitis, and emphysema observed in people exposed to severe air pollution. Asthma is an allergic supersensitivity of the bronchial

---

BOX 6-1 AIR POLLUTION DISASTERS

Donora, Pennsylvania, is a small town in the steep valley of the Monongahela River; in 1948 it had a population of 12,300. Because of the steepness of the surrounding hills it tends to be even smokier than other mill towns. In the autumn, fog is often added to the smoke, making the mixture smog (smog equals smoke plus fog in the strict sense of the word, but air pollution not involving fog, such as that found in Los Angeles, is now commonly called "smog"). On Tuesday, October 26, 1948, a thermal inversion (a layer of warm air above a layer of cold air; see Fig. 6-2) trapped fog and smoke producing a lethal situation. The red, black, and yellow smoke from Donora's huge wire factory, zinc and sulfuric acid plants, and steel factory lingered for days over the grimy town, and the upper layer of fog absorbed the sun's heat, creating more warm air above the cold and intensifying the inversion. The smog persisted through Sunday, and 6,000 people, nearly half the people in the area, were made ill as a result. Fifteen men and five women died, and the lives of many others may have been shortened.

A similar smog occurred in London in 1952; the combination of fog and thermal inversion was accompanied by severe cold weather. London's homes were heated by coal, and the cold greatly increased fuel consumption and the production of smoke. The atmospheric content of sulfur dioxide rose to double its usual level. The episode started on Friday, December 5, and by Sunday the smog had reduced visibility to only one yard in parts of London, and created multitudes of hard-to-credit situations. For example, so much smog seeped into theaters that only people in the first four rows could see the cinema screen. People inadvertently walked off of quays along the Thames and fell into the river. A pilot trying to taxi to the terminal at London Airport after an instrument landing got lost, as did the party sent to search for him. The consensus is that about 4,000 deaths were directly attributable to the London smog.

There have, of course, been other smog disasters, as well as many close calls. Two often-cited cases occurred in the Meuse Valley of Belgium in 1930 and at Poza Rica near Mexico City in 1950. When the next smog "diasaster" will come, no one knows. But in August 1969 citizens of both Los Angeles and St. Louis were warned by doctors not to play golf, jog, or do anything that involved deep breathing because of the air-pollution hazards that prevailed. The activities of school children in the Los Angeles basin are curtailed on doctors' orders with increasing frequency, and attrition of the health of asthmatics and others with respiratory or cardiovascular problems continues.

tree, the set of branching tubes that carry air from the trachea to the lungs (Fig. 6-1). An asthmatic attack causes the muscles that encircle the "twigs" of the bronchial tree to contract and narrow the tubes. The victim is able to inhale air, but is unable to exhale with sufficient force to clear the lungs. The result is a distension of the lungs: input exceeds output. Carbon dioxide builds up in the lungs, and the victim also suffers oxygen deprivation. Asthma attacks kill several hundred Americans a year; even those that are not lethal often last for long periods and may lead to more or less permanent changes in the breathing apparatus.

Bronchitis, inflammation of the bronchial tree, leads to difficulty in expelling foreign matter from the lungs by coughing. The muscles surrounding

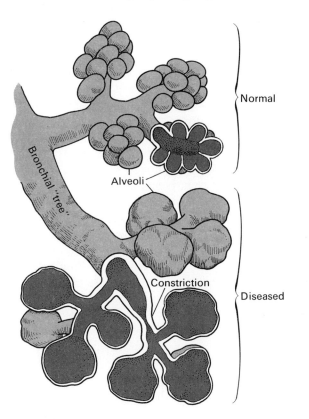

FIGURE 6-1
Bronchitis-emphysema, a disease that is caused or aggravated by air pollution. In the normal lung the bronchial tubes branch into millions of tiny chambers (alveoli), where transfer of oxygen to blood takes place. In the diseased lung the alveoli coalesce, reducing the amount of surface available for oxygen transfer. Furthermore, the "twigs" of the bronchial tree are constricted, reducing the rate at which air is exchanged. [After McDermott, "Air Pollution and Public Health." Copyright © 1961 by Scientific American, Inc. All rights reserved.]

the bronchial tubes weaken, and mucus accumulates. There is a progressive loss of breathing ability. Bronchitis is often accompanied by emphysema, a disease of the air sacs in the lungs. These air sacs tend to fuse, essentially coalescing from clusters of small pouches to form larger ones. This is accompanied by a narrowing of the finer branches of the bronchial tree. The combined results are a reduction of total surface area for the exchange of oxygen between air and blood stream and a reduction of the amount of air flow through the lungs. This process takes place gradually over a period of years, while the lungs become progressively less capable of providing oxygen for activity. The victim of emphysema ultimately dies of suffocation.

Nitrogen oxides affect man in much the same way as carbon monoxide, by reducing the oxygen-carrying capacity of the blood. The hydrocarbon pollutants are a diverse lot and, among other things, are almost certainly involved in rising cancer death rates (the best known suspected carcinogen is the complex benzpyrene molecule). Similarly, some components of "particulate" pollution, such as asbestos and certain metals, are strongly suspected of contributing to the cancer load of the human population. Unfortunately, it is difficult to make definitive statements about the precise health effects of air pollution, for reasons explained in Box 6-2.

In spite of these problems, the evidence pointing to the seriousness of air pollution as a definite hazard is now massive. Consider just a few sample findings. Cigarette smokers from smoggy St. Louis, Missouri, have roughly four times the incidence of emphysema as smokers from relatively smog-free Winnipeg, Canada. At certain times, air pollution increases the frequency of head colds. Ten years after the Donora smog disaster of 1948, those residents who had reported severe effects during the smog showed the highest subsequent death rates. (This, of course, does not *prove* that the smog hurried them toward their graves; perhaps only previously weakened people suffered severe effects.) Pneumonia deaths are more frequent in areas of high pollution. Chronic bronchitis is more serious among British postmen who work in areas of high air pollution than in those who serve in relatively smog-free areas. Emphysema death rates have skyrocketed as air pollution has increased. England has higher overall rates of air pollution than the United States, and death from lung cancer is more than twice as common among British men as it is among American men. The lung cancer death rates in England are correlated with the density of atmospheric smoke. The lung cancer rate for men over 45 in the smoggiest part of Staten Island, New York is 55 per 100,000. In a less smoggy area just a few miles away, the rate is 40 per 100,000.

Any one of the examples we have given might be open to question, but taken *in toto* the picture is clear. Air pollution kills. It usually kills slowly and unobtrusively, and the resulting deaths are not dramatically called to the attention of the public.

If current trends are allowed to continue, death from air pollution *will* become obtrusive. The Public Health Service predicts that annual sulfur dioxide emission will increase from the 1960 level of 20 million tons to 35 million by the year 2000. Similarly, nitrogen oxides will increase from 11 to almost

30 million tons, and particulates from about 30 million to more than 45 million tons. Unless the United States alters present trends in transportation, the number of automobiles will quadruple between the years 1960 and 2000, as will the number of gallons of fuel consumed. Although population and environmental limitations make it unlikely that these trends will continue to the end of this century, these projections do give some indication of what we may have to live with as long as they do continue. One can hope that public awareness of the problem will lead to change early in the 1970's, that perhaps the internal combustion engine will come to play a much smaller role in American life and that pollution control will become more effective. The first practical step might be to reduce the size and compression ratios of internal combustion engines until such time as they can be replaced by some nonpolluting alternative, whether by another type of engine for personal cars or by efficient forms of mass transportation, or even some entirely new system combining both.

BOX 6-2   ASSAYING THE HAZARDS OF AIR POLLUTION

The effects of cigarette smoking on health might be considered a problem in "micro air pollution." We now know that cigarette smoking has many harmful effects. Yet even with the great advantage of being able to measure the amount and length of exposure, and having a relatively uniform pollutant source, it took many years to do the research required to convince doctors, scientists, and eventually the general public of the extreme hazards of smoking.

In contrast, here are some of the problems of assaying the dangers of air pollution:

1. Pollutants are numerous and varied, and many of them are difficult to detect. Their concentrations vary geographically. In many areas techniques for monitoring pollutants are highly inadequate, and long-term records are unavailable. Long periods of study are usually needed to reveal delayed and chronic effects.

2. It is usually impossible to determine with precision the degree of exposure of a given individual to specific pollutants.

3. Degree of air pollution is correlated with other factors, such as degree of exposure to various kinds of stress, other kinds of

pollution, and food additives. Such factors must be considered in data analysis.

4. Research is complicated because pollutants that do not cause problems when tested alone may be dangerous in combination with other pollutants. For instance, many of the asbestos particles inhaled by nonsmokers are carried out of the lungs in an ever-moving sheet of mucus propelled by the beating of cilia (tiny active appendages of living cells). Smoking interferes with this natural cleansing function, and increases the chance of coming down with an asbestos-induced mesothelioma, a kind of cancer of the lungs. Sulfur dioxide also tends to interfere with this cleaning function. It is thought that the length of exposure of lung surface to airborne carcinogenic hydrocarbons as benzpyrene may determine whether a cancerous growth is started. When benzpyrene occurs as a pollutant in combination with sulfur dioxide, the exposure and the hazard are greatly increased. Such interactions are called *synergistic;* the danger from the two combined pollutants is greater than the sum of the individual dangers.

Air Pollution and Population Growth

The clear connection between air pollution and population growth may be seen by examining the history of pollution in Los Angeles. Even four centuries ago, Juan Rodriquez Cabrillo recorded in his diary that smoke from Indian fires in the basin went up for a few hundred feet and then spread to blanket the valley with haze. Because of this phenomenon, he named what is today called San Pedro Bay "The Bay of Smokes." Cabrillo was observing the effect of a thermal inversion. Normally the temperature of the atmosphere decreases steadily with increased altitude, but during an inversion a layer of warm air overlying cooler air below severely limits vertical mixing of the atmosphere, and pollutants accumulate in the layer of air trapped near the earth's surface (Fig. 6-2). Because of the wind patterns in the eastern Pacific and the ring of mountains surrounding the Los Angeles Basin, it is an ideal place for the formation of inversions, usually at about 2,000 feet above the floor of the basin. They occur there on about 7 days out of every 16.

Los Angeles has abundant sunshine, another climatic feature that contributes to its air-pollution problems. Sunlight acts on a mixture of oxygen, nitrogen oxides, and hydrocarbons to produce what is known as photochemical smog. Characteristic of photochemical smog are such compounds as peroxyacetyl nitrates. Combustion products from well over 3 million cars are exhausted into the atmosphere of the Los Angeles Basin in addition to

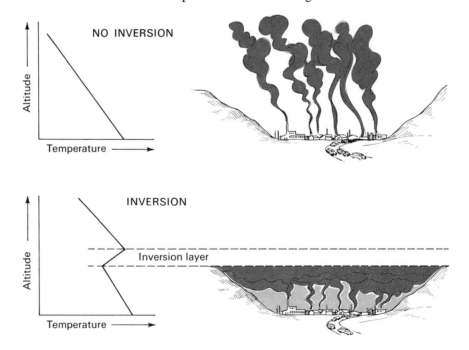

FIGURE 6-2
Temperature inversion, in which a layer of warm air overlies a layer of cooler air, trapping air pollution close to the ground.

the wastes discharged by oil refineries and other industries. As a result, the air that residents of Los Angeles breathe contains far more than the usual mixture of nitrogen, oxygen, and carbon dioxide; it also contains carbon monoxide, ozone, aldehydes, ketones, alcohols, acids, ethers, peroxyacetyl nitrates and nitrites, alkyl nitrates and nitrites, benzpyrene, and many other dangerous chemicals.

Smog first became prominent in Los Angeles during World War II. Since then the Los Angeles County Air Pollution Control District (APCD) has pursued a vigorous policy of smog abatement. A "Devil's Dictionary of Air Pollution" published in a San Francisco newspaper in 1969 defined *Air Pollution Control* as "a phrase used in answering the telephone at many public agencies which are involved in watching the growth of air pollution. It describes a modern myth." This definition might be accurate for most agencies, but not for the APCD. The district has imposed strict controls on industry, setting rigid emission standards for power plants, refineries, and other sources of pollution. Some 1.5 million domestic incinerators, a dozen large municipal incinerators, 57 open burning dumps, and most incinerators in commercial buildings have been eliminated. Coal burning has been made illegal, and so has (for most of the year) the burning of oil with a high sulfur content. Control is exercised over the escape of vapors from petroleum storage tanks and gasoline loading facilities; also controlled are commercial processes that require organic solvents, the olefin content of gasoline sold in Los Angeles County, and many other contributors to air pollution. Furthermore, all cars sold in California are required to have smog-control devices designed to reduce crankcase emissions of hydrocarbons.

And what has all this effort accomplished? At best, it has more or less permitted a holding of the line. There has been no improvement in the air quality in the Los Angeles Basin since 1960. Unexpectedly, pollution from nitrogen oxides has soared, largely because manufacturers have increased the compression ratios of automobile engines, and perhaps in part because of the fitting of crankcase antismog devices, which were designed to reduce the emissions of hydrocarbons. Fortunately, hydrocarbon levels have remained about even, as have those of carbon monoxide. Sulfur oxides have fluctuated, but they are currently decreasing. Since 1962 there has been an increase in the number of smog alerts in which public health warnings are broadcast. Furthermore, although there has been no spectacular rise in the *density* of smog since 1960, the *volume* of heavily polluted air is increasing. The smog is spreading in area and in height as the heat generated by the city forces the base of the inversion cap higher. According to one estimate, the Los Angeles basin now receives only 94 percent of its heat from the sun; fully 6 percent comes from the burning of fossil fuels. Air pollution is now reported to be causing damage to living plants growing hundreds of miles east of Los Angeles.

Why is Los Angeles unable to improve its air quality in spite of the strenuous efforts of the APCD? The basic answer is population growth. Even though the per capita amount of pollution has declined, the number of people has increased. Each new worker is faced with the virtual necessity of using an automobile to move around in an immense city that lacks an adequate public transportation system. And, of course, more people means more business and industry, which in turn tend to attract more people. In California the situation is especially critical, but many urban areas of the U.S.A. face similar problems. More people and more automobiles, plus systematic resistance to smog control from industry and industry-hungry local governments, combine to work against successful pollution abatement.

Water Pollution

In many communities direct threats to human health arrive through the faucet as well as through the air. The drinking water that flows from the tap in some localities has already passed through seven or eight people. Graffiti in public washrooms in numerous towns along the Mississippi River read: "Flush the toilet, they need the water in St. Louis." Yet the water in St. Louis is chlorinated and filtered, and therefore it should be safe to drink. Unfortunately, the water in many cities is often unsafe to drink (Box 6-3). Although proper chlorination may help, there is growing evidence that high contents of organic matter in water can somehow protect viruses from the effects of chlorine. Infectious hepatitis is spreading alarmingly in the United States, and a major suspect for the route of transmission is the "toilet-to-mouth pipeline" of many water systems not made safe by chlorination. Indeed, the safety of purifying water with chlorine has been questioned by Nobel Laureate Joshua Lederberg of Stanford University who wrote in his *Washington Post* newspaper column in 1969, "Many geneticists have raised

---

BOX 6-3   IS YOUR WATER SAFE TO DRINK?

Where did you live in the late 1960's? In Wilmington, Delaware; New London, Connecticut; Chattanooga, Tennessee; or Eugene, Oregon, the quality of your water was not completely protected from the source to your tap. Did you live in Grand Junction, Colorado; Fort Myers, Florida; or Bayonne, New Jersey? Your water in those cities did not come from the purest possible source. In Savannah, Georgia, or North Platte, Nebraska? Your water was not checked frequently enough for dangerous bacteria. Fairbanks, Alaska? Your local regulations were not adequate to prevent health hazard. Pueblo, Colorado? Surveys to detect potential health hazards were too infrequent. Wilmington, North Carolina? The bacterial level in your water was too high. Altoona, Pennsylvania? There were too many chemical impurities in your water. Charleston, South Carolina? Your water department used nonapproved tests. Some of the above-mentioned cities had more than one of these problems, and many other cities have similar ones. These facts were revealed in a Public Health Service Provisional List, in which water supplies of more than 60 American cities were rated as "unsatisfactory" or "potential health hazard." If you are living in one of the cities mentioned you might wish to check with your public health agency as to the current status of your water supply. Indeed, periodic inquiry would be a good idea no matter where you live.

cautions about chemicals that may cause mutations, and I will join them by adding chlorine to the lengthy list that cry out for close scrutiny." The principal difficulty with chlorination is that certain chlorine compounds, which are sometimes formed by the chlorination process, cause mutations; but considering the high level of dangerous germs in many of our water supplies, we probably will have to continue to accept any risks involved in chlorination.

As the populations of many municipalities grow, their sewage treatment facilities, though once adequate, are quickly outgrown. Funds for new facilities can be obtained only at the expense of those needed for better schools, police departments, water systems, roads, and other public services. Inevitably, it seems, the available funds are insufficient to meet all of these needs, which are created in part by increases in population. Lax inspections and public health standards permit construction of septic tanks too close together or in unsuitable soils in many of the rural and suburban areas where there are no general sewage facilities. In some rural areas public health measures are so lax that many people have no sanitation facilities at all; people "just go to the woods."

As population grows so does industry, which pours into our water supplies a vast array of contaminants: lead, detergents, sulfuric acid, hydrofluoric acid, phenols, ethers, benzenes, ammonia, and so on. As population and industry grow, so does the need for increased agricultural production, which results in a heavier water-borne load of pesticides, herbicides, and nitrates. A result is the spread of pollution not just in streams, rivers, lakes, and along seashores, but also (and most seriously) in groundwater, where purification is almost impossible. With the spread of pollution goes the threat of epidemics of hepatitis and dysentery, and of poisoning by exotic chemicals.

Another hazard is the problem of nitrate pollution. Current agricultural practices result in the flow of a heavy load of nitrates into our water supply; nitrates also accumulate in high concentrations in our crops. Nitrates themselves are not especially dangerous, but when certain bacteria are present in the digestive tract, they convert the nitrates into highly toxic nitrites. In addition, conversion of nitrates to nitrites can occur in any opened container of food, even if it is subsequently refrigerated. Farm animals and human infants are particularly likely to include in their digestive tracts the proper types of bacteria and the appropriate conditions for the conversion of nitrate to nitrite. When this nitrite is absorbed into a baby's bloodstream, it reacts with the oxygen-carrying pigment of the red blood cells, forming methemoglobin, which does not have hemoglobin's oxygen-transport capability. The resulting disease, methemoglobinemia, is characterized by labored breathing; in some cases, it terminates in suffocation. Nitrate water pollution in lakes, streams, and wells probably is most dangerous in the central valley of California, where it is a severe public health hazard and where doctors often recommend that infants be given only pure bottled water. It is also serious, however, in some other states, such as Illinois, Wisconsin, and Missouri. The city of Elgin, Minnesota, was forced by nitrate pollution to find a new water supply.

A United States Department of Agriculture official estimated that the use of inorganic nitrogen fertilizer would be increased some ten times between 1970 and 2000. Should this occur, it would contribute to a general ecological catastrophe, as well as to the possible poisoning of large numbers of children and farm animals.

Water pollution with sewage provides one of the classic examples of diseconomies of scale accompanying population growth. If a few people per mile live along a large river, their sewage may be dumped directly into the river and natural purification will occur. But if the population increases, the waste-degrading ability of the river becomes overstrained, and either the sewage or the intake water must be treated if the river water is to be safe for drinking. Should the population along the river increase further, more and more elaborate and expensive treatments will be required to keep the water safe for human use and to maintain desirable fishes and shellfishes in the river. In general, the more people there are living in a watershed, the higher the *per capita* costs of avoiding water pollution will be.

Solid Wastes

An extremely serious problem facing the United States and other affluent countries is the accumulation of solid wastes in open dumps or inadequate fills. These dumps are not just aesthetic disasters; if they are burned they contribute to air pollution, water percolating through them pollutes groundwater supplies, and they serve as breeding grounds for such annoying and disease-bearing organisms as rats, cockroaches, and flies. Each year in the United States we must dispose of some 55 billion cans, 26 billion bottles and jars, 65 billion metal and plastic bottle caps, and more than half a billion dollars worth of other packaging materials. Seven million automobiles are junked each year, and the amount of urban solid wastes (trash and garbage) collected annually is approximately 150 million tons. If current trends continue, sometime in the next decade every man, woman and child in the United States will, on the average, be producing a ton of refuse annually. In addition to junked cars, some 10 million tons of iron and steel are scrapped each year, more than 3 *billion* tons of waste rock and mill tailings are dumped near mine sites, and huge amounts of slag, ash, and other wastes are produced by smelters, power plants, and other industries.

It is becoming universally recognized that current methods of dealing with the solid waste problem are utterly inadequate. A report by the Department of Health, Education and Welfare recently labeled 94 percent of the 12,000 disposal sites in the United States as "unacceptable." Many cities are facing disposal crises as population growth simultaneously produces more waste and reduces the available land for dumping. Waste disposal is another classic case where per capita costs tend to go up as population grows. San Francisco and other cities have considered having their refuse hauled to distant dumping sites by train. But, curiously enough, people living near the selected sites were not happy with the idea, and costs would be very high. Sanitary landfill, where space is available, is a more satisfactory (and expensive) solution than dumping, but it also generates many problems. Water pollution continues, dust pollution is created, and nonbiodegradable materials (those not quickly broken down by microorganisms) which do not compact easily, lessen the utility of the fill. Incineration of wastes is another answer which in France and other European countries has been combined with power production in trash-fired power plants. Unless great care is taken, of course, this answer may merely substitute air pollution for land pollution.

Besides the obvious necessity of limiting the size of the human population, a number of other measures would help ameliorate the solid waste problem. Laws might be passed that would place heavy taxes upon any product or wrapping that is designed to be discarded rather than returned or recycled, and the manufacture of nonbiodegradable products could be prohibited. Heavy deposits, perhaps 25 cents per beer can or "pop" bottle, should be required to encourage the return of such containers. Then even those that might be discarded would be gleaned from roadsides and beaches by ambitious small boys. Many of our products, as well as our refuse-collection system, could be so designed that the materials which could be used as soil conditioners could be separated from those that could be recycled in other ways. Automobiles could be designed not only to minimize air pollution, but also for ease of disassembly into recyclable components. Indeed, in the face of the obvious need to minimize the wasteful scattering of nonrenewable resources, the design of all of man's manufactured devices, from home appliances to computers, should take into account the possibility of recycling their components.

General Pollution—
Pesticides and Related Compounds

Some substances, such as chlorinated hydrocarbons, lead, mercury, and fluorides reach us in so many ways that they must be considered as general pollutants. Chlorinated hydrocarbons are the most ubiquitous molecules man has manufactured. Of these, DDT has been employed the longest, having been put into mass use late in World War II. It is the most commonly used and most thoroughly studied of all synthetic insecticides. It often occurs in concentrations of more than 12 ppm in human fat, and as high as 5 ppm in human milk (though the usual range is some 0.05 to 0.26 ppm). Most mother's milk in the United States contains so much DDT that it would be declared illegal in interstate commerce if it were sold as cow's milk; the permissible level in cow's milk is set by the FDA at 0.05 ppm. The DDT intake of infants around the world is now about twice the daily allowable maximum in standards recommended by the World Health Organization (WHO). Other chlorinated hydrocarbon insecticides, including aldrin, dieldrin, and benzene hexachloride, have also been found in recent years in human milk.

Recently another class of chlorinated hydrocarbon compounds, polychorinated biphenyls (PCBs), have also been found to be a serious pollutant. These compounds are used in a variety of industrial processes, and are released into our environment in a variety of ways. They vaporize from storage containers, are emitted from factory smokestacks, are dumped into rivers and lakes with industrial wastes, and, along with a variety of other hydrocarbons, are added to the load of particulate atmospheric pollutants as automobile tires are worn down. Like the pesticides, they show up in the milk of nursing mothers. Zoologist Robert W. Risebrough of the University of California recently stated that PCBs "are highly toxic to man when inhaled as vapors, and the more heavily chlorinated components have greater toxicity. No tolerance limits have been set for human food supplies, and their cancer-causing properties remain to be determined."

Chlorinated hydrocarbons are present in our drinking water, in our fruits and vegetables, and in the air we breathe. At times the dosage is direct and high. Farmers sometimes far exceed legal dosages of insecticides on their crops and get away with it because inspection is lax. Some ill-informed grocers spray their produce to kill fruit flies. In the summer of 1968, our research group found leaking cans of chlordane dust (a chlorinated hydrocarbon insecticide) on a narrow shelf above the onion bin in a supermarket. The dust was present on the produce. The manager, on being informed, took prompt corrective action—but not before some of his customers had added to their loads of chlorinated hydrocarbons. By the summer of 1969 the pesticides had reappeared on the shelf over the produce, and complaints had to be renewed. Obviously the sale of all pesticides should be prohibited in food stores.

A colleague of ours has observed massive anti-roach spraying—presumably of chlordane—in a restaurant kitchen, where the spray drifted over exposed food. Some restaurants formerly used lindane vaporizers; fortunately these have now been banned. Regardless of whether such practices and the resultant heavy doses are common or not, continuous "light" exposure is virtually unavoidable. For example, at least a dozen states have reported that residual pesticide levels in fishes are well above the FDA recommended levels, and some DDT concentrations are ten times higher.

Can this light exposure be dangerous? Doesn't the government specify how much exposure to these chemicals is safe on the basis of long-term experiments? Haven't the medical and biological sciences protected us? Isn't it true that DDT has been proven to have no adverse effects on humans unless taken in massive doses? Unfortunately the answer to the last three questions is a resounding "No!". But there is no reason why the average citizen should know that, even though the dangers of pesticide poisoning have been given increasing and much-needed attention in the news media during the past decade. Because of the variety of problems enumerated above in the discussion of air pollution, it has been very difficult to evaluate the long-term and chronic effects of pesticides. Biologists have long been warning that we have no evidence that DDT, even though its effects may not be immediately obvious, might not have subtle or long-term effects. In fact, we have every reason to believe that these biologically active molecules are downright dangerous. Rachel Carson wrote, "For the population as a whole, we must be more concerned with the delayed effects of absorbing small amounts of the pesticides that invisibly contaminate our world." But, as often happens, the possibility of subtle effects have been discounted by industry, ignored by the government, and forgotten by the public.

People can understand acute poisoning, but they find subtle physiological changes difficult to grasp. Why should it matter if high concentrations of chlorinated hydrocarbons are being stored in our bodies? Haven't scientists carried out experiments in which convicts ate DDT without apparent harm? Hasn't a study of workers in a DDT plant and another done with convicts shown that no ill effects resulted from heavy exposure? The answer is that these two studies attesting to the "safety" of DDT were poorly designed and utterly inadequate to assure us of its long term safety. Both were done with people whose first exposure occurred as *adults,* and the convict study followed individuals over *less than two years.* The study of exposed workers did not investigate what had happened to workers who were no longer employed. The effects on the delicate developmental systems of fetuses and infants were not investigated. No attempt was made to investigate the possible effects of DDT exposure on large populations over several decades, and the causes of death in large numbers of people with high and low exposures were not statistically compared.

Biologists have just started to get an inkling of what our "harmless" chlorinated hydrocarbon load may be doing to us over the long run. Animal studies give us some clues. In high doses DDT has recently been shown to increase the incidence of cancers, especially liver cancers, in mice. At around 10 ppm DDT has been shown to induce abnormally high levels of certain liver enzymes which break down many prescribed drugs and render them ineffective. What may be worse, as pharmacologist Richard M. Welch of the Burroughs Wellcome Research Laboratory has pointed out, is that DDT in rats not only induces the production of these enzymes, but also increases the weight of the uterus and the deposition of dextrose in the uterus. More disturbing, it stimulates the production of estrogen, the female sex hormone. We know that DDT affects the sex hormones of rats and birds, and we know that rat reproductive physiology is very similar to human reproductive physiology. We do not know whether hormonal changes are induced in man, or what their effects will be if they are.

Results of other recent studies are even more ominous. One study, the results of which were obtained by autopsies, showed a correlation between DDT levels in human fat and cause of death. Concentrations of DDT and its breakdown products, DDE and DDD, were significantly higher in the fat of patients who died of softening of the brain, cerebral hemorrhage, hypertension, portal cirrhosis of the liver, and various cancers than in groups of patients who died of infectious diseases. Significantly higher concentrations of dieldrin, another chlorinated hydrocarbon pesticide, also were correlated with suspicious causes of death. The histories of the patients in the study showed that concentrations of DDT and its breakdown products in their fat were strongly correlated with home use of pesticides, heavy users having much higher concentrations than light or moderate users.

More conclusive investigations of these effects are urgently needed, but in the light of what is known about the deleterious affects of chlorinated hydrocarbons on laboratory animals, the results of this study alone leave little room for complacency. Neurophysiologist Alan Steinbach of the University of California at Berkeley claims that DDT is an irreversible nerve poison. There is also some evidence that chlorinated hydrocarbon exposure can cause abnormal changes in electroencephalograph (brain wave) patterns. These observations are not surprising, since experiments with other animals indicate that exposure to chlorinated hydrocarbons caused changes in the central nervous system. For example, in experiments conducted by J. M. Anderson and M. R. Peterson, biologists at Carleton University, Ottawa, Canada, trout exposed to 20 parts per billion DDT showed a complete inability to learn to avoid an electric shock, whereas *all* unexposed fishes learned to do so quite easily. Furthermore, previously trained fish lost their ability to avoid electric shock after exposure to DDT.

There is some evidence that the amount of DDT stored in human tissue has not increased over the past decade or so in the United States, but has probably reached a mean concentration of some 7–12 ppm. At a given exposure level it apparently takes about one year for an equilibrium to be established between intake and loss through excretion, after which continued exposure produces no increase in DDT load. The mean concentration of DDT in human populations varies widely from one geographic location to another, both within and between countries. It also varies with diet, race, age, and undetermined individual differences. Table 6-1 shows the DDT concentrations that have been found in a series of studies.

Generally, people in the most northern countries, where growing seasons are short and insects less of a year-round problem, have substantially smaller DDT loads than people in the United States. Intensive agriculture in Israel, as well as increased household usage of pesticides, is doubtless responsible for the high levels found there. Unfortunately, there are no available reports of DDT loads from other countries with intensive agriculture, such as Japan and the Netherlands. High levels in Delhi, India, may be related to the use of DDT to preserve stored food. Racial and sexual differences in the U.S.A. and elsewhere are probably due to dietary differences and undetected variations in occupational exposure.

In a recent study of individuals from Dade County, Florida, a significantly lower DDT-DDE concentration was found in children under 5 years of age, suggesting that they had not yet reached their equilibrium levels. Six stillbirths and fetuses were examined, and found to have loads more closely reflecting concentrations in their mother's tissues. Passage of DDT across the placental membrane into the fetus has now been demonstrated to take place as early as the 22nd week of pregnancy, and may occur well in advance of that.

It is difficult at this juncture to evaluate the magnitude of the direct threat to human health represented by the present chlorinated hydrocarbon load, to

TABLE 6-1
Mean Concentration of DDT in Human Body Fat

Population	Year	Number in sample	DDT (*ppm*)
United States	1942	10	0
United States	1950	75	5.3
United States	1955	49	19.9
United States	1954–1956	61	11.7
United States	1961–1962	130	12.6
United States	1961–1962	30	10.71
United States	1962–1963	282	10.3
U.S. (all areas)	1964	64	7.0
U.S. (New Orleans)	1964	25	10.3
U.S. (white, over 6 yrs.)	1968	90	8.4
U.S. (nonwhite, over 6 yrs.)	1968	35	16.7
Alaskan Eskimo	1960	20	3.0
Canada	1959–1960	62	4.9
Canada	1966	27	3.8
United Kingdom	1961–1962	131	2.2*
United Kingdom	1963–1964	65	3.3
United Kingdom	1964	100	3.3*
Germany	1958–1959	60	2.2
Hungary	1960	50	12.4
France	1961	10	5.2
Israel	1963–1964	254	19.2
India (Delhi)	1964	67	26.0

SOURCE: Various. DDT is expressed as DDT plus its breakdown product DDE converted to equivalent DDT units. Some figures include minor amounts of other breakdown products.
* Geometric mean.

say nothing of whatever loads might be incurred in the future. Most of the analyses completed have dealt with DDT, although human beings are also being exposed to a wide range of related compounds, some of which have considerably higher immediate toxicity. There are indications that dieldrin, perhaps four times as toxic as DDT, may be involved in portal cirrhosis of the liver, and that benzene hexachloride may contribute to liver cancer. The critical question is not immediate toxicity, but long-term effects. The oldest people who have been exposed to high concentrations of DDT since conception are now just in their early twenties. It is possible that their life expectancies may already have been dramatically reduced; it is also possible that there will be no significant reduction of life expectancies. We will not know until more time has passed. Breast-fed babies in Sweden get 70% more than what is considered the maximum acceptable amount of DDT, and British and American breastfed babies consume about 10 times the recommended maximum amount of dieldrin. Some babies in Western Australia are exposed to as much as *30 times* the maximally acceptable amount of dieldrin.

What effect these poisons may be having on the sensitive developmental systems of infants is unfortunately unknown. Göran Löfroth of the Institute of Biochemistry, University of Stockholm, wrote in 1968 that "Many parents are faced by a difficult choice. Should they expose their child . . . to an unknown and high amount of organochlorine pesticides, or should they deprive the child of nutritious milk and warm contact with its mother? The danger notwithstanding, it looks as if the positive advantages of breast-feeding outweigh the organochlorine hazard. But the outlook for the future is, to say the least, distinctly disturbing."

At any rate, we shall almost certainly find out what the overall effect of the chlorinated hydrocarbon load will be, since the persistence of these compounds guarantees decades of further exposure, even after their use has been discontinued. The continued release of chlorinated hydrocarbons into our environment is tantamount to a reckless global experiment, and we humans, as well as all other animals that live on this globe, are playing the role of guinea pigs.

Lead Pollution

Although biologists are just beginning to understand the effects of chlorinated hydrocarbons on people, and are beginning to realize that they previously underestimated the danger, there is no lack of understanding with regard to lead poisoning. We *know* what lead does. Chronic lead poisoning symptoms include loss of appetite, weakness, awkwardness, apathy, and miscarriage; it causes lesions of the neuromuscular system, circulatory system, brain, and gastrointestinal tract. It is a sobering thought that overexposure to lead was probably a factor in the decline of both the Greek and Roman civilizations. As Doctor S. C. Gilfillian has pointed out, the Romans lined their bronze cooking, eating, and wine-storage vessels with lead. They thus avoided the characteristic unpleasant taste of copper and the obvious symptoms of copper poisoning, trading them for the pleasant flavor of lead and the more subtle symptoms of lead poisoning.

Although lead pipes were commonly used to carry water, it is doubtful whether much of the lead that accumulated in the bones of Roman citizens entered their systems through the water supply. The reason is that most waters are slightly alkaline, and insoluble compounds would have formed on the surfaces of the pipes, thus preventing the metal from entering the water. Most of the lead undoubtedly entered their bodies with food and drink, particularly their wines. The acids in foods and in wines combine with lead to form soluble salts that can be absorbed by the body. Examination of the bones of upper class Romans of the classical period shows high concentrations of lead; this poisoning may have been one cause of the famous decline of Roman leadership. The lower classes lived more simply, drank less wine from lead containers, and thus may have picked up less lead.

We too are constantly exposed to lead in our environment, in the form of air contamination from lead smelting and the combustion of gasoline containing tetraethyl lead. We are exposed to lead in various other ways as well —via pesticides, paints, solder used to seal food-cans, lead piping, abraded particles of lead-containing ceramics and glassware, and so forth. As Clair C. Patterson, a geochemist at the California Institute of Technology, stated in 1965, "There are definite indications that residents of the United States today are undergoing severe chronic lead insult. The average American ingests some 400 millionths of a gram of lead per day in food, air, and water, a process which has been viewed with complacency for decades."

The pattern of increase in the lead contamination of the atmosphere has been revealed by studies of the lead content of the Greenland ice cap. The ice cap "lead load" increased some 400 percent between 1750 and 1940, and it rose another 300 percent between 1940 and 1967! By comparison, studies show that the content of sea salts in the Greenland ice cap have not changed since 1750, indicating that changes in the overall pattern of deposition of materials in the ice is not the cause of the lead increase. That similar patterns of lead contamination are not found in Antarctic snows lends strong support to the thesis that atmospheric lead pollution originated first with lead smelting and then more recently with the combustion of gasoline. Both sources of contamination are concentrated in the Northern Hemisphere, and the spread of pollution to Antarctica and the Southern Hemisphere in general is largely blocked by atmospheric circulation patterns.

It is now suspected that airborne lead is becoming a major source of exposure, at least for people in urban areas, although the overall exposure from food and beverages is still higher. But in Los Angeles and a few other cities, it is possible that more lead is now being absorbed through the lungs than through the digestive tract. Since 1924 the American consumption of tetraethyl lead in automobile fuel has risen from less than one million pounds per annum in 1924 to 285 million in 1950 and 700 million in 1968. In 1968 another 50–60 million pounds were used in aviation gasoline. About 75 percent of this ends up in the atmosphere. The average concentration of lead in the blood of Americans in 1968 was about 0.25 ppm, which is a little less than half the level at which removal from exposure is recommended for people who work with lead in industry. Garage mechanics and parking lot attendants tend to have about 0.34–0.38 ppm in their blood. Future projections for lead pollution all point to an increase.

Lead is a cumulative cellular poison. It seems hardly prudent to wait until much of the population begins to show chronic or acute symptoms before we attempt to lower its level in the environment. Chronic lead poisoning is unusually difficult to diagnose, and low-level effects could be quite common already. Moreover, there is always the possibility of synergistic interactions with the other poisons to which we are exposed. It is estimated that to add anti-knock properties to gasoline by using substances other than tetraethyl lead would mean a one-cent-per-gallon rise in the price of gasoline. That would seem like quite a bargain, provided that the substituted additives did not cause equal or worse problems.

Fluoride Pollution

Fluoridation of water supplies is an emotion-charged subject, but it is linked with a potentially serious health hazard, fluoride pollution, and it must be discussed. The scientific evidence supporting the efficacy and safety of mass fluoridation is not as good as it ought to be, but neither is there convincing evidence that it is harmful. Although there are certainly some "cranks" in the antifluoridation school, there are also some serious and competent scientists and responsible laymen who have been unmercifully abused because of the position they have taken on this controversial issue. Individual treatment with fluoride is simple and can be supplied cheaply on public funds for those desirous of using it.

Fluoride pollution is definitely a serious problem. Fluorides are discharged into the air from steel, aluminum, phosphate, glass, pottery, and brick works. It can add to the fluoride uptake of individuals who drink fluoridated water. In addition, increased fluoride concentration has been detected in foods and beverages processed in communities supplied with fluoridated water. The difference between "safe" and "unsafe" levels of fluoride uptake is small, and it is clear that some people in fluoridated communities and elsewhere are now taking in more than the official "safe" level (there is evidence that even this level may be unsafe for certain people). Fluoride pollution and water fluoridation should be monitored much more closely, and a way must be found to assay the benefits and dangers of fluoridation in a much calmer atmosphere than has prevailed over the past decade or so.

Radiation and Chemical Mutagens

No increase in the prevailing level of radiation on the surface of our planet is anything but harmful. As Sheldon Novick has said in his book, *The Careless Atom* (1969), ". . . the environment which supports us has only a limited capacity for radiation, and that capacity can only be used once." One cost of each additional increment of radiation to which a population is exposed is a future increase in genetic deformities, cancers, and stillbirths. Ionizing radiation causes mutations—random changes in the structure of DNA, the long molecule that contains the coded genetic information necessary for the development and functioning of a human being. Because mutations occur at random, the vast majority of them are harmful, just as a random change in any complex apparatus, such as a TV set, is much more likely to do harm than good. When a cell in which a mutation has occurred is in the germ line —that is, any cell that will produce sperm or eggs—the mutation may be passed on to future generations. Another cost of increased radiation is paid by individuals of the current generation; for them the price in increased radiation exposure is often cancer. Of course, the costs of increased exposure to radiation (like those of all kinds of pollution) must be balanced against whatever social benefits are perceived as deriving from the activities responsible for the increased exposure.

Exposure to radiation comes from several sources, including isotope therapy and X-ray diagnosis and therapy. Another source is fallout from the testing of nuclear weapons. Still another is radiation pollution from nuclear reactors used to generate power to meet the needs of exploding populations.

The hazard for Americans thus far created by fallout amounts to about 1 percent of that from normal "background radiation" from cosmic rays and other natural sources. This risk is small even compared with those of X-ray exposure. But even this tiny increase may have been responsible for up to 12,000 genetically defective babies and 100,000 cases of leukemia and bone tumors. Dr. Ernest Sternglass of the University of Pittsburgh has claimed recently that infant mortality has been greatly increased by strontium-90 entering milk after nuclear testing. His results have been strongly contested, and we believe them to be incorrect. The resultant controversy, however, has underlined once again the difficulty of obtaining facts, sorting out factors, and arriving at a consensus about the huge "natural experiments" we are carrying out by changing our environment. According to geneticist Joshua Lederberg, while Sternglass is probably wrong about the level of damage caused by strontium-90, one of its decay products, yttrium-90, may be causing genetic damage (although almost certainly not at the level postulated by Sternglass).

The amount of radiation pollution to be expected from nuclear power stations is still an open question. Although these plants do not produce the kinds of air pollutants associated with the burning of fossil fuels, their radioactive waste products may prove to be a bad substitute. The Atomic Energy Commission (AEC) seems to have made a good case for the solidification of the bulk of radioactive fission products and their storage in empty salt mines, but that will not remove all the hazard. It has been estimated that by the year 2,000, more than 3,000 6-ton trucks will be in transit at any given time carrying such wastes to burial sites. Truck accidents will be a constant serious threat.

Perhaps more dangerous than bulk radioactive wastes are the number of isotopes continually released in small quantities into the air and water by nuclear plants. There is, at present, no economically feasible way of containing these emissions. In some areas such isotopes have already turned up in potentially serious concentrations. This situation will be further aggravated by the projected enormous increases in nuclear power generation. The projected release of one isotope *alone,* krypton-85, could, within the next century, raise the level of radiation exposure of the general population to 60 percent of the maximum permissible level set by the National Committee on Radiation Protection and Measurement. Krypton-85 is just one of some 200 radioactive substances released at "low levels" by fission reactors. Although it has frequently been stated that the eventual advent of fusion reactors will free us from these difficulties, at least one authority, F. L. Parker of the International Atomic Energy Agency, takes a more cautious view. He contends that the escape of radioactive tritium from fusion power plants may prove even more hazardous than the escape of isotopes from fission reactors.

The permissible level of krypton-85 and those of the AEC for various radioactive substances have recently been shown by careful analysis to be *set much too high*. In a devastating report, medical physicists John W. Gofman and Arthur R. Tamplin, of the Lawrence Radiation Laboratory of the University of California, press for the setting of new guidelines "absolutely above reproach and question, for the consequences of error can even mean the deterioration of the human race on earth." They contend that the basis of the establishment of permissible levels, the concept that below certain threshold levels of exposure radiation is harmless, is not justified by the available evidence.

It is abundantly clear that nuclear power programs are being pushed too rapidly for safety. The AEC, which has unfortunately been cast in the role of both promoter and regulator of nuclear power, is promoting more vigorously than it is regulating. Though the hazards may possibly be reduced technologically in the future, they are much too high now. If serious explosion hazards are not completely designed out of the plants, then the dangers of catastrophic radiation accidents, which could lead to hundreds of thousands of deaths and the contamination of very large areas will persist. These hazards are now so great that private insurance companies have refused to cover the risk. As a result, Congress was persuaded to pass the Price-Anderson act, which, in essence, makes the taxpayer pay the huge price of liability insurance for the utility companies. If it were not for this and other huge subsidies for research and development, nuclear power could not come close to competing with conventional power sources. It is hardly reassuring to know that even the Price-Anderson act allows for only enough insurance to cover 8 percent of the damage that the government *itself* estimated would be caused *to property alone* by the most serious "hypothetical accident" for a moderate-sized installation. The estimated cost, $7 *billion,* is now thought to have been a very *low* estimate. Heavily documented discussions of the technical problems and serious hazards of nuclear power generation can be found in the books by Novick and by Curtis and Hogan, both of which are listed in the bibliography.

We must, of course, bend every effort toward reducing the hazards posed by the use of nuclear reactors to generate electricity. The advantages of saving our dwindling supplies of oil and coal are great, as is the potential for reducing pollution. At the moment, however, nuclear power simply substitutes more subtle and dangerous radioactive pollutants for those pollutants from the fossil-fueled plants that plague us today. The AEC has a very poor record in the area of environmental pollution, which began when they underplayed the seriousness of fallout from nuclear weapons tests in the 1950's. Judging from statements made in 1969 by its chairman, Glenn T. Seaborg, the AEC has not profited from those early mistakes. His claim of an "excellent safety record" in the nuclear power field is based on the relatively few deaths that have been directly associated with reactor accidents. The reluctance of private companies to supply nuclear power plants with liability insurance is based in part on the "near misses" in the reactor field, such as the accident in 1966 at the Fermi Plant outside Detroit, which potentially could have killed millions of people and rendered a substantial part of the U.S. uninhabitable. Prior to 1964 there had been twelve reactor accidents involving serious damage to the installation, radiation overexposure for individuals, or release of radioactivity to the environment. Some of these incidents exceeded the "maximum credible accident" for the installation involved. This concept is itself an indication of the euphemistic AEC approach to safety, for the "maximum credible accident" is defined as the worst one which could occur in the absence of human error and with all safety devices working perfectly. Since human beings make mistakes and safety devices are prone to failure, this is hardly reassuring. It is clear that until the AEC can be reorganized to provide cautious and intelligent control of immediate and long-term environmental hazards, constant vigilance by Congress and concerned citizens will be necessary to avoid running grave risks.

Biologists have recently become seriously concerned about sources of mutations other than radiation, namely chemical mutagens. Increased interest in the causes of congenital defects, combined with the progress being made toward an understanding of the chemical basis of heredity, have led to an awareness that mankind is being exposed to many thousands of synthetic chemicals whose mutagenic potential is unknown. Such chemicals as caffeine and LSD have been alleged to be dangerously mutagenic in man, but the results of tests on experimental animals have been variable and therefore inconclusive. Caffeine has been shown to be mutagenic in fruitflies, but not in mice. Among the many other chemicals that have been shown to be capable of causing mutations are nitrogen mustards, hydrogen peroxide, formaldehyde, cyclohexylamine (a breakdown product of the artificial sweetener cyclamate), and nitrous acid (this is what the food additive sodium nitrite becomes in the stomach).

In order to get through the next few decades with civilization intact, we will have to focus our attention primarily on the *quantity* of *Homo sapiens*. But it would be foolish for us to neglect, even in the face of crisis, the question of the future *quality* of the human population. Every reasonable effort should be made to determine the extent of mutational hazards and to reduce them.

Noise Pollution

People everywhere have recently become aware of a new kind of pollution—noise pollution. The problem has been thrown into sharp focus by the discovery that some teen-agers were suffering permanent hearing loss following long exposures to amplified rock music, and by public concern about the effects of sonic booms that will be caused by the Federal Aviation Agency's supersonic transport (SST) project. Possible serious effects of the SST, in addition to the booms, are discussed later in this chapter.

Noise is usually measured in decibels. A 10-fold increase in the strength of a sound adds 10 units on the decibel scale, a 100-fold increase adds 30. Silence, an arbitrary threshold level, is represented by zero decibels. The formula definition of the decibel scale is decibels 10 $\log_{10}$ (measured intensity/average human hearing threshold intensity). Table 6-2 gives the decibel values of some representative sounds.

Even a brief exposure to intense noise can cause temporary loss of hearing acuity. Permanent loss of hearing follows chronic exposure to high noise levels. Noise levels as low as 50–55 decibels may delay or interfere with sleep and result in a feeling of fatigue on awakening. Recently there has been growing evidence that noise in the 90-decibel range may cause irreversible changes in the autonomic nervous system. Noise may be a factor in many

TABLE 6-2
Noise Levels

Threshold of hearing	1
Normal breathing	10
Leaves rustling in breeze	20
Whispering	30
Quiet office	40
Homes	45
Quiet restaurant	50
Conversation	60
Automobile	70
Food blender	80
Niagara Falls at base	90
Heavy automobile traffic, or jet aircraft passing overhead	100
Jet aircraft taking off, or machine gun at close range	120

stress-related diseases, such as peptic ulcer and hypertension, although present evidence is only circumstantial. In any case, noise pollution is clearly a growing threat to our health and happiness. Even if we are not subjected to the booms of the SST, the problem of noise abatement will continue to be a serious one for our society. Fortunately, however, the problem is more readily solvable with technology, imagination, and determination than most pollution problems.

"Quiet, Please," an article on aircraft noise by pioneer aviator Wolfgang Langewiesche, appeared in the April 1969 issue of *Air Facts,* a magazine for pilots. The article contains a series of excellent suggestions for suppressing aircraft noise, as well as a moving statement of Langewiesche's attitude: "To me, the sound of an airplane is the most poetic sound in the world . . . the sound of one of man's great adventures. But it's got to stop now, that's quite clear."

Geological Hazards

Geological hazards, such as landslides—or even earthquakes—are sometimes caused by human activities. These include changing the land for housing or industrial construction or the building of large dams to meet the need of growing populations for additional supplies of fresh water.

When Lake Mead was created (1935–1939) following the completion of Hoover Dam, thousands of seismic events—the largest of which was an earthquake with a magnitude of 5 on the Richter scale—were recorded in that previously inactive area. Large dams in other usually inactive regions of the world have caused numerous earthquakes with magnitudes greater than 6, large enough to do substantial damage to urban areas. An earthquake that registered 6.4 on the Richter scale and that was triggered by the filling of the Kogna Dam in India in 1967 caused 200 deaths. Some geologists suspect that the lowering of water tables (underground water), now a worldwide occurrence, could have similar effects.

In 1967 the consequences of four years of pumping fluid chemical wastes into an underground reservoir near Denver became clear. A series of earthquakes occurred, the three largest of which had magnitudes of about 5; slight damage was reported in Denver. The amount of energy released in the series of earthquakes was slightly greater than that released by a one kiloton A-bomb, more energy than was expended in pumping the fluid into the reservoir. The remaining energy had been stored in the Earth's crust by geologic processes, and its release was triggered by the injection of fluid into the underground reservoir.

Underground nuclear explosions also have the potential for releasing such stored energy. Although the widely discussed Amchitka test in 1969 did not induce a major quake, that in no way guarantees that future tests will not serve as triggers to set off earthquakes which may be far more serious than any yet caused by human intervention in the dynamics of the Earth's crust.

The Environment of Modern Cities

The deterioration of the environment, both physically and aesthetically, is most apparent in our cities. The dehumanizing effects of life in the slums and ghettoes particularly, where there is little hope for improving conditions, have often been cited as contributing causes of urban rioting and disturbances. Crime rates usually reach their zenith in these neighborhoods. Such symptoms of general psychological maladjustment suggest that modern cities provide a less than ideal environment for human beings.

There seems to be abundant evidence that traditional cultural patterns break down in cities, and also that the high numbers of contacts with individuals not part of one's circle of regular social acquaintances may lead to mental disturbance (defined here merely as behavior generally considered "disturbed" by the majority of the society). It is important to note that antisocial behavior and "mental illness" are found in all cultures, and that indeed the same disorders recognized by Western psychiatrists are found even in primitive peoples. Therefore we can be reasonably certain that lack of an evolutionarily "natural" environment is not the sole cause of such behavior. Nevertheless, that lack may well serve to aggravate the problems of people living in our most crowded, smoggy, and impersonal metropolises.

Stanford psychologist P. G. Zimbardo has concluded that urban pressures are transforming Americans into potential assassins. He based his conclusions on experimental studies of the connection between anonymity and aggression, and on field studies of vandalism. He noted an estimated 230 violent urban outbreaks in the period 1964–1969, and reported that in 1967 vandals in New York City alone wrecked 360,000 pay telephones, broke 202,712 school windows, and did damage to parks and transit systems costing some $850,-000. Cars were abandoned on streets of a large city (New York) and a small one (Palo Alto, California), and secretly watched to see if there was a difference in vandalism between the two localities. The New York car was virtually demolished within three days by 23 separate attacks by looters and vandals, nearly all in view of passers by and during the daytime. The Palo Alto car was not molested during more than a week. How much (if any) of such behavior might be reduced if density were lowered is unknown, but at least the anecdotal evidence seems to indicate that high density is a factor in such problems. Crime rates are some five times as high in urban as in rural areas. Though some of this difference may be due to disparities in reporting, not all of it can be explained on this basis. Rates for violent crimes have been shown to be positively correlated with actual population densities in American cities. This general correlation held for statistics taken in three different years, 1940, 1950, and 1960, in the same cities. The rises in assault and robbery with higher density were particularly striking, although murder and rape both also reflected the trend. Robbery is the only one of the four that does not most commonly occur between acquaintances. Interestingly, crime rates in the suburbs have been rising in the past few years, especially among teenagers from relatively affluent areas, although their crimes are more often acts against property than crimes of violence.

Some recent psychological studies suggest that individuals who commit violent crimes may have a lower than normal tolerance for crowding. Psychiatrist A. F. Kinzel of the Columbia-Presbyterian Medical Center in New York has found that prisoners convicted of crimes of violence were four times likelier to interpret the close approach of another person as "threatening" than were prisoners convicted of offenses involving property. Evidently, there are great differences in amounts of tolerance for crowding among individuals as well as among different cultures.

Other symptoms of mental disturbance and emotional stress are also prevalent in cities, although by no means exclusive to them. Incidence of divorce, suicide, child abuse, and various forms of mental breakdown are higher in urban areas. In an intensive study conducted in the late 1960's in Manhattan on the effects of crowding on people, all but 18.5 percent of the people interviewed were found to be suffering from some degree of neurotic or psychotic disturbance. This survey did not include the poorest neighborhoods, nor did it include people who were hospitalized. A different study of mental problems among children in Manhattan indicated that only 12 percent of these children were entirely free of any mental problems, and that 12 percent were seriously disturbed. Poverty and discrimination were found to be associated with mental disturbance, especially after the onset of adolescence. But the evidence is conflicting, and some studies tend to indicate that little or no increase of mental illness accompanies urbanization. Much more work is needed before the effects of urbanization and crowding can be clearly separated from other factors.

Diseases associated with stress, particularly ulcers, coronary disease, and high blood pressure, are also prevalent in cities. Lung cancer, associated with air pollution, is much more common in cities, even among nonsmokers, than in the country. But so are several other forms of cancer, the causes of which are unknown. Studies with animals, especially rats, which, like people, also form social systems (but whose social systems differ from those of men), indicate that overcrowding leads to severe stress on individuals. Under extreme conditions of crowding, the social system of rats breaks down and various sorts of aberrant behavior appear, including cannibalism, violent aggression, and gross neglect of offspring. Miscarriage and failures of reproduction become more common and the death rate rises. Autopsies of these animals reveal exhaustion of the adrenal cortex, brought on by stress. Similar symptoms of stress pathology were found in autopsies of many people who died in World War II concentration camps. Although there has been no direct investigation of adreno-cortical stress as a factor in deaths of urban dwellers, the prevalence of stress-related diseases in cities suggests that there might be a relationship. The possibility that our cities could eventually deteriorate to the point of causing complete social breakdown is something to consider.

Urban renewal, when carried on without regard for the social structure of a neighborhood and the style of life preferred by its inhabitants, has been shown to have extremely disruptive effects on the lives of the people involved. At its worst it evicts poor people without satisfactorily fulfilling the obligation to relocate them. Many, if not most, of the present hazards of city life could be eliminated or mitigated by more creative design of houses and neighborhoods, by the development of alternative, nonpolluting means of transportation, by finding solutions to the problems of the minorities and the poor in general, and by more efficient and equitable forms of administration. Of course, all of this requires vast infusions of time, talent, imagination, and money. But no amounts of these, however vast, can bring lasting success as long as our cities continue to grow rapidly.

Aesthetic Considerations

Some destitute mountain folk from the Appalachians, who were moved to New York where jobs were available, promptly fled back to the mountains, preferring poverty amid pleasant surroundings to life in such a horrible place.

The aesthetic poverty of our cities and suburbs has reached such a degree that most citizens are aware of it. Newspapers are replete with stories describing slums, ghettos, rats, trash and garbage. This is one of the reasons why weekends and holidays invariably bring on a mass exodus from the cities. Unfortunately, our frontier habits of thoughtless littering and defacement seem likely to reduce our attractive rural areas and state and national parks to similar levels of ugliness.

Studies with young animals and indirect evidence from young children indicate that a rich sensory environment early in life may determine the extent of later mental development. Sensory stimulation in young rats resulted in measurably larger brain sizes in adulthood than in their sensorily deprived litter-mates, and it affected their learning and problem-solving abilities as well. Children who have been exposed to a variety of sights, sounds, and experiences when they are very young may learn faster, and later on be more likely to develop attitudes of inquiry and exploration.

Yet our cities, once a rich source of varied sensory experiences, are becoming more monotonous and dismal. Modern urban development programs flatten blocks at a time—blocks that once included a mixture of buildings of different ages and styles—and then replace them with concrete monoliths that lack aesthetic quality. The variety of sounds, at least some of which were pleasing to hear, in smaller towns and on farms, is also coming to be replaced by an incessant din of traffic, construction, and household appliances.

A zoologist with an interest in environmental psychology, A. E. Parr of the American Museum of Natural History, has written that city children of a generation or two ago spent much of their time exploring and participating in the activities of the city, while today children are confined to dreary school rooms, their homes, and the local park. Poorer ones may play in the streets, and in this respect perhaps they are luckier. But many of today's city children are being deprived of firsthand knowledge about the city they live in and how the social organizations within it function, which creates a sort of alienation from their surroundings. At the same time their surroundings are becoming more and more monotonous and less attractive. Children's urges toward inquisitiveness, exploration, and ingenuity (qualities we will desperately need during the next generation) may thus be stifled outside the schools as well as in them.

Suburbs are often better than the cities in aesthetic qualities and sensory stimulation, but not invariably so. Although the environment is usually more natural and includes trees and gardens, many suburbs tend to be monotonous and reduce everything to a common denominator. All the houses in a given area are similar if not identical, and so are the gardens, parks, and shopping centers. Each modern real estate development is generally inhabited by people of about the same age, type of employment, and economic status. There is not much opportunity for children to meet people whose points of view differ from their own or those of their parents. Although the children may be freer to explore in the suburbs than in the city, there is sometimes even less of interest to find there than in the city. The absence of men most of the time may result in an even greater alienation of youngsters (and wives as well) from the functioning society. Of course, television may compensate somewhat for the lack of sensory and social variety in our lives, but it does not encourage inquisitiveness or offer opportunities for exploration or ingenuity or direct experience. On the contrary, it seems to foster passiveness and a tendency to regard life as a spectator sport.

Pollution and Climate

The climate of the Earth is largely determined by its heat balance. Most of the sun's energy reaches the Earth in the form of radiation of relatively short wavelengths—visible- and near-ultraviolet light. The air is almost transparent to these wavelengths, and very little energy is absorbed until the radiation reaches the surface. Absorption of energy warms the Earth's surface, and the heat is then reradiated from the surface as infrared radiation. But some constituents of air are not transparent to the long wavelengths of infrared radiation. Water vapor, water droplets, and carbon dioxide absorb outbound energy in the infrared and reradiate about half of it back toward the surface. If this "trapping" of heat did not occur the surface of the Earth would have an average temperature around $-10°F$ instead of about $+60°F$. This phenomenon of heating, which is due to the differential transparency of the atmosphere to long and short wavelengths, is called the *greenhouse effect*. Glass in a greenhouse lets light in, but absorbs the infrared reradiated by the warmed plants and earth of the greenhouse. The glass reradiates some of the infrared back into the greenhouse, which is the reason that greenhouses normally have higher daytime temperatures than their surroundings. Similarly, cloudy nights tend to be warmer than cloudless nights, other things being equal. At night the Earth's surface radiates heat accumulated during the day, and clouds absorb part of the heat and reradiate it toward the surface, thus adding to the greenhouse effect.

Another important determinant of the Earth's temperature is the reflectivity, or *albedo,* of the planet. The albedo is the fraction of incoming light *directly* reflected as short wavelengths instead of being absorbed (the infrared reradiated by the warmed planet is not part of the albedo). The higher the albedo the less energy is absorbed to warm the planet. Between 10 and 30 percent of the light reaching the land surface is not absorbed, but is reflected. Forests and cultivated land reflect less than do deserts. The seas reflect on the average some 5–15 percent, depending largely on the angle of elevation of the sun. Snow and ice may reflect as little as 30 percent or more than 90 percent, depending on their condition. Clouds, which cover about half of the planet at any given time, contribute greatly to its albedo. They reflect about 60 percent of the incoming solar energy back into space. Clouds thus play an important dual role in the heat balance, contributing to the albedo during the day and to the greenhouse effect night and day.

That is a simplified outline of the major factors affecting the average temperature of the Earth's surface. Energy from the sun is partly reflected and partly absorbed by the surface. In the process of absorption the surface is warmed and reradiates infrared radiation, part of which is trapped by the greenhouse effect. But the average temperature is not the whole story of climate. Many other factors determine how the energy received from the sun actually drives the global weather system. These are not entirely understood, but it is known that differential heating is very important, especially the degree of contrast between the equator and the poles. This means, for instance, that raising the overall temperature of the planet a degree or two would not necessarily mean a warmer climate for all the world's population. Its main effect might be to speed up circulation patterns and to bring arctic cold further south and antarctic cold further north.

How can man's activities affect the climate of the Earth? One obvious way is by influencing the overall heat balance. For instance, when fossil fuels are burned, carbon dioxide (CO_2) is added to the atmosphere, and CO_2 contributes to the greenhouse effect. Since 1880 the CO_2 content of the atmosphere has increased about 12 percent, and until the 1940's there was a concomitant rise in temperature. All of this increase in CO_2 may not be accounted for by burning of fossil fuels, since some increase in the amount of radioactive carbon (carbon-14) in the atmosphere has been reported. Carbon-14 is present in living and recently dead plant materials, but *not* in fossil fuels. Therefore the release of CO_2 by burning of fossil fuels would not increase the atmospheric load of carbon-14. Part of the increase in CO_2 undoubtedly has come from agricultural burning, and part from the slow oxidation of peat bogs which occurred as the climate warmed. The whole CO_2 picture is made immensely complex by interactions between the atmospheric pool of CO_2 and plant life (which uses CO_2 in photosynthesis) and the oceans (which absorb CO_2 at different rates in different areas). Unquestionably, man is influencing the climate when his activities add CO_2 to the atmosphere, but the degree and significance of that influence are uncertain.

Since the 1940's there appears to have been a decline in the average temperature of the Earth, in spite of a continued increase in the CO_2 content of the atmosphere. The consensus among meteorologists seems to be that this is a result of increases in the albedo caused by dust, other particulate pollution, and also increased cloud cover produced by the contrails of high-flying jet aircraft. This increase in reflectivity has more than counterbalanced the increased greenhouse effect from the CO_2. A veil of pollution now completely covers the planet. In the last decade there has been, for instance, a 30 percent increase in the turbidity (dustiness) of the atmosphere on the island of Hawaii, which is a long way from major sources of pollution. One major source of atmospheric dust is agriculture; thus food-growing activities change the weather, upon which the success or failure of crops ultimately depends. Automobiles, aircraft, power plants, trash burning, deforestation (leading to wind-erosion of soil) and many other devices and activities of mankind add to the turbidity of the atmosphere.

Another important source of dust in the atmosphere is volcanic activity. A look into history can give us some idea of what might be in store for man if he continues increasing particulate pollution, or if there should be an upsurge in volcanic activity. In 1815 the eruption of Mount Tambora on the island of Sumbawa in Indonesia put an estimated 150 cubic kilometers of ash into the atmosphere. The climatic effects were staggering. In 1816 there was "no summer" in the northern United States, and the English summer was one of record cold. The mean July temperature in England was 13.4°C (56°F), in contrast with a 250-year average of 15.7°C (61°F). In fact, the three coldest decades in England's summary weather statistics were 1781–1790, 1811–1820, and 1881–1890, the decades of the eruptions of Mount Asama in Japan and Mount Skaptar in Iceland (both 1783), Mount Tambora (1815), and Krakatoa (1883). It is sobering to consider what a Tambora-scale eruption today would do to the world food supply.

Increases in the planetary albedo resulting from man's activities are not limited to those caused by particulate pollution. Contrails, the long thin clouds produced by the passage of high flying aircraft, also add to the albedo. Contrails often dissipate rather rapidly, but sometimes they apparently trigger the formation of high cirrus clouds. Meterologists R. A. Bryson and W. M. Wendland have estimated that contrails are responsible for a 5–10 percent increase in cirrus clouds over North America, the Atlantic Ocean, and Europe. Contrails from SSTs could be an especially important factor, since they will be formed above the level of the atmosphere where rapid mixing occurs and could be extremely persistent. Bryson and Wendland indicate that under certain conditions SSTs might generate almost *total* cover in their regions of operation. On the other hand, meteorologist Louis J. Battan thinks that the formation of persistent SST contrails is unlikely because of the low humidity of the stratosphere.

Unfortunately it is impossible to predict exactly what will happen to the overall temperature of the Earth over the next few decades, or what the local effects of changes will be. It is not even known whether the amount of radiation produced by the sun is a constant—and that is essential information if changes in the heat budget of the planet are ever to be predicted. As a result, although we can be certain that man is affecting the climate (and probably accelerating change), we cannot yet isolate man's contribution to changes we observe.

It is worthwhile to consider some of the climatic changes that *might* occur. If the arctic region should become warmer, the floating ice pack of the Arctic Ocean would disappear. This could result in northward shifts in the positions of storm tracks and thus severely reduce rainfall on the plains of North America, Europe, and Asia. These areas would rapidly be converted into deserts. Simultaneously, the more northerly storm paths would bring on another age of glaciation; ice sheets would form on the northern parts of the continents. It is unlikely that the Arctic Ocean would freeze again if its mantle of ice were removed, since incoming solar radiation would no longer be reflected by the ice but would be absorbed by the water. Thus the change would not be quickly reversed.

On the other hand, should the south polar region get colder, the Antarctic ice cap could be destabilized by an increase in its thickness. As the weight of ice grew, the bottom layer would liquify, and much of the mass of the cap might slump into the Antarctic Ocean. The magnitude of such a disaster, thought possible by geologists J. T. Wilson of Victoria University, New Zealand, and J. T. Hollin of Princeton University, is difficult to imagine. It might produce a global tidal wave that could wipe out a substantial portion of mankind, and the sea level could rise 60–100 feet worldwide. Ice would cover an area of the oceans perhaps as large as Asia. There is enough ice stored in the Antarctic and Greenland ice caps together to cover the entire globe with a layer of ice almost 50 yards thick! (In a disaster such as the one just described, only part of the Antarctic ice mass would move into the water.) Polar ice is now a major reflector of solar radiation. If part of the Antarctic ice cap slumped into the sea and spread out, the area of reflecting ice would be enormously increased. The temperature balance of the planet would be drastically altered, producing an estimated average drop of 10°F, and a glacial age would begin that would last until melting and wave action broke up the ice and an interglacial period began. Evidence has been put forward that the last two ice ages began with catastrophic inundations, and that the current situation closely approximates that immediately preceding the last flooding.

Jet aircraft may change the climate in ways other than those already mentioned. For instance, astrophysicist Dr. Walter Orr Roberts of the National Center for Atmospheric Research has pointed out that naturally formed cirrus clouds may deflect jet streams, dramatically altering distant weather. A change in the course of a jet stream is suspected to have been partially responsible for starting the formation of the Sahara desert. Roberts considers it possible that contrail-triggered cirrus clouds may also alter the course of jet streams.

Climate, of course, is an ever-changing thing. The past million years or so have shown a pattern of glacial advances and retreats, changes in sea level, changes in rainfall pattern, and so forth, all having tremendous impact on the men alive at the time. Many areas of our planet show the traces of mankind flooded out, frozen out, or forced to migrate because of drought. All of the speculated climatic changes might be viewed merely as a continuation of age-old processes of change and therefore held to involve risks that have always been present in one form or another. But, unhappily, there is a difference. At just the time that man has populated the planet to the point of stretching his food resources to the maximum, he is almost certainly accelerating climatic changes. When climate changes, so must agriculture, and, as has been observed, man is conservative in his agricultural behavior. Consequently, any rapid change of climate, in whatever direction is bound to decrease food supply. Should rapidly accelerating air pollution, a new volcanic incident, or melting of the North Polar ice pack destroy the Northern Hemisphere's granaries in the next decade or so, even worse famines than those previously predicted would be inevitable.

The Epidemiological Environment

Today the population of *Homo sapiens* is the largest in the history of the species, it has the highest average density, and it contains a record number of undernourished and malnourished people. The population is also unprecedentedly mobile. People are in continual motion around the globe, and they are able to move from continent to continent in hours. The potential for a worldwide epidemic (pandemic) has never been greater, but people's awareness of this threat has probably never been smaller.

We do not completely understand the behavior of viruses but we do know that the spontaneous development of highly lethal strains of human viruses and the invasion of humanity by extremely dangerous animal viruses are possible. We also know that crowding increases the chances for development of a virus epidemic. Should, say, an especially virulent strain of flu appear, it is doubtful that the United States and other developed countries could produce enough vaccine fast enough to save most of their populations. Needless to say the problem would be even more severe in the UDCs. Certainly little effort could be made to save most of humanity. Consider, for example, the difficulty the United States had in coping with the mild Asian flu epidemic of 1968. It was not possible to manufacture enough vaccine to protect most of the population, and the influenza death rate in 1968 was more than four times as high as that of 1967. Only 613 deaths were attributed to flu, but society paid a high price for the disease in extra medical care and loss of working hours.

In 1967 an outbreak of a previously unknown disease occurred among a shipment of vervet monkeys that had been imported into laboratories in Marburg, Germany, and in Yugoslavia. This severe, hemorrhagic disease infected twenty-five laboratory workers who came into contact with the monkeys and their tissues. Seven of these people died. Five secondary infections occurred in individuals who came into contact with the blood of the original patients; all of these individuals survived. Mankind was extremely fortunate that the first infections of *Homo sapiens* by Marburgvirus occurred around laboratories where the nature of the threat was quickly recognized, and the disease contained (it was not susceptible to antibiotics). If it had escaped into the human population at large, and if the disease had retained its virulence as it passed from person to person, an epidemic resulting in hundreds of millions or even billions of deaths might have occurred. Among well-fed laboratory workers with expert medical care, 7 out of 30 patients died. Among hungry people with little or no medical care, mortality would be much higher. The infected monkeys passed through London airport in transit to the laboratories. If the virus had infected airport personnel, it could have spread over the entire world before anyone realized what was happening.

Our highly mechanized society is also extremely vulnerable to disruption by such events as power failures, floods, and snowstorms. What would happen if the United States were confronted with an epidemic that kept masses of sick people from work and caused the uninfected to stay home or flee the cities because of their fear of infection? This might slow or even stop the spread of the disease, but hunger, cold (in the winter), and many other problems would soon develop as the services of society ceased to operate. We have substantial knowledge of the almost total breakdown of much less complex societies than ours in the face of the "Black Plague"—a breakdown that occurred among people far more accustomed to a short life, hardship, disease, and death than the population of the Western World today. The panic may well be imagined if Americans were to discover that "modern medical science" either had no cure for a disease of epidemic proportions, or had insufficient doses of the cure for everyone. The disease itself would almost certainly impede the application of any ameliorating measures. Distribution of vaccines, for instance, would be difficult if airlines, trains, and trucks were not running.

In many parts of the world, public health conditions are developing that have a high potential for disaster. The rats that live on stored grain in India have renewed the spectre of a major outbreak of bubonic plague. Indeed, a returning Vietnam veteran could bring plague to rat-infested New York City and create an extremely dangerous situation. Nitrate pollution of water is creating conditions in which dangerous soil organisms are brought into contact with man for the first time. The organism that has recently caused cases of a fatal meningitis has been identfied as a soil-dwelling amoeba. It may be just the first of many such agents to infect man.

Irrigation projects connected with the Aswan Dam are spreading the conditions that promote the serious parasitic disease bilharzia. The broadcast use of chemotherapy and antibiotics has created a serious medical problem through the induction of resistance in bacteria and other parasites. Modification of the climate would also inevitably influence disease patterns; for example, the length of time viruses remain infectious is in part a function of humidity. A trend toward drying would encourage some, whereas others would thrive in increased moisture.

As if the threat of a natural pandemic were not gruesome enough, there is always the threat of biological warfare, or of an accidental escape of lethal agents from a biological warfare laboratory. Although most laymen have long been afraid of thermonuclear war, they are just beginning to grasp the colossal hazard posed by chemical and biological warfare (CBW). Any country with one or two well-trained microbiologists and even a modest budget can build its own biological doomsday weapons. Constructing lethal viruses against which there is little or no resistance in human populations can easily be done in theory; it may have already been done in practice. There recently have been rumors of the development by the American CBW establishment of a pneumonic rabies, one which, instead of being transmitted by bite, is transmitted in the same way as the common cold: from person to person via exhaled droplets. This is certainly possible, since under special conditions (such as those that sometimes occur in caves full of rabid bats) rabies has already been shown to have been transmitted through the air. Such a disease would be a disastrously effective weapon if it were transmitted by infected individuals before symptoms appear, since once they do appear rabies is 100 percent fatal. Other possibilities for lethal agents are many—anthrax, plague, tularemia, and Q-fever, to name a few. These might be disseminated in their natural form or in the form of special "hot" strains that are drug resistant or superlethal. Besides direct assaults on man, overt or covert attacks on a nation's food supply might be made by introducing plant diseases. The more crowded a population is, and the smaller its per capita food supplies, the better a target it would be for a biological warfare attack.

Why would nations develop such weapons? For the same reason they develop others. They hope to immunize or otherwise protect their own populations and thus avoid a biological backlash. These weapons have a special appeal for small and poor powers, which see themselves threatened by larger, richer ones, and which lack the funds and expertise to develop nuclear weapons systems. Presumably CBW would hold a special interest for countries like Taiwan, Cuba, Egypt, Israel, North Vietnam, and Yugoslavia.

Probably the full arsenal of CBW will never be used but that does not rule out the possibility of an accident. Virus laboratories, especially, are notoriously unsafe. To date, some 2,700 laboratory workers have become accidentally infected with viruses transmitted by insects, and there have been 107 fatalities. These deaths were caused by just one group of viruses. Fatal accidents occur in laboratories where work is done on other kinds of viruses, as well as other microorganisms. The inability of government CBW agencies to avoid accidents has been made clear by the Skull Valley, Utah CBW disaster of 1968, in which many thousands of sheep were poisoned when a chemical agent "escaped," and by the possible escape of Venezuelan Equine Encephalitis from the Dugway, Utah, Proving Ground in 1967. Congressman Richard D. McCarthy of New York announced in 1969 that CBW agents were being transported around the country in small containers *on commercial airliners!* Biological warfare laboratories are potential sources of a man-made "solution" to the population explosion. It is essential that some way be found to block all further work on biological weapons—the risk for mankind is simply too great.

In November 1969, President Nixon announced the unilateral renunciation by the United States of the use of biological warfare, even in retaliation. He directed that U.S. stocks of biological agents were to be destroyed and that further work on defenses against biological weapons was to be transferred from the Department of Defense to the Department of Health, Education and Welfare. President Nixon's warning that ". . . mankind already carries in its own hands too many of the seeds of its own destruction" is one that must be heeded by people in all nations. Even though this action might be reversed by reactionary leadership in this country or nullified by actions elsewhere, it is encouraging that the President of the world's most powerful nation has taken this most constructive step.

Bibliography

Anderson, J. M., and M. R. Peterson, 1969. DDT: sublethal effects on brook trout nervous system. *Science,* vol. 164, pp. 440–441.

Bates, Marston, 1968. Crowded people. *Natural History* (Oct.)

Berelson, B., and G. A. Steiner, 1964. *Human Behavior: An Inventory of Scientific Findings.* Harcourt, Brace & World, Inc. An invaluable source for information on subjects ranging from perception to mental illness and cultural change.

Battan, Louis J., 1966. *The Unclean Sky: A Meterologist Looks at Air Pollution.* Doubleday and Co., New York.

Battan, Louis J., 1969. *Harvesting the Clouds, Advances in Weather Modification.* Doubleday and Co., New York. See especially Chapter 12, "Changing climates," and 13, "Plants, animals, people, the law, and the weather."

Berger, Rainer, and W. F. Libby, 1969. Equilibration of atmospheric carbon dioxide with sea water: possible enzymatic control of the rate. *Science,* vol. 164, pp. 1395–1397. Illustrates the complexity of the role played by the ocean in regulating the CO_2 content of the atmosphere.

Bryson, R. A., 1968. All other factors being constant . . . A reconciliation of several theories of climatic change. *Weatherwise* (April).

Bryson, R. A., and W. M. Wendland, 1968. Climatic effects of atmospheric pollution. Paper presented at the A.A.A.S. meeting, Dallas.

Burnham, David, 1969. Psychologist says pressures of big-city life are transforming Americans into potential assassins. *New York Times,* April 20, p. 49. An account of Dr. Philip G. Zimbardo's studies on aggression and vandalism in large and small cities.

Calhoun, John B., 1962. Population density & social pathology. *Scientific American,* vol. 206, no. 2 (Feb.). Studies of crowding in rats.

Carr, Donald E., 1965. *The Breath of Life.* W. W. Norton & Co., Inc., New York. A general discussion of air pollution.

Cooper, D. F., and William C. Jolly. 1969. *Ecological Effects of Weather Modification.* University of Michigan, School of Natural Resources. This report, sponsored by the Department of the Interior, is an excellent, balanced summary of possible consequences of purposeful weather modification and contains much material related to the effects of gradual climatic change. Good bibliography.

Cole, LaMont C., 1966. Man's ecosystem. *BioScience,* vol. 16, no. 4 (April).

Curley, A., and R. Kembrough, 1969. Chlorinated hydrocarbon insecticides in plasma and milk of pregnant and lactating women. *Arch. Environmental Health,* vol. 18, pp. 156–164.

Curtis, Richard, and Elizabeth Hogan, 1969. *Perils of the Peaceful Atom: The Myth of Safe Nuclear Power Plants,* Doubleday & Co., New York.

This and Novick's book (below) summarize the dangers in today's headlong rush to use nuclear energy to produce electrical power.

Deevey, E. S., Jr. 1958. Bogs. *Scientific American,* vol. 199, no. 4 (Oct.). Describes bog contribution to CO_2 in atmosphere.

Dubos, Rene, 1967. *Man Adapting.* Yale Univ. Press, New Haven.

Falk, H. L., S. J. Thompson, and Paul Koten, 1965. Carcinogenic potential of pesticides. *Arch. Environmental Health,* vol. 10, pp. 848–858.

Fischer, Ames, 1967. Community psychiatry and the population explosion. *California Medicine,* vol. 106, pp. 189–195. Contains information on relation between high population density and incidence of mental illness.

Flohn, Hermann, 1969. *Climate and Weather.* McGraw-Hill, New York. A fine summary.

Gofman, John W., and Arthur R. Tamplin, 1969. Studies of radium-exposed humans: the fallacy underlying a major "Foundation of NCRP, IRCP, and AEC Guidelines for Radiation exposure to the Population-at-Large." Supplement to testimony presented before the Sub-committee on Air and Water Pollution Committee on Public Works, U.S. Senate, Nov. 18.

Graham, Frank, Jr., 1966. *Disaster by Default. Politics and Water Pollution,* M. Evans & Co., Inc., New York.

Gross, Edward, 1969. Digging out from under. *Science News,* vol. 96, pp. 278–279. Discusses the problem of disposal of solid wastes.

Hall, E. T., 1966. *The Hidden Dimension.* Doubleday, Garden City, New York. The basic source on man's use of personal space.

Hanson, R. P., S. E. Sulkin, E. L. Buescher, W. McD. Hammon, R. W. McKinney, and T. H. Work, 1967. Arbovirus infections of laboratory workers. *Science,* vol. 158, pp. 1283–1286. Describes incidence of laboratory accidents with arthropod-borne viruses.

Hass, Ernst, 1968. Common opponent sought . . . and found? *Bulletin of the Atomic Scientists* (Nov.). Popular description of Wilson's ice-age theory, and description of possible technological preventions.

Hayes, W. J., Jr., W. F. Durham, and C. Cueto. 1956. The effect of known repeated oral doses of chlorophenothane (DDT) in man. *Journal of American Medical Association,* vol. 162, pp. 890–897. In this study high oral doses of DDT did not produce detectable symptoms in adult men over a period of 1–2 years. It is often erroneously cited as "proof" that DDT is harmless to human beings.

Herber, Lewis, 1968. *Crisis in our Cities.* Prentice-Hall, Inc., Englewood Cliffs, N.J. Describes the negative aspects of the urban environment.

Hersh, Seymour M., 1969. *Chemical and Biological Warfare.* Doubleday (Anchor Book), Garden City, N.Y.

Hersh, Seymour M., 1969. Dare we develop biological weapons? *N.Y. Times Magazine,* Sept. 28.

Hollin, John T., 1965. Wilson's theory of ice ages. *Nature,* vol. 208, no. 5005 (Oct. 2). Describes partial check of Wilson's ice-age theory.

Keyfitz, Nathan, 1966. Population density and the style of social life. *BioScience,* vol. 16, no. 12, pp. 868–873 (Dec.). An interesting discussion of urbanization and the differences between DC and UDC cities.

Kissling, R. E., R. Q. Robinson, F. A. Murphy, and S. G. Whitfield, 1968. Agent of disease contracted from green monkeys. *Science,* vol. 160, pp. 888–890.

Kyllonen, R. L., 1967. Crime rate vs. population density in United States Cities: A model. *Yearbook of the Society for General Systems Research,* vol. 12, pp. 137–145.

Laws, E. R., Jr., A. Curley, and E. F. Biros. 1967. Men with intensive occupational exposure to DDT. *Archives of Environmental Health,* vol. 15, pp. 766–775. This study, like that of Hayes et al. cited above, tends to indicate little or no toxicity of DDT to adults over periods of a decade or more. It says nothing about the effects of exposure over longer time stretches, especially when exposure begins before birth. Information on the causes of death of men who have worked for chlorinated hydrocarbon manufacturers would be of greater interest on the subject of adult toxicity than this sort of study.

Lerner, I. Michael, 1968. *Heredity, Evolution, and Society.* W. H. Freeman and Company, San Francisco. Excellent background reading for hazards associated with mutagenesis.

Lewis, Howard R., 1965. *With Every Breath You Take.* Crown Publishers, New York. Another general discussion on air pollution.

Lewis, Oscar, 1966. The culture of poverty. *Scientific American,* vol. 215, no. 4 (April).

MacDonald, G. J. F., 1968. How to wreck the environment. *In* N. Calder (ed.) *Unless Peace Comes.* Viking Press, pp. 181–205. Describes purposeful weather modification for military purposes.

MacDonald, G. J. F., 1969. The modification of planet earth by man. *Technology Review,* Oct./Nov. See especially the section on man-made earthquakes.

Marine, Gene, 1969. *America the Raped.* Simon & Schuster, New York.

Mitchell, J. M., 1968. A preliminary evaluation of atmospheric pollution as a cause of the global temperature fluctuation of the past century. Paper presented at the A.A.A.S. meeting, Dallas.

Novick, Sheldon, 1969. *The Careless Atom.* Houghton-Mifflin, Boston.

Novick, Sheldon, 1969. A new pollution problem. *Environment* (May). Discussion of mercury pollution. The same issue of *Environment* contains two other articles on the same subject.

Parr, D. E., 1967. Urbanity and the urban scene. *Landscape,* vol. 16, no. 3, Contrasts the psychological impact of city life today with that of two generations ago, especially on children.

Parr, D. E., 1968. The five ages of urbanity. *Landscape,* vol. 17, no. 3. Describes the impact of modern city life on people of different ages.

Poppy, John, 1969. Violence: we can end it. *Look,* vol. 33, no. 12.

President's Science Advisory Committee, Environmental Pollution Panel, 1965. *Restoring the Quality of Our Environment.* Washington, D.C. Somewhat out of date but still a useful reference.

Radomski, J. L., W. B. Deichman, E. E. Clizer, and A. Rey, 1968. Pesticide concentrations in the liver, brain and adipose tissue of terminal patients. *Food and Cosmetic Toxicology,* vol. 6, pp. 209–220. This study is one of the most frightening yet to appear on the direct threat of the human chlorinated hydrocarbon load.

Reinow, Robert, and Leona T., 1967. *Moment in the Sun.* Dial, New York.

Revelle, R., and H. E. Suess, 1967. Carbon dioxide between atmosphere and ocean and the question of an increase of atmospheric CO_2 during the past decades. *Tellus,* vol. 9, no. 1, pp. 18–27 (Feb.).

Sachs, David O., 1968. Drink at your own risk. *McCalls* (Nov.), p. 100. Describes the state of water supplies in a series of American cities. Based on data from the Public Health Service.

Sanders, Howard J., 1969. Chemical mutagens. 1. The road to genetic disaster. 2. An expanding roster of suspects. *Chemical and Engineering News,* May and June. An excellent popular summary of what is known about chemical mutagens.

Sax, Karl, and Hally J. Sax, 1968. Possible mutagenic hazards of some food additives, beverages and insecticides. *Japan Journal of Genetics,* vol. 43, no. 2, pp. 89–94.

Smith, C. E. G., D. I. H. Simpson, E. T. W. Bowen, and I. Zlotnik, 1967. Fatal human disease from vervet monkeys. *Lancet,* vol. 2 for 1967, no. 7526, pp. 1119–1121. See also pp. 1129–1130 of the same issue.

Sommer, Robert, 1969. *Personal Space.* Prentice-Hall, Inc., Englewood Cliffs, N.J.

T.-W.-Tiennes, R. N., 1963. Stress in a crowded world. *New Scientist,* no. 357, pp. 595–6 (Sept. 19).

Wexler, Harry, 1952. Volcanoes and world climate. *Scientific American,* vol. 186, no. 4 (April).

Wilson, A. T., 1964. Origin of ice ages: an ice shelf theory for pleistocene glaciation. *Nature,* vol. 201, no. 4915 (Jan. 11). The basic source of the antarctic ice-cap-slump theory of glacial periods.

Wright, Jim, 1966. *The Coming Water Famine.* Coward-McCann, Inc., New York.

Zaron, M. R., R. Tyre, and L. Lattore, 1967. Chlorinated hydrocarbon pesticide levels in newborn. *Proc. Conf. Biological Effects Pesticides Mammalian Systems.* N.Y. Academy of Sciences (in press).

CHAPTER 7

Ecosystems in Jeopardy

*". . . the fouling of the nest which has been typical of man's
activity in the past on a local scale now seems to
be extending to the whole world society."*

Kenneth Boulding
*The Economics of the Coming
Spaceship Earth* (1966)

The plants, animals, and microorganisms that live in an area and make up a
biological community are interconnected by an intricate web of relationships,
which includes the physical environment in which these organisms exist.
These interdependent biological and physical components make up what
biologists call an *ecosystem.* The ecosystem concept emphasizes the functional relationships among organisms and between organisms and their physical environments. These functional relationships are exemplified by the food
chains through which energy flows in ecosystems, as well as by the pathways along which the chemical elements essential to life move through the
ecosystem. These pathways are generally circular; the elements pass through
the system in cycles. The cycling of some elements is so slow, however, that
in the time span of interest to us, movement appears to be one-way. An understanding of the flow of energy and the cycling of materials in ecosystems
is essential to our perception of what is perhaps the most subtle and dangerous threat to man's existence. This threat is the potential destruction, by
man's own activities, of those ecological systems upon which the very existence of the human species depends.

Food Webs

The food web of a Long Island estuary has been thoroughly investigated by biologists George Woodwell, Charles Wurster, and Peter Isaacson. The relationships they discovered are illustrated in Figure 7-1; their study shows several important characteristics of most food webs. One is complexity. Although only some of the kinds of plants and animals in this ecosystem are shown in this figure, it is evident that most of the consumers feed on several different organisms, and that most prey organisms are attacked by more than one predator. To put it another way, the food chains are interlinked. Ecologists believe that complexity is in part responsible for the stability of most

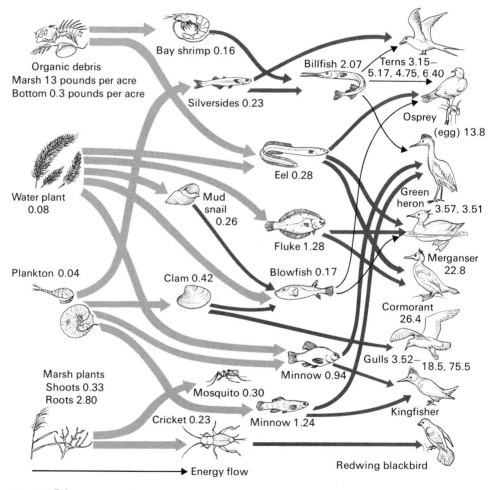

FIGURE 7-1
Portion of a food web in a Long Island estuary. Arrows indicate flow of energy. Numbers are the parts per million of DDT found in each kind of organism. [After Woodwell, "Toxic Substances in Ecological Cycles." Copyright © 1967 by Scientific American, Inc. All rights reserved.]

ecosystems. Apparently, the more food chains there are in an ecosystem, and the more cross-connecting links there are among them, the more chances there are for the ecosystem to compensate for changes imposed upon it.

For example, suppose that the marsh plant-cricket-redwing blackbird section of Figure 7-1 represented an isolated entire ecosystem. If that were the case, removing the blackbirds—say, by shooting—would lead to a cricket plague. This in turn would lead to the defoliation of the plants, and then to the starvation of the crickets. In short, a change in one link of such a simple chain would have disastrous consequences for the entire ecosystem. Suppose, however, that the cormorants were removed from the larger system. Populations of flukes and eels would probably increase, which in turn might reduce the population of green algae (*Cladophora*). But there would be more food for mergansers and ospreys, and their populations would probably enlarge, leading to a reduction of eels and flukes. In turn, the algae would recover.

Needless to say, things do not normally happen that simply and neatly in nature. But we have both observational and theoretical reasons to believe that the general principle holds: complexity is an important factor in producing stability. Complex communities, such as the deciduous forests that cover much of the eastern United States, persist year after year if man does not interfere with them. An oak-hickory forest is quite stable in comparison with an ultrasimplified community, such as a cornfield, which is a man-made stand of a single kind of grass. A cornfield has little natural stability and is subject to almost instant ruin if it is not constantly managed by man. Similarly, arctic and subarctic ecosystems, which are characterized by simplicity, tend to be less stable than complex tropical forest ecosystems. In arctic regions the instability is manifested in frequent, violent fluctuations in the populations of such northern animals as lemmings, hares, and foxes. In contrast, outbreaks of one species do not occur as often in complex tropical forests. Ecologist Robert MacArthur suggested in 1955 that the stability of an ecosystem is a function of the number of links in the web of food chains. He developed a measure of that stability using information theory. Although the bases of stability now appear somewhat more complicated than those proposed by MacArthur in his pioneering work, the idea that complexity promotes stability still appears to be theoretically sound.

Concentration of Toxic Substances in Ecosystems

Nowhere is man's ecological naiveté more evident than in his assumptions about the capacity of the atmosphere, soils, rivers, and oceans to absorb pollution. These assumptions all too often take the following form: if one gallon of poison is added to one billion billion gallons of water, then the highest concentration of poison to which anything will be exposed is about one part per billion billion. This might be approximately true if complete mixing by diffusion took place rapidly, which it often does not, and *if only physical systems were involved*. But because biological systems *are* involved, the situation is radically different. For example, filter-feeding animals may concentrate poisons to levels far higher than those found in the surrounding medium. Oysters make their living by constantly filtering the water they inhabit, and they live in shallow water near the shore, where pollution is heaviest. Consequently their bodies often contain much higher concentrations of radioactive substances or lethal chemicals than the water in which they live. For instance, they have been found to accumulate up to 70,000 ppm of chlorinated hydrocarbon insecticides, many thousands of times the concentration found in their environment. Food chains lead to the concentration of toxic substances; as biologist Barry Commoner of Washington University once put it, they act as a kind of "biological amplifier." The diagram of the Long Island estuary food web (Fig. 7-1) shows how the concentration of residues of DDT and its derivatives tend to increase in food chains from one trophic level to another. This tendency is especially marked for the chlorinated hydrocarbons because of their high solubility in fatty substances and their low water solubility. Although the clam and the mud snail are at the same trophic level, the filter-feeding clam accumulates more than half again as much DDT as the mud snail because of the difference in their food-capturing habits.

The mechanism of concentration is simple. Because of the second law of thermodynamics, the mass of herbivores normally cannot be as great as the mass of plants they feed on. With each step upward in a food chain the *biomass* is reduced. Energy present in the chemical bonds of organisms at one level does not all end up as bond energy at the next level, because much of the energy is degraded to heat at each step. In contrast, losses of DDT and related compounds along a food chain are small compared to the amount that is transferred upward through the chain. As a result, the concentration of DDT increases alarmingly at each level. Concentrations in the birds at the end of the food chain are from tens to many hundreds of times as high as they are in the animals further down in the chain. In predatory birds, the concentration if DDT may be a *million* times as high as that in estuarine waters.

Clear Lake, in California, has long been a favorite of fishermen, and now attracts water-skiers and vacationers of all kinds. Unfortunately, a midge (known locally as the Clear Lake "gnat") reproduces in great numbers in certain years. This insect is considered a pest merely because it is phototropic (attracted to light), and for no other reason. In an attempt to control the gnat, a spraying program was begun in the late summer of 1949 with DDD, a less toxic but equally persistent relative of DDT. The rate of application was about 0.02 ppm. The first application of what was then thought to be a relatively harmless pesticide eliminated about 99 percent of the gnats, as did the next application in 1954. By the time the lake was sprayed for the third and last time in 1957, the gnat plus almost 150 species of insects and other pests had developed some immunity to the pesticide. (It should be pointed out that within two weeks after each spraying, no DDD could be detected in the lake waters.)

One of the first signs of ecological damage became apparent in 1950. Before 1950 Clear Lake had been a nesting ground for about 1,000 pairs of western grebes (ducklike diving birds that feed primarily on small fishes and other aquatic organisms). Not only did many grebes die soon after the 1954 and 1957 sprayings, but fairly large die-offs occurred in subsequent years. Furthermore, the survivors were rendered unable to reproduce. From 1950 to 1961 no young were produced; in 1962 a single grebe hatched. Reproduction remained unsuccessful until 1969, many years after the first introduction of DDD into the environment. Studies designed to determine the concentration of DDD from the lowest trophic levels to the highest revealed that the microscopic plankton of the lake contained about 250 times that of application (the original concentration in the lake water). The concentration in frogs was 2,000 times that of application, in sunfish, about 12,000, and in grebes, as high as 80,000 times. The figures given for frogs and the other animals higher in the food chain are for the visceral fat. The flesh of several species of game fish were also examined. Some white catfish contained almost 10,000 times the original concentration of DDD in the water. These data make it obvious why no DDD could be detected in the lake water only two weeks after application: because of its high solubility in the fatty materials of biological systems, the insecticide had been absorbed almost completely by the *living* components of the lake's ecosystem.

Biogeochemical Cycles

Energy from the sun is constantly entering and passing through the Earth's ecosystems. But our ecosystems have no similar extraterrestrial source of the carbon, nitrogen, potassium, and sulfur, and many other substances that are required for life. These substances must be continually recycled through the ecosystem if the ecosystem is to persist. Let us now consider the cycling of three of these essential elements: carbon, nitrogen, and phosphorous.

CARBON CYCLE

Carbon is the basic constituent of all the large molecules characteristic of living beings. In a real sense life on Earth is "carbon-based"; life is possible only because of the properties of this element. The major reservoir of carbon is the gas carbon dioxide (CO_2), which occurs in the atmosphere of our planet and in solution in its waters. As shown in Figure 7-2, the process of photosynthesis forms the primary pathway by which carbon (as CO_2) is withdrawn from the carbon dioxide "pool" and is used by plants to build carbohydrates and other organic compounds. These compounds transfer the carbon to herbivores, which eat the plants. When herbivores are eaten by carnivores, the carbon moves further along the food chain. Both plants and animals extract energy from these organic compounds by the complex biochemical process called *cellular respiration*. Photosynthesis is the process by which energy from the sun is used to form the bonds of chemical energy that hold organic molecules together. The inorganic raw materials used in photosynthesis are CO_2 and water. Oxygen, which is released into the atmosphere, is one of its most important by-products. In respiration, which

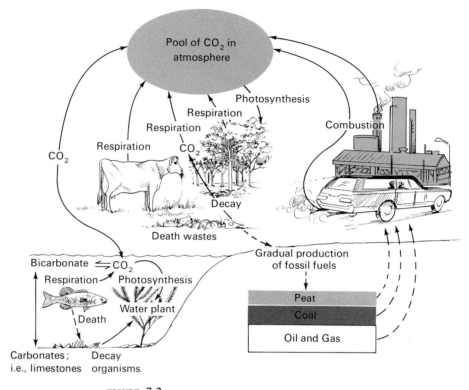

FIGURE 7-2

Carbon cycle. Solid arrows represent flow of CO₂.

occurs in both plants and animals, the organic molecules are broken down by oxidation (a slow combustion), and the energy of their chemical bonds is extracted. The end products of respiration are water and carbon dioxide.

Thus an essential part of the carbon cycle is the movement of carbon molecules from the pool of CO_2 in air and water to plants and animals further up the food chain. From plants and animals at various positions along the chain, respiration returns CO_2 to this pool. Carbon is also returned to the pool through the agency of the bacteria and fungi that cause decay. These microorganisms serve as the ultimate link in food chains, reducing the complex carbon-containing molecules of dead plant and animal matter, and animal wastes, to their simple components.

Not all the carbon built into the molecules of living organisms by the process of photosynthesis is returned quickly to the CO_2 pool. Some of it leaves the carbon cycle for millions of years and enters the crust of the Earth. This happens when incompletely decomposed organic matter accumulates and is transformed by geologic processes into fossil fuels—coal, oil, and natural gas. Carbon also is temporarily withdrawn from the cycle by the formation of limestone, often through the life processes of organisms (as in the formation of coral reefs). Such carbon is returned to the CO_2 pool by the burning of fossil fuels and by the weathering of limestone rocks.

NITROGEN CYCLE

Air is almost 80 percent nitrogen, another element required by all living systems (it is an essential ingredient of proteins). Nitrogen moves within ecosystems through a series of complex pathways, some of which are shown in Figure 7-3. Unlike the oxygen and carbon dioxide of the atmosphere, gaseous nitrogen cannot be used directly by most organisms. But some microorganisms, such as certain bacteria and blue-green algae, can convert gaseous nitrogen into more complex compounds that can be utilized by plants and animals. The best known of these nitrogen-fixing organisms are the bacteria associated with the special nodules on roots of legumes, which are plants of the pea family. These and other nitrogen-fixing bacteria that live free in the soil use the atmospheric nitrogen directly in making their own proteins. Nitrogen-containing compounds become available to plants when these bacteria die, and eventually to animals that eat the plants.

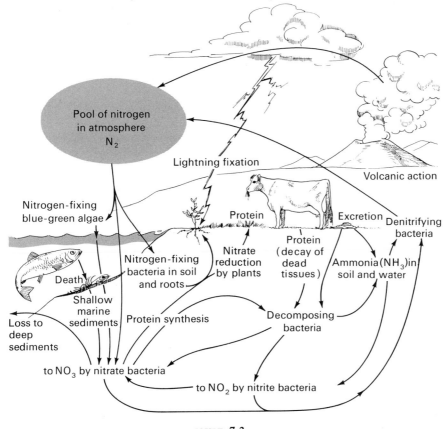

FIGURE 7-3
Nitrogen cycle.

Decay of dead plants and animals (by bacteria and fungi) leads to the production of ammonia, as does animal excretion. A special group of bacteria, nitrite bacteria, utilizes the energy in the chemical bonds of the ammonia, degrading it to nitrites (compounds containing nitrogen atoms each combined with two oxygen atoms—in the shorthand of the chemist, NO_2). Then another group of bacteria, nitrate bacteria, changes the nitrites to nitrates (compounds with combinations of single nitrogen atoms with three oxygen atoms, NO_3). The nitrate bacteria remove more energy in degrading NO_2 compounds to NO_3. Nitrates are the commonest form in which plants obtain nitrogen from the soil; thus a loop of the nitrogen cycle may be completed without the formation of gaseous nitrogen.

Nitrogen, then, enters the living part of the cycle in two ways: directly from the atmosphere via nitrogen-fixing bacteria, and as nitrates taken up from the soil by plants:

$$NO_3 \longrightarrow protein \longrightarrow ammonia \longrightarrow NO_2 \longrightarrow NO_3.$$

Another kind of bacteria, denitrifying bacteria, returns nitrogen to the atmosphere. These bacteria break down nitrates, nitrites, and ammonia, and liberate gaseous nitrogen.

Some nitrogen is lost to the system. In the form of nitrates, which are highly soluble, it is washed from the soil and eventually becomes deposited as deep-sea sediments.

PHOSPHORUS CYCLE

A famous German biochemist introduced the epigram: "Ohne Phosphor kein Leben"—without phosphorus there is no life. Phosphorus is an essential element in the DNA and RNA molecules involved in the transmission of genetic information (heredity), and phosphorus compounds are the prime energy-manipulating devices of living cells. Phosphorus does not cycle in ecosystems as readily as nitrogen does. The principal phosphorus reservoirs are phosphate rocks, deposits of guano (sea-bird excrement), and deposits of fossilized animals (Fig. 7-4). Phosphorus is released from these reservoirs through natural erosion and leaching, and through mining and subsequent use as fertilizer by man. Some of this released phosphorus becomes available to plants in the form of phosphates in the soil, and thus enters the living part of the ecosystem. It may pass through several animals and microorganisms before returning to the soil through decay. Much of the phosphate washed or dug from rock deposits eventually finds its way to the sea—man's mining and distributing activities accelerate this process. There it may be utilized by marine ecosystems or deposited in shallow or deep marine sediments. Although some of this may be returned by upwelling currents, much of it is lost semipermanently. It can be returned by geological processes leading to the uplifting of sediments, but it seems unlikely that these in the future will be sufficient to balance the loss.

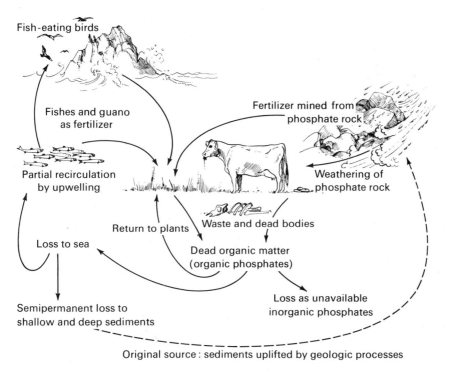

Fish-eating birds

Fishes and guano
as fertilizer

Fertilizer mined from
phosphate rock

Partial recirculation
by upwelling

Weathering of
phosphate rock

Loss to sea

Return to plants

Waste and dead bodies

Dead organic matter
(organic phosphates)

Loss as unavailable
inorganic phosphates

Semipermanent loss to
shallow and deep sediments

Original source : sediments uplifted by geologic processes

FIGURE 7-4
Phosphorous cycle.

THE ATMOSPHERE

It is important to remember that the atmosphere as we know it is largely a product of the activities of organisms. The atmosphere of the primitive Earth is thought to have been made up mainly of water vapor, methane, ammonia, and hydrogen. The presence of large amounts of free oxygen is a result of the photosynthetic activities of plants. They produced the surplus we now have, and they are essential for maintaining it. Similarly, it is the nitrogen cycle that maintains the nitrogen content of the atmosphere, and respiration and combustion are responsible for the CO_2 content of the atmosphere. Most life on Earth depends on maintaining the mixture of roughly 21 percent oxygen, 78 percent nitrogen, and 0.03 percent carbon dioxide. Mankind evolved to live in exactly that kind of atmosphere and would find significant deviations from this combination extraordinarily unpleasant, to say the least.

Modifying Ecosystems

Let us look now at some of the ways in which mankind modifies ecological systems. Obviously, some ecosystems are destroyed outright by such diverse activities as planting crops, logging forests, starting fires, building dams, applying defoliants to jungles, and constructing buildings and laying pavement. The results of man's activities are as varied as the activities themselves. When prairie is converted to cornfield, an unstable, simple ecosystem replaces a stable, complex one. Man's attempts to stabilize such systems artificially can lead to further destabilization and bring about changes elsewhere as well.

Wholesale logging of forests creates extreme changes that effectively destroy the forest ecosystem. Many animals that depend on the trees for food and shelter disappear. Many of the smaller forest plants depend on the trees for shade; they and the animals they support also disappear. With the removal of trees and plants, the soil is directly exposed to the elements, and it tends to erode faster. Loss of topsoil reduces the water-retaining capacity of an area, diminishes the supply of fresh water, causes silting of dams, and has other serious consequences for man. The flooding along many of the world's rivers, from the Yang-tse in China to the Russian River in California, is greatly aggravated by heavy logging in their watersheds. Deforestation changes the water cycle in other ways. It reduces the amount of water transferred from ground to air by the trees in the process known as "transpiration." This modifies the weather downwind of the area, usually making it more arid and subject to greater extremes of temperature. Finally, if reforestation is not carried out, the deforested area is invaded by "pioneer" weedy plants that often have much less desirable characteristics for human use than did the forest that was removed.

Man's activities have already produced a great increase in the amount of desert and wasteland. In 1882 land classified as either desert or wasteland amounted to 9.4 percent of the total land on Earth. In 1952 it had risen to 23.3 percent. During the same period land classified as carrying inaccessible forest *decreased* from 43.9 percent to 21.1 percent. The vast Sahara desert itself is largely manmade, the result of overgrazing, faulty irrigation, deforestation, perhaps combined with a shift in the course of a jet stream. Today the Sahara is advancing southward on a broad front at a rate of several miles per year. The great Thar Desert of western India is also the result of man's influence. Some 2000 years ago, what is now the center of this desert was a jungle. The spread of this desert, formed primarily because of lumbering and overgrazing, has accelerated recently. For almost a century now the desert has been advancing into the surrounding country at about five miles per decade around its entire perimeter; it has increased in size by some 60,000 square miles. Man's activities can lead to repetition of the Sahara and Thar stories all over the globe.

Erosion is an increasingly serious problem. Although thousands of years may be required to build up an inch of soil, many places on Earth lose topsoil at rates measured in inches per year! It is estimated that one-half of the farmland in India is not adequately protected from erosion, and on fully one-third of the farmland erosion threatens to remove the topsoil completely. As Georg Borgstrom has pointed out, soil-conservation procedures are especially difficult to institute in areas where the population is poorly fed. He cites a study that recommended a one-fifth *reduction* in the amount of cultivated land and a one-third reduction in the size of livestock herds in Turkey. It was hoped that these reductions would help to diminish the danger of catastrophic erosion caused by overgrazing. Unfortunately, the program was not initiated, presumably because the local people were dependent upon the land and the herds for food and other necessities.

Insecticides and Ecosystems

Besides being direct threats to human health, synthetic insecticides (Box 7-1) are among man's most potent tools for simplifying ecosystems. The increase in the concentration of the most persistent of these compounds with each upward step in a food chain exposes the populations *least* able to survive poisoning to the highest concentrations.

There are several reasons why the organisms that occupy positions near the upper end of food chains are less able to cope with the poisons than are, for example, herbivores. The first reason traces back again to the second law of thermodynamics. Because of the loss of energy at each transfer along food chains, the higher the position that a population occupies in a food chain, the smaller that population will be. This means that if a poison were applied that would kill most of the predators and herbivores in an area, it would be more likely to exterminate the population of predators than the population of herbivores, simply because there are fewer predators. Purely by chance, members of the larger population would be more likely to survive. It would not be necessary to kill all individuals of any one species of predator to force it to extinction. If survivors were too scattered for the sexes to find one another and produce offspring, extinction would surely follow. Or, if survivors were few, various genetic problems might result from inbreeding and cause the population to dwindle to zero.

Another reason that small populations of animals occupying high positions in food chains are more vulnerable is that larger populations tend to have greater stores of genetic variability. Assume, for instance, that one individual per hundred thousand in each of two insect populations, *A* and *B*, carries a mutant gene that makes it naturally resistant to pesticide *X*. Assume that *A* is a herbivore and that its population in a field consists of one million individuals. Assume that *B* is a parasite on *A* and that its population is one hundred thousand individuals. If the field is thoroughly treated with pesticide *X*, ten individuals of *A* will survive, but only one of *B* will survive, each of these being naturally resistant mutants. In this oversimplified example, the consequences are clear. The small group of resistant *A* insects can quickly reproduce a large population, free of the attack of *B*. But because most individuals of the new population of *A* will be resistant, the next treatment with insecticide *X* will have little effect. If dosage of *X* is increased, species *A* will respond by becoming more and more resistant with each new generation. The development of resistance is not, of course, confined to herbivorous pests. Other large populations can do so easily; for example, resistance to DDT has developed in many mosquito populations and has hampered malaria control programs.

In many actual cases differential kill of predators has released some of their prey species from their natural restraints. It is fair to say, for instance,

---

BOX 7-1 SYNTHETIC INSECTICIDES

Two groups of compounds contain the majority of synthetic insecticides: chlorinated hydrocarbons and organophosphates.

Chlorinated Hydrocarbons

This group includes DDT, benzene hexachloride (BHC), dieldrin, endrin, aldrin, chlordane, lindane, isodrin, toxophene, and similar compounds designed to kill insects. DDT is the most thoroughly studied of the chlorinated hydrocarbons, and much of the following discussion is based on it. In its behavior it is more or less typical of the group, although other chlorinated hydrocarbons are more soluble in water, more toxic, less persistent, etc. In insects and other animals these compounds act primarily on the central nervous system in ways that are not well understood, but the effects range from hyperexcitability to death following convulsions and paralysis. Chronic effects on vertebrates include fatty infiltration of the heart, and fatty degeneration of the liver which is often fatal. Fishes and other aquatic animals seem to be especially sensitive to chlorinated hydrocarbons. Oxygen uptake is somehow blocked at the gills, causing death from suffocation. That chlorinated hydrocarbons apparently can induce the production of enzymes may account for their wide range of effects.

Chlorinated hydrocarbons tend to be selectively soluble in fats and fatty tissues. In animals this means that they may be stored at sites remote from the primary active site in the nervous system and rendered relatively harmless. Chlorinated hydrocarbons vary a great deal in their toxicity to plants.

They are known to slow the rate of photosynthesis, but the exact cause of this effect is unknown. Their affinity for fats may lead them to concentrate in plant cell membranes (which, like those of animals, have a fatty component). Photosynthesis is carried on in membranous structures within the plant cell; malfunctioning of active transport systems in these membranes due to the presence of insecticides may well be the basis of the inhibition of photosynthesis.

The greater toxicity of chlorinated hydrocarbons in insects as compared to mammals is primarily a function of the greater ease with which these compounds are absorbed through insect cuticle compared with mammalian skin. Four properties make chlorinated hydrocarbons a potent threat to ecosystems:

1. Chlorinated hydrocarbons have a wide range of biological activity that is not well understood; they are broad-spectrum poisons.

2. They have great stability. It is not clear, for instance, how long DDT persists in ecosystems. Fifty percent of the DDT sprayed in a single treatment may still be found in a field 10 years later. This does not mean, however, that the other 50 percent has been degraded to biologically inactive molecules; it may only have gone somewhere else. Probably DDT (including its biologically active breakdown product DDE) has an average half-life (time required before 50 percent has been degraded) of much more than a decade. Indeed, DDE may be virtually immortal.

that mites, as pests, are a *creation* of the pesticide industry. Careless overuse of DDT and other pesticides has "promoted" many of these little insect-like relatives of spiders to pest category by killing off the insects that previously preyed on the mites and kept them under control. The emergence of the European red mite as a major pest in apple orchards followed the use of

3. Chlorinated hydrocarbons are very mobile. For example, the chemical properties of DDT cause it to adhere to dust particles and thus get blown around the world. Four different chlorinated hydrocarbons have been detected in dust filtered from the air over Barbados; insect populations in unsprayed areas high in the Sierra Nevada mountains of California are polluted with DDT. Furthermore, DDT codistills with water; when water evaporates and enters the atmosphere, DDT goes with it.

4. Finally, chlorinated hydrocarbons become concentrated in the fats of organisms. If you think of the world as being partitioned into nonliving and living parts, then these pesticides may be thought of as moving continually from the physical environment into living systems. To attempt to monitor DDT levels merely by testing water (as has frequently been done) is ridiculous. Water is saturated with DDT—that is, can dissolve no more—when it has dissolved 1.2 parts per billion. Besides, the chemical does not remain for long in water; it quickly enters any organisms that live in the water.

It is these four properties—extreme range of biological activity, stability, mobility, and affinity for living systems—that cause biologists' fears that DDT and its relatives may destroy the life-support systems of our planet. If any one of these properties were lacking, the situation would be much less serious, but in combination they pose a deadly threat.

Organophosphates

This group includes parathion, malathion, Azodrin, diazinon, TEPP, phosdrin, and several others. These poisons are descendants of the nerve gas Tabun (diisopropyl-fluorophosphate), developed in Nazi Germany during World War II. All of them are cholinesterase inhibitors; they inactivate the enzyme responsible for breaking down a nerve "transmitter substance," acetylcholine. The result is, in acute cases of poisoning, a hyperactivity of the nervous system; the animal dies twitching and out of control. In general, organophosphates do not build up in tissues or show chronic effects. Moreover, unlike chlorinated hydrocarbons, they are not long-lived and tend not to produce chronic effects in ecosystems.

Organophosphates inhibit other enzymes as well as cholinesterase. Indeed, some of those that show relatively high insect toxicity and low mammalian toxicity do so because they poison an esterase that is more critical to the functioning of insect than of mammalian nervous systems. Malathion, which is violently poisonous to insects, is relatively nontoxic to mammals because the mammalian systems contain an enzyme, carboxy-esterase, that destroys malathion. But toxic effects on mammals can occur when malathion is used in combinations with other organophosphates, which apparently inhibit the carboxy-esterase enzyme.

DDT to control the codling moth. This is but one of many examples in which pesticides have killed off one pest but led to the flourishing of others. The usual response of the pesticide industry to such situations is to develop more potent poisons which then create another array of pollution problems; for instance, some miticides seem to be powerful carcinogens.

There is an additional reason why our artificial poisons are so much more effective against predators and parasites than they are against herbivores. For many millions of years plants have been evolving defenses against the assaults of herbivores. Many of these defenses are familiar to everyone. They include the spines of the cactus, the thorn of the rose bush, and a wide variety of compounds ranging from the irritants in poison ivy and poison oak to such useful substances as quinine and pepper. These plant substances are natural pesticides; in fact, mankind has utilized some of them, such as nicotine (extracted from tobacco) and pyrethrins (extracted from a small marigold-like flower) for their original purposes—as insect poisons. Although the use of nicotine as an insecticide has fallen off since the introduction of synthetic pesticides, pyrethrins are still the active ingredient in many insect sprays intended for home use.

Insects, of course, have in turn evolved mechanisms for evading the plants' chemical defenses. Long before man appeared, this reciprocal "coevolutionary war" was being waged between the plants and insects; the plants continually building better defenses, the insects countering with better attacks. Small wonder that herbivorous insects have had little trouble in dealing evolutionarily with man's recent attempts to poison them.

Agriculture and Ecology

World agriculture today is an ecological disaster area. We carefully breed out of plants their natural chemical defenses. The poisons usually don't taste good to us, although some of our spices, which we use in small quantities, are produced by plants to serve as insecticides. We plant our crops in tight, simple monocultures, inviting pest outbreaks, to which we then respond with synthetic pesticides, often killing a higher proportion of some nontarget insect populations than we kill of the target population of pests. There are a few hopeful signs that ecologically sound agricultural practices may eventually be adopted, but so far the general trend has been in the opposite direction.

The percentage of crop losses to insects in the U.S. seems to have remained about the same for more than 20 years, despite enormously increased use of pesticides. In 1948, ecologist William Vogt noted in his book, *Road to Survival,* that "$\frac{1}{10}$ of all crop plants are destroyed by insects in the U.S. every year." Vogt based his comment on statistics published by the USDA. In 1969, Georg Borgstrom, also using USDA figures, observed that crop losses due to insects amount to the yield from about a fifth of our total acreage, or about a sixth of the cash value of our total crop production. When the storage-loss component is subtracted, the field losses amount to slightly more than a tenth of total production, about the same as 1948. The President's Science Advisory Committee Panel on the World Food Problem estimated insect losses in the field during the 1950's as between 4 percent and 14 percent, depending on the crop. In 1948, according to zoologist Robert L. Rudd of the University of California, DDT, benzene hexachloride, and lead arsenate were the only insecticides of any significance used. By 1958, production of DDT in the U.S. had increased seven-fold (about half was then exported), production of lead arsenate had dropped about a third, and production of six other chlorinated hydrocarbons amounted to nearly five times the 1948 production of DDT. The production of Benzene hexachloride tripled by 1953, then dropped again in 1958 to about half the 1953 figure. In *Pesticides and the Living Landscape* (1964), Rudd points out that it is difficult to get accurate estimates of pest losses and that standards of pest damage have changed through time. Nevertheless, the consistency of insect loss estimates over time is rather striking. Despite huge inputs of insecticides, insects still claim a substantial share of the American farmers' greatly increased agricultural production.

What proportion of this increased production is due to the use of synthetic pesticides? Certainly not as much as the pesticide industry would like us to believe, but synthetic pesticides may play a more significant role than is indicated in the relatively constant percentage loss figures. High-yield strains of crops, heavily fertilized, probably require more protection than lower yield strains. That is, one might expect a higher percentage loss in fields today if we were still using the control techniques of 1940.

Could similar or greater yields have been achieved since World War II with control methods which are more ecologically sophisticated than current pesticide practices? It is the opinion of systems ecologist K. E. F. Watt of the University of California that when measured against successful biological and integrated control programs, "most pesticide projects have been failures." We believe that the procedures in use in the 1950's and 1960's will eventually be seen as one of mankind's most tragic blunders, and that when the total accounting is done, it will be found that other methods of control would have provided higher yields at less direct cost and with fewer deleterious consequences for mankind.

Of all the synthetic organic pesticides, probably more is known about DDT than any other. It is the oldest and most widely used chlorinated hydrocarbon insecticide. It is found everywhere—not only where it has been applied, but all over the Earth. Virtually every kind of animal on Earth has been exposed to it. As noted earlier (Table 6-1), concentrations in the fat deposits of Americans average about 12 ppm and the people of India and Israel have much higher concentrations. More startling and significant in some ways has been the discovery of DDT residues in the fat deposits of Eskimos, and in antarctic penguins and seals. Seals from the east coast of Scotland have been found to have concentrations of DDT as high as 23 ppm in their blubber. Pesticide pollution is truly a worldwide problem.

Because DDT breaks down so slowly, it lasts for decades in soils. For instance, in the Long Island estuary studied by Woodwell and his colleagues, the marsh had been sprayed for 20 years for mosquito control. Up to 32 pounds per acre of DDT were found in the upper layer of mud there. Such concentrations are not unusual. As a result of the concentration of DDT as it moves up food chains the danger to the life and reproductive capacity of fish-eating birds is extreme. Nesting failures among bald eagles have now reached proportions that bring the survival of the species into severe jeopardy. In addition, reproductive difficulties in populations of such diverse birds as the peregrine falcon, the brown pelican, and the Bermuda petrel have been traced to residues of DDT and other chlorinated hydrocarbon insecticides. These chemicals severely interfere with the birds' ability to metabolize calcium, which results in the laying of eggs whose shells are so thin that they are crushed by the weight of the nesting parents. Similar lethal effects have been documented for the polychlorinated biphenyls (chlorinated hydrocarbons used extensively in industry), which are closely related to the insecticides. They apparently share with the insecticides the blame for high rates of nesting failure in raptorial birds, and they may be as much as five times more potent killers than DDT.

The evidence against DDT in the case of birds' eggs is now overwhelming. Studies have been done of the thickness of raptorial bird eggshells in museum collections. Among those species that feed high on food chains, there is virtually always a sharp drop in eggshell thickness for the period 1945–1947, when DDT was generally introduced (Fig. 7-5). The exceptions make the case even more convincing. The shells of one Florida population of bald eagles first thinned not in 1945–1947, but in 1943. Investigations disclosed that this population lived in a county where large-scale DDT testing took place in 1943. One pair of peregrine falcons on the coast of California was an exception to the general rule of nesting failure. Examination of their nest revealed that they were feeding inland on mourning doves. Mourning doves are herbivores; thus the peregrines were feeding much lower in the food chain than if they had been sharing their cohorts' fish-diet. They got less DDT, and were therefore able to reproduce.

Experimental feedings of DDT to mallard ducks, American sparrow hawks, and Japanese quail all produced thin egg shells and reduced hatch rates. DDE, the widely distributed, stable breakdown product of DDT, has also been shown to reduce the thickness of mallard egg shells and to reduce hatchability, and dieldrin produced similar results with sparrow hawks. The exact mechanism of this effect is not clear. In birds the steroid hormone, estrogen, plays an important role in calcium metabolism. Both DDT and dieldrin have shown the ability to induce the production of enzymes which break down estrogen in the liver. This could lead to the observed symptoms of calcium deficiency. So could impairment of medullary bone deposition, inhibition of the action of thyroid or parathyroid glands, impairment of the absorption of calcium from food, inhibition of an enzyme (calcium anhydrase) in the shell-forming gland, or excess nervousness leading to premature egg-laying.

Birds are not the only organisms suffering from the chlorinated hydrocarbon load. Coho salmon in Lake Michigan, which also feed at high trophic

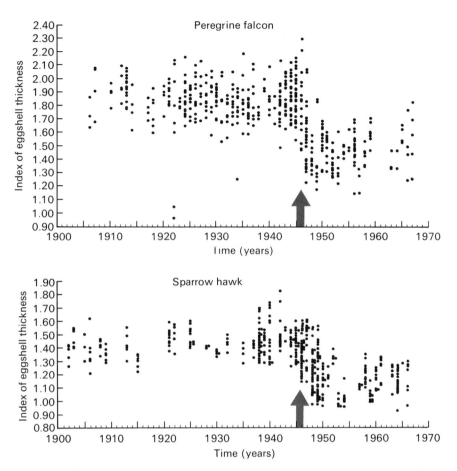

FIGURE 7-5
Changes in thickness of eggshells of peregrine falcon and sparrowhawk in Britain. Arrows indicate first use of DDT. [After Ratcliffe, "Decrease in Eggshell Weight in Certain Birds of Prey." *Nature,* vol. 215, pp. 208–210, 1967.]

levels, have been laying eggs that contain DDT residues. In 1968 almost 700,000 young salmon died as they absorbed the last DDT-rich drop of oil from their yolk sacs. Trout have been having similar problems, and rising DDT levels are now found in such commercially important marine fishes as tuna, mackerel, and hake.

Pesticides, especially the persistent ones, simplify the ecosystems to which they are applied, and into which they are transported by wind and water. The results of direct application are all too often the same: the freeing of pests from natural restraints. The pest, at first seemingly controlled, is soon back in even larger numbers than before. This destabilizing effect of pesticides is so common that it is often cited in the scientific literature as evidence that ecosystem simplification leads to instability. Unfortunately, things do not end there in agricultural practice, and higher doses of pesticides are applied creating further difficulties.

The history of attempts to control cotton pests in the coastal Cañete Valley of Peru has been reported by entomologist Ray F. Smith of the University of California. Against the advice of ecologically sophisticated entomologists, who recommended the use of cultural control methods and inorganic and botanical insecticides, synthetic organic pesticides were widely introduced in the valley in 1949. At first the use of these pesticides, principally the chlorinated hydrocarbons, DDT, BHC, and toxaphene, was very successful. Cotton yields increased from 494 kilograms per hectare (440 lbs/acre) in 1950 to 728 kilograms per hectare (648 lbs/acre) in 1954. The cotton farmers concluded that if more pesticide were applied, more cotton would grow. Insecticides "were applied like a blanket over the entire valley. Trees were cut down to make it easier for the airplanes to treat the fields. The birds that nested in these trees disappeared. Other beneficial animal forms such as insect parasites and predators disappeared. As the years went by, the number of treatments was increased; also, each year the treatments were started earlier because of the earlier attacks of the pests."

Trouble started in 1952 when BHC proved no longer to be effective against aphids. In 1954 toxaphene failed against the tobacco leafworm. Boll weevil infestation reached extremely high levels in 1955–1956, and at least *six brand new pests had appeared,* pests that were not found in similar nearby valleys that had not been sprayed with organic pesticides. In addition, the numbers of an old pest, larvae of the moth *Heliothis virescens,* exploded to new heights, and showed a high level of DDT resistance. Synthetic organic phosphates were substituted for the chlorinated hydrocarbons, and the interval between treatments was shortened from one or two weeks down to 3 days. In 1955–1956 yields dropped 332 kilograms per hectare in spite of the tremendous amounts of insecticide applied. Economic disaster overtook the valley. In 1957 an ecologically rational "integrated control" program was initiated in which biological, cultural, and chemical controls were combined. Conditions improved immensely.

This example should not be taken to mean that ecologically unsound pesticide programs have been instituted only in other places and in former times. Many examples can be cited of mistakes made here in the United States. For example, in both California and Arizona, profit margins have been dropping for cotton farmers because of insect attacks and the rising costs of chemical pesticide applications. In an attempt to evaluate the control measures used by agriculturalists, biologists uncovered some astounding facts. The programs designed to "control" cotton pests in these states were reviewed in 1968 by entomologist Kevin Shea, Scientific Director of the Committee for Environmental Information. Shea reported that "controlled experiments on small plots suggest that cotton growers in California may have spent thousands of dollars to fight an insect, the lygus bug, that has no appreciable effect on the final production per acre." Reduction of the number of lygus bugs per acre *did not lead to increased yields,* apparently because the bugs fed on "surplus" bolls of cotton, which would not ripen in any case. Spraying for lygus bugs early in the season with some pesticides not only did not help yields, but lowered them by killing insect predators of the bollworm.

What is still more intriguing is that recent research has begun to indicate that the bollworm itself may not be a threat to yields even at population levels considerably higher than what had previously been considered a dangerous infestation.

Most disturbing of all is the Azodrin story. Azodrin is a broad-spectrum organophosphate insecticide manufactured by the Shell Chemical Company (a subsidiary of the Shell Oil Company). Azodrin kills most of the insect populations in a field, but like other organophosphates (and unlike the chlorinated hydrocarbons) it is not persistent. Its effects are of course most devastating in populations of predatory insects. Therefore, when the field is reinvaded by pests, or when pest survivors make a comeback, their natural enemies are often absent, and overwhelming population booms of the pest may occur. Experiments by University of California entomologists clearly indicated that, rather than controlling bollworms, Azodrin applications, through their effect on the bollworms' natural enemies, actually *increased* bollworm populations in treated fields. Figure 7-6 summarizes the experimental results.

Other Azodrin experiments, and the similar results obtained with the use of other broad-spectrum pesticides, make it clear that the control procedure, rather than helping the farmer, often has precisely the opposite effect. One might reasonably expect the pesticide manufacturer to withdraw his product, or at least warn customers and advise them how to avoid these disastrous effects. However, Shea writes: "Shell Chemical Company, manufacturer of Azodrin, was aware of the University's findings through publications and from a seminar given at the Shell Research Center in Modesto. Nevertheless, the Company decided to promote the material for use on cotton pests in the San Joaquin Valley. Shell mounted a massive sales campaign. Radio, television, billboards, bumper stickers, and trade journal ads were employed to move Azodrin out of the warehouses and into the fields. Azodrin was heralded as being unmatched in its ability to kill every major insect likely to damage cotton."

Shell further has been promoting the use of Azodrin on a fixed schedule, whether pests are present or not. But fixed schedule spraying is recognized as having lethal effects on nontarget organisms and ecosystems. Aside from enhancing these effects, which are discussed below, such programs promote the development of resistant strains of pests and the extinction of natural enemies. Of course, this guarantees the "need" for heavier and heavier doses of Azodrin. As one Azodrin advertisement put it, "even if an overpowering migration (*sic*) develops, the flexibility of Azodrin lets you regain control fast. Just increase the dosage according to label recommendations." The pesticide manufacturer is clearly the only beneficiary of such practices.

But it would be unfair to blame the petrochemical industry alone for the destruction of the Earth's ecosystems. The United States Department of Agriculture has also contributed heavily to environmental deterioration. That agency has had a long history of promoting pesticides, often displaying a high degrees of ecological incompetence in the process. An outstanding example can be found in the history of the fire ant program, in which the USDA,

176

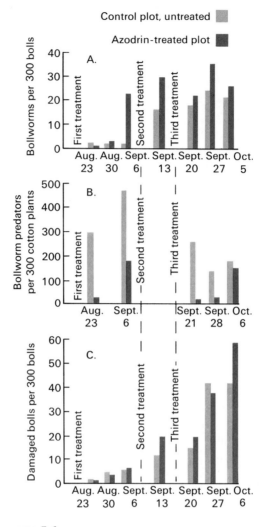

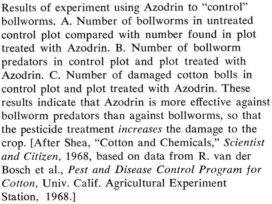

FIGURE 7-6
Results of experiment using Azodrin to "control"
bollworms. A. Number of bollworms in untreated
control plot compared with number found in plot
treated with Azodrin. B. Number of bollworm
predators in control plot and plot treated with
Azodrin. C. Number of damaged cotton bolls in
control plot and plot treated with Azodrin. These
results indicate that Azodrin is more effective against
bollworm predators than against bollworms, so that
the pesticide treatment *increases* the damage to the
crop. [After Shea, "Cotton and Chemicals," *Scientist
and Citizen,* 1968, based on data from R. van der
Bosch et al., *Pest and Disease Control Program for
Cotton,* Univ. Calif. Agricultural Experiment
Station, 1968.]

against the advice of many biologists, attempted to "exterminate" this insect over a large portion of the United States by spraying a huge area with chlorinated hydrocarbons. The ensuing disaster is examined in some detail in Appendix 4. Because the program was terminated in the early 1960's, enough time has passed to allow us to assess the results of programs that ignore the basic principles of ecology, since the outcome is now a matter of record.

In the summer of 1969 the USDA proposed to use 69,000 pounds of dieldrin to treat 2,300 acres of Kelly Air Force Base (near San Antonio, Texas) against possible importation of insects from Vietnam. Such proposals might lead one to conclude that the entire staff of the USDA is ecologically incompetent, and unable to learn from past experience. That this is not true is shown by the ecologically sophisticated pest control programs that have been initiated by various individuals within the Department. Perhaps the most brilliant was that against the screwworm, a fly whose larvae (maggots) can be an extremely serious pest on cattle. Annual losses in livestock have been estimated to be as high as $40 million a year. Under the leadership of entomologist E. F. Knipling, the USDA embarked on a massive program of sterilizing male screwworm flies by irradiation and releasing them in infested areas. The female screwworm only mates once. By flooding infested areas with sterile males, the screwworm was effectively eradicated from the southeastern United States. The effectiveness of this biological control program makes an interesting contrast with the futile and destructive fire ant fiasco.

The literature on pesticide effects on nontarget animals is now of encyclopedic proportions. Among the organisms involved (other than insects) are robins, amphipods, whitefish, earthworms, old-squaw ducks, warblers, rabbits, quail, lake trout, mosquito fish, foxes, opossums, mice, ospreys, muskrats, pheasants, turkeys, seagulls, fiddler crabs, salmon, snakes, and big-game mammals. Poisoning of these organisms, of course, always affects the ecosystems in which they function.

One spectacular example of the destruction of nontarget organisms is described in detail by reporter Frank Graham, Jr. in his fine book *Disaster by Default*. He recounts the story of the great Mississippi fish kill in the early 1960's. Rough estimates give the total loss in the four years 1960–1963 as between 10 and 15 million fishes in the lower Mississippi and its bypass, the Atchafalaya. The fishes killed included several kinds of catfish, menhaden, mullet, sea trout, drumfish, shad, and buffalo fish. The die-offs were ruinous to the local fishing industry. A thorough investigation by government (Public Health Service) and private laboratories placed the blame primarily on the highly toxic insecticide endrin and one of its derivatives. It was found not only in the blood and tissues of dying fishes and water birds but also in the mud in areas where fishes were dying. In experiments, extracts, made both from the mud and from the tissues of dying fishes, killed healthy fishes. It was found that fish kills were greatest in 1960 and 1963, when endrin was used commonly to treat cotton and cane crops in the lower Mississippi valley, and that fish kills were smallest in 1961 and 1962 when very little endrin was used.

The Public Health Service found that runoff from agricultural lands following dusting and spraying was one major source of the endrin. The other source was the Memphis plant of the Velsicol Chemical Corporation; waste endrin from the manufacturing process was getting into the river. Graham describes the interesting reaction of the Velsicol Corporation:

"Velsicol, under fire, shot back. Bernard Lorant, the company's vice-president in charge of research, issued strong denials. In a statement to the press, he said that endrin had nothing to do with the Mississippi fish kill, that the symptoms of the dying fish were not those of endrin poisoning, and that Velsicol's tests proved that the fish had died of dropsy."

Unfortunately for the Velsicol defense, dropsy happens to be a disease of fishes that is *never epidemic*. Considering the facts cited above, and the small detail (apparently ignored by the Velsicol researchers) that the fishes had the symptoms of endrin poisoning, one would have to conclude that some 10 million fishes had simultaneously contracted a new form of dropsy that produced the symptoms of endrin poisoning and that, coincidentally—perhaps only to confuse investigators—the fishes had even produced endrin in their tissues and excreted it into the mud of the Mississippi! With this example in mind, we can only hope that the approximately one million humans who drink Mississippi water will not come down in future years with a comparable form of "dropsy"—one that is delayed in its appearance and produces the symptoms of cirrhosis of the liver, liver cancer, hypertension, or softening of the brain.

At a 1964 conference on the Mississippi fish kill, a theme promoted by the pesticide industry was that only Communist sympathizers would criticize the extravagent way pesticides are used. This approach is exemplified by a statement made well before the conference by Parke C. Brinkley, president of the National Agricultural Chemicals Association: "Two of the biggest battles in this war [against Communism] are the battle against starvation and the battle against disease. No two things make people more ripe for Communism. The most effective tool in the hands of the farmer and in the hands of the public health official as they fight these battles is pesticides."

In June 1969 a vast fish kill occurred in the river Rhine. Preliminary investigations indicated that containers holding at least 200 pounds of the insecticide Endosulfan, which had dropped off a barge, were responsible. The encouraging increase in public understanding between 1964 and 1969 of the ecological dangers of pesticides was perhaps indicated by the refreshing absence of any comments from the pesticide industry about either dropsy or communists.

Another example will illustrate how complex, subtle, and far-reaching the effects of pesticide pollution may be. Ecologist L. B. Slobodkin of the State University of New York has described a plan to block the seaward ends of lochs in western Scotland and use them as ponds for raising fishes. One of the problems has been to find ways to raise the young fishes in the laboratory so that they can be "planted" in the ponds. It has been discovered that newly hatched brine shrimp serve as a satisfactory food for the kinds of fishes that will be raised. These may be obtained from brine shrimp eggs that are gathered commercially in the United States and sold to tropical fish fanciers for use in feeding young tropical fishes. The American supplies come from two places: San Francisco Bay in California, and Great Salt Lake in Utah. Sufficient eggs for the project can no longer be obtained from San Francisco Bay because of the demands of local aquarists and because large areas of former brine shrimp habitat are now residential subdivisions. Unfortunately, the Utah supply is of no use to the British, because brine shrimp hatched from Utah eggs kill their young fishes. The Utah shrimp have absorbed the insecticides that drain into Great Salt Lake from surrounding farmlands. Thus insecticide pollution in Utah hampers fish production in Scotland!

Insecticides and Phytoplankton

The effects of insecticides in water are not confined to aquatic animals. Perhaps the most frightening ecological news of 1968 was contained in a short paper entitled "DDT Reduces Photosynthesis by Marine Phytoplankton," which was published in the journal *Science*. The author, ecological chemist Charles F. Wurster, Jr., of the State University of New York, reports that DDT reduced photosynthesis in both experimental cultures and natural populations of marine phytoplankton (algae, diatoms, etc.), the tiny green plants that float free in the waters of the oceans. Effects were noted at DDT concentrations of only a few parts per billion (ppb), well below quantities that are commonly found in waters near land sites treated with DDT. Water at a distance from treatment sites ordinarily has DDT concentrations averaging less than 1 ppb, but biological systems clearly have the power and propensity to amplify these amounts.

The effects of DDT on phytoplankton in nature are difficult to evaluate. Phytoplankton are the primary producers responsible for most of the food we take from the sea. If photosynthesis is significantly reduced in marine phytoplankton, the amount of life in the seas will be reduced; if marine photosynthesis ceased, all sea life would die. But significant qualitative changes in the phytoplankton community seem more probable than large quantitative changes. Phytoplankton populations are differentially susceptible to DDT; even extremely low DDT concentrations might result in shifts of dominance, leading to huge blooms of one or a few species. These shifts would, in turn, produce serious consequences throughout the oceanic food web. One possibility is that phytoplankton less acceptable to large herbivores would take over, so that many larger animals would be eliminated. This shortening of food chains might leave man only microscopic plants and animals as a source of food from the sea. Another possibility is that phytoplankton communities near the shore could become dominated by smaller species, lengthening food chains and dramatically reducing the size of populations of fishes at the upper trophic levels.

Similarly, the problems besetting our inland waters (discussed below) may be aggravated by the effects of DDT on fresh-water phytoplankton. As Wurster says, "Such effects are insidious and their cause may be obscure, yet they may be ecologically more important than the obvious, direct mortality of larger organisms that is so often reported." No one knows how long we can continue to pollute the seas with chlorinated hydrocarbon insecticides, polychlorinated biphenyls, and hundreds of thousands of other pollutants without bringing on a worldwide ecological disaster. Subtle changes may already have started a chain reaction in that direction.

Insecticides and Soils

The effects of insecticides on soils are difficult to evaluate. Soils are not just collections of crushed rock; they are extraordinarily complex ecosystems in their own right. The animals of the soil are extremely numerous and varied. In forest communities of North Carolina, an estimated 125 million small invertebrates live in each acre of soil, more than 30,000 per square meter. Some 70 percent of these are mites, a group of arthropods that may eventually prove to be as diverse as the insects. In a study of pasture soils in Denmark, up to 45,000 small oligochaete worms, 10 million nematodes (round-worms), and 48,000 small arthropods (insects and mites) were found in each square meter. Even more abundant are the microflora of the soil. More than a million bacteria of one type may be found in a gram (0.035 ounce) of forest soil, as well as almost 100,000 yeast cells, and about 50,000 bits of fungus mycelium. A gram of fertile agricultural soil has yielded over 2.5 billion bacteria, 400,000 fungi, 50,000 algae and 30,000 protozoa.

The plants, animals, and microorganisms of the soil are absolutely essential for its fertility. The roles that some of these organisms play in the ecology of the soil were indicated in the discussion of the nitrogen cycle. Everyone is familiar with the beneficial effects of earthworms, but most people are completely unaware of the myriad other complex (and in many cases still poorly understood) plant-animal relationships within the soil that make it a suitable substance for the growth of oak trees, chaparral, corn, or any other plants. For instance, the roots of higher plants are coated with the microorganisms that are responsible for the conversion of nitrogen to forms available to the plants. These microorganisms are often also responsible for the production of usable forms of phosphorus and sulfur. Many trees have been found to depend on an association with fungi. The fungi get carbohydrates and other essential substances from the roots, and the root-fungus complex is able to extract from the soil minerals that could not be extracted by the root alone. Such mycorrhizal associations are just beginning to be understood, but it is clear that in many areas the "visible" plant community would be drastically altered if the mycorrhizal fungi were absent from the soil.

Recognizing as they do that most of the complex physical and chemical processes responsible for soil fertility are dependent upon soil organisms, environmental biologists are appalled by continuing treatment of soils with heavy dosages of deadly and persistent poisons. Consider, for instance, a recent study of persistence of chlorinated hydrocarbons in a sandy loam soil at an experimental station. Table 7-1 summarizes the results, which, because of the conditions of the study, may be close to the upper limits for persistence. Of half of these insecticides more than one-third of the amounts applied remained in the soil 14 or more years after treatment.

Considerable evidence already exists that the use of insecticides may reduce soil fertility, especially in woodland soils, which are subject to spraying but not artificial cultivation. Populations of earthworms, soil mites, and insects are dramatically changed, and these in turn affect the soil fungi, which are their principal food. Even if bacteria were not affected directly, there is

TABLE 7-1
Persistence of Insecticides in Soils

Insecticide	Years since treatment	Percent remaining
Aldrin	14	40
Chlordane	14	40
Endrin	14	41
Heptachlor	14	16
Dilan	14	23
Isodrin	14	15
Benzene hexachloride	14	10
Toxaphene	14	45
Dieldrin	15	31
DDT	17	39

SOURCE: Nash and Woolson, *Science,* vol. 157, pp. 924–927.

no question that the general effects on the soil ecosystem would carry over to these and other microorganisms. But it would be fatuous to assume that the bacteria are not directly affected. It is known that a few microorganisms can degrade DDT to DDD under the proper conditions; so far none has been found that can degrade dieldrin. Our ignorance of the interactions of pesticides with soil microorganisms is immense. Our general lack of attention to the possible long-range effects of these and similar subtle problems in our environment could ultimately prove to be fatal to mankind.

Alternatives to Present Patterns of Insect Control

It is commonly claimed that only current patterns of chemical control stand between us and starvation or death from insect-borne disease. Nothing could be further from the truth; the alternatives are not death or the continued dosing of ourselves and our environment with chlorinated hydrocarbons. First of all there is a wide variety of highly effective insecticides that are not persistent, and that are thus much less dangerous ecologically (although some may cause considerable environmental disruption and may have much higher immediate toxicity for human beings). These include the organophosphates, carbamates, and botanical compounds, such as pyrethrum and rotenone. Some of these may be more expensive now than the chlorinated hydrocarbons, but if the chlorinated hydrocarbons are banned it seems likely that the petrochemical industry will find ways to reduce the costs of producing the other compounds, especially if the present government subsidies for DDT, which are provided through our agricultural aid programs, are shifted to these other compounds.

The most desirable alternative of all is to shift as completely as possible to ecological pest management—that is, to what is often called "integrated control." Integrated control has as its goal the maintenance of potential pest populations below the level at which they cause serious health hazards or economic damage. It does not attempt to exterminate pests—a goal that, incidentally, has never been accomplished by chemical control programs. Integrated control involves using one or more techniques appropriate to the particular pest situation. Mosquitos may be controlled by draining swamps in which some of the larvae live, stocking lakes with mosquito-eating fishes, and perhaps applying small amounts of nonpersistent insecticides to any standing water that will not support fishes and cannot be drained. Similarly, a crop may be protected by practices such as planting it in mixed cultures with other crops, destroying pest reservoirs adjacent to fields, introducing and encouraging appropriate predators and parasites, breeding more resistant crop strains, luring pests from fields with baits, and using nonpersistent insecticides. Insect development may be disrupted by the use of hormonal insecticides. These and other practices may be combined to achieve both a high level of desirable control and a minimum of damage to the ecosystems of the world. Sometimes, as in the successful screwworm program, no chemical control will be necessary; at other times chemical methods may play a major role.

The transition away from the relatively simple chemical techniques will require planning and training, and will perhaps produce some temporary economic stress. Since we must not delay banning the chlorinated hydrocarbons, more expensive methods may have to be used temporarily. But there is no reason that the transition should lead to serious consequences for human health or nutrition. The step would be necessary even if such consequences *were* foreseen as serious, since continued use of persistent insecticides will result sooner or later in an unprecedented catastrophe for the entire planet. In fact, in many areas positive benefits would be immediate, particularly where the development of DDT-resistant mosquitoes is reducing the effectiveness of mosquito control programs. It is important to remember, above all, that the consequences of any control programs, integrated or not, require intelligent surveillance and periodic re-evaluation. *Any* tinkering with an ecosystem may result in unforeseen and deleterious consequences.

Herbicides and the Ecosystems

In recent years there has been an enormous upsurge in the use of herbicides as a substitute for farm machinery and labor in cultivating crops, for keeping roadsides, railroad rights of way, and powerline cuts free of shrubs, and as military defoliants in Vietnam. The rate of increase in herbicide use far outstrips that of synthetic pesticide use. Two kinds of herbicides are in wide use (Box 7-2). Members of one group (2,4D; 2,4,5-T; picloram, etc.) are similar to plant hormones, and cause metabolic changes in the plant that lead to death or leaf drop. The other group (simazin, monuron, etc.) interferes with a critical process in photosynthesis, causing the plant to die from lack of energy. Although their direct toxicity to animals is low, herbicides have great impact on animal populations through their modification and eradication of plant populations, since all animals depend, at least indirectly, on plants for food. Furthermore, as a result of the coevolutionary interactions discussed earlier, most herbivorous animals are specialized to feed on one kind or just a few kinds of plants.

In the light of these considerations, it is possible to evaluate the statements that American government officials have made concerning the lack of danger to animals or the uncertainty of effects on animals of our defoliation activities in Vietnam. The reasons for concern on the part of biologists become very plain. Defoliation of tropical jungles inevitably leads to the local extinction of many populations of insects, birds, arboreal reptiles, and arboreal mammals. But, of course, "animals" in official statements can all too often be translated "elephants, tigers, and other large mammals." In temperate forests there is generally a less distinct canopy fauna, but changes in

---

BOX 7-2   HERBICIDES

Chloraphenoxy Acid Herbicides

This group includes 2,4-D, 2,4,5-T, picloram, and several others. These compounds are chemically similar to the growth-regulating substance indolacetic acid. This plant hormone (or auxin) controls such diverse things as shoot growth, root growth, apical dominance, and phototropism. Overdoses of these herbicides function by causing uncontrolled growth and metabolism; the plant, in essence, grows itself to death.

Indolacetic acid does not function as a growth substance in animals, and therefore it is not surprising that these herbicides have essentially no direct effect on animals. Differential toxicity to broadleafed plants (as opposed to narrowleafed grasses) is a function of the greater ease with which the compounds are absorbed. Some of these herbicides, such as 2,4-D, are rapidly metabolized in woody plants, which usually localize the damage; they are defoliated, but not killed. Other herbicides, such as picloram, remain active for long periods in trees and ecosystems.

Symmetrical Triazines and Substituted Ureas

These include simazine, fenuron, diuron, and monuron. Both of these classes of compounds block a critical step in photosynthesis, known as the Hill reaction. The plant, in essence, starves to death. Since animals do not photosynthesize, they are not directly affected by these compounds, with the exception of possible mutagenic effects of the triazines.

animal populations in response to large-scale defoliation would certainly be tremendous.

We know very little about direct effects of herbicides on soil microorganisms. Some herbicides, such as 2,4-D, are quickly degraded by bacteria and persist for only a few weeks or months; others (2,4,5-T and presumably picloram) are more persistent. Soil microorganisms (primarily bacteria and fungi) do not photosynthesize; they are consumers, not producers. Therefore, they probably will not be affected by herbicides that block photosynthetic processes, although there could, of course, be other metabolic effects. Herbicides that function as simulated plant hormones are unlikely to disturb the growth processes of the soil flora, since there is no evidence that the plant hormone simulated by these substances functions in bacteria or fungi. These herbicides may of course have other physiological effects, since, as noted above, some are metabolized by soil bacteria.

We now know nothing about the effects of herbicides on aquatic life, but the runoff of herbicides—especially those that interfere with photosynthesis —into inland and coastal waters could be more serious than the effects of herbicides on soil fertility. The photosynthetic processes of phytoplankton, as well as the growth processes of other plants, could be interfered with. Again, it is important to remember that changes in basic producer populations will inevitably affect populations higher up in the food chains.

Although we need to know much more about the ecological effects of herbicides, one statement can be made with assurance. The use of such long-lasting herbicides as picloram in tropical areas raises the threat of laterization. In most tropical areas the soils are extremely poor. They cannot maintain large reserves of minerals needed for plant growth, such as phosphorus, potassium, and calcium, primarily because of heavy rainfall and a resultant high rate of water flow. The soils also have very high contents of iron and aluminum oxides in their upper levels. Most of the nutrients in a tropical jungle are concentrated not in the soil, but in the vegetation, and nutrients that enter the soil through the decay of dead plant parts are quickly returned to the living vegetation. Since most jungle trees are evergreen, this process is continuous. There is no chance for nutrients to build up in the soil as they do in temperate deciduous forests, which are dormant each year following a general leaf fall.

When a tropical forest is cleared for agriculture, or defoliated, this continual recycling of nutrients is interrupted. Heavy rains wash away the thin supply of soil nutrients, and the last substances to leach out are iron and aluminum oxides. The soil is exposed to sun and oxygen, and a series of complex chemical changes takes place, often resulting in the formation of a rocklike substance called *laterite* (from *later,* the Latin word for brick). Such laterization has occurred over wide areas of the tropics, starting long ago and continuing in recent years. Those who have been fortunate enough to visit Angkor Wat in Cambodia have seen magnificent cities and temples built by the Khmers some 800 to 1,000 years ago. The construction materials were sandstone and laterite, and laterization may have been a principal reason for the disappearance of the Khmer civilization.

Farming small clearings for a year or two and then letting the jungle re-claim them is the ancient method of agriculture in many areas where soils are subject to laterization. Tropical forests are usually able to reinvade small areas before laterization is complete. Whether large areas that have been kept cleared for substantial periods of time can be reforested is an open question. Reforestation has been successful in some areas where the soil crust has been carefully broken up, fertilizers applied, and the whole system carefully cultivated. But natural reforestation seems unlikely, and even most of the attempts supported by man have failed. Laterization is con-tinuing throughout the tropics and will doubtless proceed more rapidly as mankind gets increasingly desperate for food. According to geologist Mary McNeil, "The ambitious plans to increase food production in the tropics to meet the pressure of the rapid rise of population have given too little con-sideration to the laterization problem and the measures that will have to be undertaken to overcome it." Along with other data supporting her conten-tion, she provides a description of the fiasco at Iata in the Amazon Basin, where the government of Brazil attempted to found a farming community. Laterization destroyed the project when, "in less than five years the cleared fields became virtually pavements of rock."

Nitrogen, Phosphates, Heat, and Ecosystems

Most of the nitrogen in natural soils is contained in humus, the organic matter of the soil. Humus is a poorly understood complex of compounds of high molecular weight. Inorganic nitrogen in such soils normally accounts for less than one-half of 1 percent of the nitrogen present; the vast majority is tied up in the large organic molecules of humus, which are derived from such varied sources as the fibrous remains of woody plant tissues, insect skeletons, and animal manure. These substances, in addition to their chemical value, in-crease the capacity of the soil to retain water. The presence of humus makes the soil a favorable medium for the complicated chemical reactions and mineral transport needed for the growth of higher plants. Bacteria in the soil decompose humus to form nitrates and other nutrient substances re-quired by plant roots.

Roots require oxygen in order to do the work necessary for the uptake of nitrates and other nutrients, but oxygen is not available if the soil is tightly compacted. Thus another important benefit of humus is to maintain soil porosity and so permit oxygen to penetrate to the roots of plants.

In natural soil systems the nitrogen cycle is "tight." Not much nitrogen is removed from the soil by leaching or surface runoff, nor does much leave the soil and enter the atmospheric nitrogen pool. It has been shown experi-mentally that by maintaining the supply of humus with careful manuring, the fertility of soil can be perpetuated. Unfortunately this is not possible when fertilizers containing inorganic nitrogen (nitrates) are employed. Experi-ments with these fertilizers have shown that although yields remained high (as compared with yields from untreated control plots), the soil's content of humus and organic nitrogen dropped. With decreased amounts of humus, the efficiency of the transfer of nitrate from soil to plant also dropped. Compaction of the soil made oxygen penetration more difficult, and this effect in turn interfered with the processes by which the roots absorb nutrients. The nitrates that were not utilized were leached out by water moving through the soil or were converted to forms of nitrogen which plants could not utilize, some of which entered the atmosphere.

Unfortunately, the quality of the soil, or at least its organic nitrogen content, cannot be restored simply by adding more inorganic fertilizer. Attempts to maintain soil fertility by additional applications of inorganic compounds merely result in large amounts being flushed from the soil by runoff or lost from the soil into the atmosphere. In short, if these fertilizers are used in place of techniques that build humus, the depletion of humus "loosens" the soil cycles and permits large amounts of nitrogen to escape. The use of inorganic fertilizers in the United States has been multiplied some 12-fold in the past 25 years. One result of this dramatic increase has been a concomitant rise in the nitrogen content of our surface water, atmosphere, and rain. Another has been a 50 percent reduction of the original organic nitrogen content of Midwestern soils.

The results of the added nitrogen content of our waters are exemplified in part by the now well-documented fate of Lake Erie. In the late 1950's when I was doing postdoctoral research at the Chicago Academy of Sciences with zoologist Joseph H. Camin, we did a study of natural selection in populations of water snakes on the islands in the western end of Lake Erie. The problem was fascinating, and we wish we could continue the study today. But all we can do is reminisce. The snakes are almost gone, as are many of the fishes on which they fed. The mayflies, a wonderful fish food, have also disappeared. The once-beautiful lake is now a stinking, septic mess. The waters of Lake Erie are so polluted that the U.S. Public Health Service has urged ships on the lake not to use lake water taken within five miles of the United States shore. The water is so badly contaminated that neither boiling nor chlorination will purify it; although the organisms in it would be killed, the dangerous chemicals it contains would not be removed or broken down.

The sources of Lake Erie's pollution are many. A report to the Federal Water Pollution Control Agency cites as the main source of pollution the raw sewage dumped into the lake by lakeside municipalities, especially Cleveland, Toledo, Akron, and Euclid, Ohio; and Wayne County (Detroit), Michigan. The report cites industry as another major source of pollution, and names the Ford Motor Company, Republic Steel, and Bethlehem Steel as significant polluters. Finally, the basin of Lake Erie contains an estimated 30,000 square miles of farmland, and another important source of pollution is runoff from these farmlands.

Let us examine the last source first. The waters draining the farmlands of the Middle West are rich in nitrogen as a result of the heavy use of inorganic nitrogen fertilizers. Indeed, they have an estimated nitrogen content equivalent to the sewage of some 20,000,000 people—*about twice the total human population of the Lake Erie basin.* Thus, besides fertilizing their farms with nitrogen, the farmers are also fertilizing Lake Erie; their nitrogen contribution is of the same order of magnitude as that of the municipalities and the industrial pollutors. The nitrogen balance of the lake has been seriously disturbed, and the abundance of inorganic nitrates encourages the growth of certain algae. In recent years these algae have produced monstrous blooms—big masses of algae that grow extremely quickly, cover huge areas, foul beaches, and then die.

The bacterial decay of these masses of algae consumes oxygen, reducing the amount of oxygen available for fishes and other animals. Such blooms and oxygen depletions are characteristic of lakes undergoing *eutrophication,* which may be loosely translated as "overfertilization." Lake Erie is not only overfertilized by nitrates, it is also overfertilized by phosphates, partly from the runoff of phosphate fertilizers and partly from municipal and industrial sources (phosphate levels have increased 27-fold in U.S. surface waters in recent years). The basic sequence is simple in outline. Inorganic nitrates and phosphates pollute the lake. These inorganic chemicals are converted into organic forms as huge blooms of algae develop; these deplete the water of oxygen and kill off animals that have high oxygen requirements. Much of the nitrate and phosphate remains in the lake, settling to the bottom with the decaying mass of algae. The bottom of Lake Erie now has a layer of muck that varies from 30 to 125 feet in thickness; this layer is immensely rich in phosphorous and nitrogen compounds. These compounds are bound by a "skin" of insoluble iron compounds that covers the mud. Unfortunately the iron compounds change to a more soluble form in the absence of oxygen. Thus the oxygen depletion itself may cause the release into the lake of more of the nutrients responsible for the lake's troubles, and eutrophication may take place even more rapidly. Biologist Barry Commoner believes that if this breaking down of the mud skin should continue, and result in the release of large amounts of nitrogen, the lake may face a disaster that would dwarf its present troubles.

Lake Erie is just one outstanding example of a general problem that is well known to most Americans—the gross pollution of our lakes, rivers, and streams. All manner of organic and inorganic wastes end up in our inland waters: raw sewage, manure, paunch manure (the stomach contents of slaughtered animals), detergents, acids, pesticides, garbage; the list goes on and on. All of these substances affect the life in the water, all too often exterminating much of it, and at the very least modifying the ecosystems in profound ways. This pollution problem is worldwide; many of the rivers of the Earth are quickly approaching the "too thin to plow and too thick to drink" stage.

In addition to chemical pollution, thermal pollution, which results from the release of hot industrial wastes into streams and lakes is an extremely grave threat to aquatic life, much of which is highly sensitive to temperature change. Nuclear power plants in particular are serious thermal polluters. On the average they waste 60 percent more energy than plants that burn fossil fuels. It has been estimated that by 1980 nuclear plants alone will be using 20 percent of the total fresh water runoff of the United States for cooling.

Projected increases in the production of electricity indicate that by the turn of the next century it will be necessary to dissipate 20 million billion BTU's of heat from generating plants daily. This means that fully one-third of this nation's runoff of fresh water would have to flow through power plants. Thermal pollution on that scale would make many of our rivers uninhabitable by fishes.

Various solutions to thermal pollution problems have been proposed, including using the warmed water for irrigation and thus extending growing seasons for crops in some areas. Although this might be practical in some localities, in most it would not. More practical (but generally expensive) is the construction of artificial lakes and cooling towers, where the water can cool before it is returned to its source. Such devices can help solve, on a local level, what is today basically a local problem of heat pollution of streams. As the thermal load increases, however, these local problems will merely become part of the more general problem of the heat balance of the Earth. Cooling towers will not then suffice.

In the United States and some other areas, serious attempts have been made to clean up fresh-water systems. These have met with mixed success. It is impossible to know whether we are gaining, holding our own, or losing at the moment, but the situation is bad, and the outlook for the future in the United States is not encouraging. Even an isolated beauty like Lake Tahoe, a high Sierra lake shared by California and Nevada, is threatened. Barry Commoner has estimated that by 1980 urban sewage alone could consume all the available oxygen in all 25 major river systems of the nation. Similar problems exist in many other parts of the world. Lake Baikal in the Soviet Union seems to be headed for a fate similar to Lake Erie's, despite the protests of Russian conservationists. Many other lakes in Europe and Asia are beginning to show signs of eutrophication, often within 10 to 20 years after the start of human pollution. In most UDC's, rivers are simply open sewers.

Commoner has said that "farmers are hooked on nitrates like a junkie is hooked on heroin." Inorganic fertilizer applications, like applications of pesticides, generate the need for more of the same. Inorganic nitrate and phosphate fertilizers must be considered a technological success because they do succeed in raising the amounts of free nutrients in the soil, but it is precisely this success that leads to eutrophication as those nutrients are leached out of the soil by groundwater. Commoner predicts that in 25 to 50 years the ultimate crisis in agriculture will occur in the United States. Either the fertility of the soil will drop precipitously, throwing the nation into a food crisis, or the amounts of inorganic nitrates and phosphates applied to the land will be so large as to cause an insoluble water pollution problem. Furthermore, the water crisis will be made even worse by two other technological successes: our high-compression automobile engines, which produce an inorganic nitrogen fallout, and our modern sewage treatment plants, which are *designed* to produce an effluent rich in inorganic nitrates and phosphates (the significance of these inorganic nutrients has only recently been widely recognized).

In the light of these and many other assaults on the environment, it would behoove us to begin immediately to head off future threats to agriculture. As is becoming apparent even to the automobile industry, the internal combustion engine will have to be phased out, perhaps beginning with a reduction in engine sizes and compression ratios. It is imperative that either our present sewage treatment plants be completely redesigned to eliminate nutrients from the effluent or that a way be found to reclaim the nutrients for fertilizer. Also needed are new sewage plants for the many communities that still pour raw sewage into our waters. Such a program requires money and effort, some of which might be provided immediately by employing the Army Corps of Engineers for such projects. The problem of stopping the runoff of nutrients from farms is more difficult, but a first step would be to halt by law the handling of manure from farm animals as a waste product. Roughly 80 percent of American cattle are produced on feedlots, and most of their manure is treated as sewage, which more than doubles the sewage of the nation. Regardless of the cost, manure should be returned to the land to help build humus. Biologist James Bonner of the California Institute of Technology has pointed out that nitrates leach from soil because they are anions (negatively charged groups of atoms) and the capacity of the soil to retain anions is low. He suggests mixing a resin with high binding affinity for anions into the soil to increase its capacity to hold nitrates. Certainly experimental work in this area should be initiated immediately, but "solutions" of this sort must be monitored very carefully, as they have a tendency to create problems more serious than those they solve.

Ecosystems and the Atmosphere

Because of its biological origin and its maintenance by biological systems, the atmosphere is an indicator of the health of all ecosystems—in fact, of the entire ecosphere. The climate in a given area is partly a function of the organisms in that area, primarily the plants. The pattern of airflow near the ground is affected by the presence or absence of forests. The amount of water vapor in the air, the rates at which the ground heats up during the day, and thus the occurrence of updrafts, vary according to the vegetation that is present.

Many air pollutants, including hydrofluoric acid, sulfur dioxide, ozone, and ethylene, injure or kill plants, and these changes in plant life lead to drastic changes in the animal populations dependent upon the plants. Other dangerous air pollutants that can also upset ecological systems are the nitrogen oxides. It is thought that the eutrophication of Lake Mendota in Wisconsin is largely attributable to the automobiles of nearby Madison; rains deposit heavy amounts of nitrogen from auto exhausts, and the nitrogen ends up in the lake. In the State of New Jersey the rains annually bring to earth an estimated 25 pounds per acre of nitrogen from industrial and automobile sources.

Ecologists are very concerned about changes in the atmosphere that may occur, or may be occurring, as a result of man's interference with the Earth's complex biogeochemical cycles. The possible effects of general atmospheric pollution on the climate have already been discussed. But man's influence on biogeochemical cycles could pose other lethal threats. Picture, for instance, what would happen if one of the biocides that we are adding to our environment should show a special lethality for microorganisms in the soil that live by degrading ammonia to nitrites. The death of these microorganisms could be followed not only by a serious decline in soil fertility, but by a buildup of poisonous ammonia in the atmosphere.

Perhaps even more serious is the danger of interrupting the oxygen cycle, not just in lakes as a result of eutrophication, but on a planetary scale. All the oxygen in our atmosphere is produced by photosynthesis, and it is consumed by respiration, combustion, and such geochemical processes as laterization. Americans are among the world's largest per capita oxygen consumers; ecologist LaMont C. Cole of Cornell University has calculated that, for the 48 contiguous United States in 1966, oxygen production was only about 60 percent of the amount consumed.

One of man's major ecological effects on this planet appears to be the reduction of photosynthesis, and thus of the production of oxygen. So far these effects may be relatively minor, but the potential for the future is ominous. For instance, Eastern deciduous forests in the United States are estimated to have an oxygen-producing capacity per unit area roughly 1,000 times that of the average land surface, and the figure for tropical rainforests is probably even greater. Man has already replaced vast areas of both kinds of forest with plant communities less productive of oxygen, and must replace even more to increase his food supply. In addition, in the United States alone an area of land roughly equivalent in size to the state of Rhode Island is covered by new construction every six months, and built-over land produces no oxygen at all.

We are poisoning plants on land and in the sea in various ways at an alarming rate. An estimated 3,000 chemical compounds have been added to the atmosphere by man, and we are dumping as many as a half million pollutant substances into the oceans. Plants have little or no evolutionary experience with most of these substances, although many of them are known to be biologically active, and their total effect on photosynthesis is unknown. Clearly, then, it is within our capacity to reduce photosynthesis dramatically on our planet. The speed with which we would deplete our atmosphere of oxygen depends heavily on patterns of future consumption. Even if photosynthesis were completely stopped, it would take at least 1,000 years at present rates of consumption before the oxygen content at sea level was reduced to the average amount found now at an altitude of 15,000 feet. But we can take little comfort in these figures. Should photosynthesis stop, we would have little enough time to worry about oxygen depletion. We, and all other animals of the Earth, would immediately starve to death.

Ecological Accounting

It should now be apparent why ecologists are unimpressed by the claims that only blessings (and profits) have been brought by the use of synthetic pesticides and fertilizers, including the saving of lives through the use of DDT in malaria control. Ecologists and other environmental scientists wince when industrialists talk about the pollution-carrying capacity of inland waters as "a great natural resource," or when government officials caution against making water-pollution standards too high for fear of "discouraging industry."

The true costs of our environmental destruction have never been subjected to proper accounting. The credits are localized and easily demonstrated by the beneficiaries, but the debits are widely dispersed and are borne by the entire population through the disintegration of physical and mental health; and, even more importantly, by the potentially lethal destruction of ecological systems. Despite social, economic, and political barriers to proper ecological accounting, it is urgent and imperative for human society to get the books in order.

Why Have We Let Our Environment Deteriorate?

Historian Lynn White, Jr. of the University of California has suggested that the basic cause of Western man's destructive attitude toward nature lies in Judeo-Christian traditions. He points out, for instance, that before the Christian era men believed trees, springs, hills, streams, and other objects of nature had guardian spirits. These spirits had to be approached and placated before one could safely invade their territories. As White says, "By destroying pagan animism, Christianity made it possible to exploit nature in a mood of indifference to the feelings of natural objects." Christianity fostered the basic ideas of "progress" and of time as something linear, nonseparating, and absolute, flowing from the future into the past. Such ideas were foreign to the Greeks and Romans, who had a cyclical concept of time and did not envision the world as having a beginning. Although a modern physicist's concept of time might be somewhat closer to that of the Greeks than to that of the Christians, the Christian view is nevertheless the prevalent one, in which God designed and started the whole business for our benefit. The world is our oyster, made for man to dominate and exploit. The European ancestors of Americans had held and developed these attitudes long before the opportunity to exploit the Western Hemisphere arrived. The "frontier" or "cowboy" economy which has characterized the United States seems to be a natural extension of the Christian world view.

Both science and technology can clearly be seen to have their historical roots in natural theology and the Christian dogma of man's rightful mastery over nature. Therefore, as White claims, it may be in vain that so many look to science and technology to solve our present ecological crisis.

Thermonuclear Warfare

A final topic must be mentioned under the heading of environmental deterioration. Much has been written, especially by military theoretician Herman

Kahn, on the effects of thermonuclear warfare, the possibilities of limited thermonuclear warfare, and so on. Since modern societies seem bent on continuing to prepare for such conflicts, we have little sympathy for those of Kahn's critics who feel that it is immoral to try to analyze the possible results. It would be pleasant (but probably incorrect) to assume that if everyone were aware of the terrible magnitude of the devastation that could result from a nuclear war, the world's stockpiles of fission and fusion weapons would soon be dismantled. This does not mean that Kahn's analysis is sound —quite the contrary. One major flaw in his evaluation of the results of thermonuclear war is one that is common to the analyses of many physical scientists. He grossly underrates the possible environmental consequences of these projected wars. In addition to the instantaneous slaughter of humans and demolition of property, the effects of any reasonably large thermonuclear exchange would inevitably constitute an unbelievable ecological and genetic disaster—especially for a world already on the edge of nutritional and environmental catastrophe.

Consider the effects that even a rather limited nuclear exchange among the United States, Russia, China, and various European powers would have on the world food supply. Suddenly the developed world would be in no position to supply either food or any technological aid to the underdeveloped. No more high-yield seed, no more fertilizers, no more wheat shipments, no more tractors, no more pumps and well-drilling equipment, trucks, or other machines, would be delivered. The world could be pitched into massive famine almost immediately, even if most countries were untouched by the nuclear explosions themselves.

But of course no country would be left unscathed. All over the world radiation levels would rise and would prevent cultivation of crops in many areas. Blast effects and huge fires burning in the Northern Hemisphere would send large amounts of debris into the atmosphere, probably dwarfing the volcanic and pollution effects previously discussed. The entire climate of the Earth would soon be altered. In many areas, where the supply of combustible materials was sufficient, huge fire storms would be generated, some of them covering hundreds of square miles in heavily forested or metropolitan areas. We know something about such storms from experiences during the Second World War. On the night of July 27, 1943, Lancaster and Halifax heavy bombers of the Royal Air Force dropped 2,417 tons of incendiary and high-explosive bombs on the city of Hamburg. Thousands of individual fires coalesced into a fire storm about six square miles in area. Flames reached 15,000 feet into the atmosphere, and smoke and gasses rose to 40,000 feet. Winds, created by huge updrafts and blowing in toward the center of the fire, reached a velocity of more than 150 miles per hour. The temperature in the fire exceeded 1,450 degrees Fahrenheit, high enough to melt aluminum and lead. Air in underground shelters was heated to the point where, when they were opened and oxygen was admitted, flammable materials and even corpses burst into flame. These shelters had to be permitted to cool *10 days to two weeks* before rescuers could enter.

Anyone interested in further details of what a *small* fire storm is like is referred to Martin Caiden's excellent book, *The Night Hamburg Died*. From this account one can imagine the ecological results of the generation of numerous fire storms and the burning off of a large portion of the Northern Hemisphere. In many areas the removal of all vegetation would not be the only effect; the soil might be partly or completely sterilized as well. There would be no plant communities nearby to effect rapid repopulation, and rains would wash away the topsoil. Picture defoliated California hills during the winter rains, and then imagine the vast loads of silt and radioactive debris being washed from northern continents into offshore waters, the site of most of the ocean's productivity. Consider the fate of aquatic life, which is especially sensitive to the turbidity of the water, and think of the many offshore oil wells that would be destroyed by blast in the vicinity of large cities and left to pour their loads of crude oil into the ocean with no way of shutting them off. Think of the runoff of solvents, fuels and other chemicals from ruptured storage tanks and pipelines.

The survivors of any large-scale thermonuclear war would face a severely devastated environment. If a full-scale war were waged, most of the survivors would be in the Southern Hemisphere. They would be culturally depauperate, since much of mankind's technology would be irretrievably lost. If the technological structure of society is destroyed, man will find it almost impossible to rebuild it because of resource depletion. Most high-grade ores and rich and accessible fossil fuel deposits have long since been used up. Technology itself is necessary for access to what remains. Only if enough scrap metals and stored fuel remained available would there be a hope of reconstruction, and it would have to begin promptly before these rusted, drained away, or were lost in other ways. From what we know of past large disasters, it seems unlikely that survivors would psychologically be able to start rapid reconstruction.

If there were extensive use of weapons in the Northern Hemisphere, or if CBW were used simultaneously, the survivors would probably consist of scattered, isolated groups. Such groups would face genetic problems, since each would contain only a small part of mankind's genetic variability and would be subject to a further loss of variability through inbreeding. Studies of certain Japanese and Italian populations have shown that inbreeding profoundly affects infant mortality. In addition it appears that prenatal damage increases linearly with the degree of inbreeding. In such a situation it is problematical whether culturally and genetically deprived groups of survivors could persist in the face of much harsher environmental conditions than they had faced previously. In short, it would not be necessary to kill every individual with blast, fire, and radiation in order to force *Homo sapiens* into extinction.

Bibliography

Acree, Fred, Jr., Morton Beroza, and Malcolm C. Borman, 1963. Codistillation of DDT with water. *Agricultural and Food Chemistry,* vol. 11, pp. 278–280. Important paper about the mobility of DDT.

Anonymous, 1969. Mission to Vietnam (2 parts). *Scientific Research,* June 9–June 23. What two ecologists found in Vietnam following herbicide treatments.

Antommari, Phillip, Morton Corn and Lawrence De Mair, 1965. Airborne particulates in Pittsburgh. Association with p,p'-DDT. *Science,* vol. 150, pp. 1476–1477. Early paper showing presence of DDT in the atmosphere of a city.

Bitman, Joel, Helene C. Cecil, Susan J. Harris, and George F. Frees, 1969. DDT induces a decrease in eggshell calcium. *Nature,* vol. 224, pp. 44–46. Experiments with Japanese quail.

Brown, W. L., Jr., 1961. Mass insect control programs; four case histories. *Psyche,* vol. 68, pp. 75–111. A distinguished entomologist and population biologist evaluates attempts to control the Fire Ant, Gypsy Moth, Mediterranean Fruit Fly, and Screwworm.

Butler, Philip A., and Paul T. Spruger, 1963. Pesticides—a new factor in coastal environments. *Trans. Twenty-Eighth North American Wildlife and Natural Resources Conference,* pp. 378–390. Summary with good bibliography of earlier papers.

Calder, Nigel (ed.), 1968. *Unless Peace Comes.* Viking (Compass), New York. Projects effects of future weapons systems.

Clark, John R., 1969. Thermal pollution and aquatic life. *Scientific American,* vol. 220, no. 3 (March).

Carson, Rachel, 1962. *Silent Spring.* Houghton-Miffin, Boston. This classic, thought to be alarmist by many when it was published, now appears to have understated the pesticide problem.

Cole, LaMont C., 1966. Complexity of pest control in the environment. In *Scientific Aspects of Pest Control.* Pub. 1402, National Academy of Sciences, National Research Council.

Commoner, Barry, 1967. *Science and Survival.* Viking, New York. Technology and survival. See especially the material on the ecological effects of thermonuclear war.

Cottam, Clarence, 1965. The ecologists' role in problems of pesticide pollution. *BioScience,* vol. 15, no 7, pp. 457–463 (July).

Crowe, Beryl L., 1969. The tragedy of the commons revisited. *Science,* vol. 166, pp. 1103–1107. A depressing evaluation of the chances of dealing politically with the problems of the commons.

DeBach, Paul (ed.), 1964. *Biological Control of Insect Pests & Weeds.* Reinhold Publishing Corp., New York. Covers one of the ecologically sensible components of integrated control.

Edwards, Clive A., 1969. Soil pollutants and soil animals. *Scientific American,* vol. 220, no. 4 (April).

Egler, Frank E., 1964. Pesticides—in our ecosystem. *American Scientist,* vol. 52, pp. 110–136. An outspoken ecologist discusses the problems of getting ecologically sophisticated control of pests.

Elton, Charles, S., 1958. *The Ecology of Invasions by Animals and Plants.* John Wiley & Sons, New York. A basic source, written by one of the world's most distinguished ecologists.

Fiserova-Bergerova, V., J. L. Radomski, J. E. Davies, and J. H. Davies, 1967. Levels of chlorinated hydrocarbon pesticides in human tissues. *Ind. Med. Surg.,* vol. 36, no. 65.

Frost, Justin, 1969. Earth, air, water. *Environment,* vol. 11, no. 9, pp. 14–33. Discusses the major role of the atmosphere in distributing chlorinated hydrocarbons.

Gilmour, C. M., and O. N. Allen (eds.), 1965. *Microbiology and Soil Fertility.* Oregon State Univ. Press, Corvallis.

Heath, Robert G., James W. Sparn, and J. F. Kreitzer. Marked DDE impairment of mallard reproduction in controlled studies. *Nature,* vol. 224, pp. 47–48.

Hickey, Joseph J., and Donald W. Anderson, 1968. Chlorinated hydrocarbons and eggshell changes in raptorial and fish-eating birds. *Science,* vol. 162, pp. 271–273. Correlation of eggshell change with presence of chlorinated hydrocarbon residue.

Hunt, Elridge G., 1966. Biological magnification of pesticides. *Symposium on Scientific Aspects of Pest Control, Nat. Acad. Sci—Nat. Res. Council,* pp. 252–261. Information on build-up of pesticides in food chains.

Kahn H., and A. J. Weiner, 1967. *The Year 2000.* Macmillan, New York. An outstanding example of futurism which discounts problems of population, resources, and environment.

Kilgore, W. W., and R. L. Dountt, 1967. *Pest Control, Biological, Physical, and Selected Chemical Methods.* Academic Press, New York.

Kormondy, Edward J., 1969. *Concepts of Ecology.* Prentice-Hall, Englewood Cliffs, N.J.

Lichtenstein, E. P., K. R. Schulz, T. W. Fuhrmann, and T. T. Liang, 1969. Biological interaction between plasticizers and insecticides. *Journal of Economic Entomology,* vol. 62, pp. 761–765. Demonstrates toxicity of PCBs to insects and shows that these compounds may increase the toxicity of dieldrin and DDT.

Marsh, George P., 1874. *The Earth as Modified by Human Action.* Charles Scribner's Sons, New York.

Marx, Wesley, 1967. *The Frail Ocean.* Coward-McCann, Inc., New York.

Mitchell, H. H., 1961. *Ecological Problems and Postwar Recuperation: A Preliminary Survey from the Civil Defense Viewpoint.* U.S. Air Force Project and Research Memorandum. A pioneering document, somewhat over-optimistic and now out of date.

Moll, K. D., J. H. Cline, and Paul D. Marr, 1960. *Postattack Farm Problems.* Part 1: *The Influence of Major Inputs on Farm Production.* Prepared for office of Civil and Defence Mobilization under the auspices of Stanford Research Institute (SRI). Limited circulation (200 copies). One of the few attempts to investigate systematically the consequences of a nuclear attack. Others by SRI include studies of the effects of nuclear attack on railroad transport and the petroleum industry.

Moore, N. W. (ed.), 1966. Pesticides in the environment and their effects on wildlife. *Journal of Applied Ecology.* Supplement to vol. 3 (June). This supplement contains many other interesting papers on pesticide ecology.

Mulla, M. S., and Lewis W. Isaak, 1961. Field studies on the toxicity of insecticides to the mosquito fish, *Gambusia affinis. Journal of Economic Entomology,* vol. 54, pp. 1237–1242. Reports high toxicity to mosquito-eating fishes of pesticides used in mosquito abatement programs.

Olson, T. A., and F. J. Burgess (eds.), 1967. *Pollution and Marine Ecology.* Interscience Publishers, New York.

Peakall, D. B., 1967. Pesticide-induced enzyme breakdown of steroids in birds. *Nature,* vol. 216, pp. 505–506. Indicates that DDT and dieldrin can change hormone metabolism and upset breeding.

Porter, Richard D., and Stanley N. Wiemeyer, 1969. Dieldrin and DDT: effects on sparrow hawk eggshells and reproduction. *Science,* vol. 165, pp. 199–200. Controlled feeding experiments.

Ratcliffe, D. A., 1967. Decrease in eggshell weight in certain birds of prey. *Nature,* vol. 215, pp. 208–210. Demonstrates rapid synchronous decline of eggshell thickness at time chlorinated hydrocarbon pesticides introduced. This was key evidence in establishing role of these substances in decline of bird populations.

Risebrough, R. W., R. J. Huggett, J. J. Griffin, and E. D. Goldberg, 1968. Pesticides: transatlantic movements in the northeast trades. *Science,* vol. 159, pp. 1233–1236. Important paper on aerial transport of chlorinated hydrocarbons.

Roe, Frank G., 1951. *The North American Buffalo.* Univ. of Toronto Press, Toronto.

Rosato, P., and D. E. Ferguson, 1968. The toxicity of Endrin-resistant mosquito fish to eleven species of vertebrates. *BioScience,* vol. 18, pp. 783–784.

Rudd, Robert L., 1964. *Pesticides and the Living Landscape.* Univ. of Wisconsin Press, Madison. The prime source on ecological effects of pesticides.

Shea, Kevin P., 1968. Cotton and chemicals. *Scientist and Citizen* (Nov.). Gives details of the Azodrin situation.

Shepard, P., and D. McKinley (eds.), 1969. *The Subversive Science.* Houghton Mifflin, Boston. Selected readings in ecology. Excellent.

Sladen, W. T. L., C. M. Menzee, and W. L. Rechel, 1966. DDT residues in Adelie penguins and a Craberta seal from Antarctica: ecological implications. *Nature,* vol. 210, pp. 670–673.

Smith, Robt. L., 1966. *Ecology and Field Biology.* Harper & Row, New York. An excellent beginning text.

Stonier, Tom, 1963. *Nuclear Disaster.* Meridian, Cleveland. Describes ecological effects of thermonuclear war.

Thomas, William L., Jr. (ed.), 1956. *Man's Role in Changing the Face of the Earth.* An international symposium, edited with the collaboration of Carl O. Sauer, Marston Bates, and Lewis Mumford. Univ. of Chicago Press, Chicago.

Watt, K. E. F., 1968. *Ecology and Resource Management.* McGraw-Hill, New York.

White, Lynn, Jr., 1967. The historical roots of our ecological crisis. *Science,* vol. 155, pp. 1203–1207. A classic paper.

Whitten, Jamie L., 1966. *That We May Live.* D. Van Nostrand Co., Inc., Toronto. A clever piece of pro-pesticide propaganda by a U.S. Congressman. It attempts to give the impression that its conclusions are endorsed by scientists, although at least four of the most distinguished scientists interviewed in the course of its preparation disagree totally with its conclusions. Read this if you want to know your enemy. Whitten does not confine his activities to promoting pesticides. U.S. Representative Richard Bolling recently wrote, "Study the unpardonable problem of malnutrition and even starvation in this country and you'll encounter Representative Jamie Whitten of Mississippi, Chairman of the Appropriations subcommittee on agriculture and lord of certain operations of the Agriculture Department." (*Playboy,* Nov. 1969, p. 255).

Woodwell, G. M., 1967. Toxic substances and ecological cycles. *Scientific American,* vol. 216, no. 3 (March). Excellent summary.

Wurster, Charles F. Jr., 1968. DDT reduces photosynthesis by marine phytoplankton. *Science,* vol. 158, pp. 1474–1475. This may turn out to be one of the most important scientific papers of all time.

Wurster, Charles F., and B. Wingate, 1968. DDT residues and declining reproduction in the bermuda petrel. *Science,* vol. 159, pp. 979–981. Shows the effects of DDT on a bird of the open ocean. See also the exchange of letters between the authors of this paper and Lewis A. McLean of Velsicol, Inc., a company which manufactures pesticides (*Science,* vol. 161, pp. 387).

Wurster, Don H., Charles F. Wurster, and Walter N. Strickland, 1965. Bird mortality following DDT spray for Dutch Elm disease. *Ecology,* vol. 46, pp. 488–489. Good bibliography of earlier related papers.

CHAPTER 8

Optimum Population and Human Biology

*"Maximum welfare, not maximum population,
is our human objective."*

—Arnold Toynbee
"Man and Hunger," 1963

The pattern of human population growth and some of its consequences which have been described lead to the conclusion that the size of the population must be controlled. It is to be hoped that all people would agree that the only humane way to control the size of the human population is by limiting the number of births; that an increase in the number of deaths (or reduction in the life expectancy) should be avoided at all costs. But the idea of controlling the size of a population implies the existence of some standard of optimum size. Ways of determining when a population is "too large" and when it is "too small" must be established; that is, the terms "overpopulation" and "underpopulation" need to be defined.

At one extreme, human population sizes are limited by the physical capacity of the Earth itself, and at the other by the smallest group that can reproduce itself. But other factors should enter into considerations of optimum population size, including an individual's relationships with his fellow men and his psychological relationship to his environment—factors that we recognize in such concepts as "the quality of life" and "the pursuit of happiness." Because these factors involve subjective psychosocial and cultural ideals, they cannot be dealt with as directly as biological and physical constraints on population size, where we are able to apply data on resource depletion, photosynthetic efficiency, human nutrition, and thermodynamic limits. Nevertheless, it is clear that questions about the *quality* of human life are inextricably bound to those about the *quantities* of human beings on Earth. And in discussing these questions together, it is important to have some understanding of man's evolutionary background.

People Versus Earth

The idea of controlling the size of the human population is really a new one. Until very recently population limitation has been considered neither possible nor proper, or limits have been set so high that the problem of limitation would in effect, be postponed into the indefinite future. The tendency to avoid this issue still exists, even in the face of abundant evidence that very large numbers could never be supported. Discussions about fertility control are still far more likely to center on changing *rates of growth;* absolute size is often considered irrelevant to anything. Nevertheless, the *absolute size* of the human race is now so large that it is perhaps the single most important factor we have to consider in discussing man's future, and its present unprecedented rate of growth adds to the urgency of the problem.

Rapid growth rates hinder economic development in UDCs. Therefore, the population problem is perceived by economists and politicians as a problem of growth rates. That the human population is now putting stress upon the carrying capacity of the Earth itself must be recognized by all responsible people, not just by ecologists. In the next few decades our efforts to support a growing population are bound to result in much more stress, even if we immediately bend most of our efforts toward alleviating the deleterious effects of overpopulation. It is unmistakably clear that the time has come for humanity to take a careful look at its resources, its ideals, and its numbers, and try to make some serious judgments about optimum population size, both for individual countries and for the world as a whole.

Optima and Environment

In order to be meaningful, statements about overpopulation and underpopulation must be based on consideration of many environmental factors in addition to numbers of people per unit of land area. One commonly hears that South America is underpopulated because it has relatively few people per square mile in comparison with, say, Asia. It sounds logical at first to use population density as the basis for discussions of optimum population. It becomes evident on further reflection, however, that in most circumstances density alone is one of the *least* important considerations.

Much more critical than density alone will be density in relation to available resources. The Sahara Desert, for instance, might be "overpopulated" at a much lower density than the tropical island of Tahiti. More people are able to live well on the resources of the island than they could on the resources of an isolated piece of desert of the same size. Of course, the discovery of valuable resources like oil or water under the desert might alter the situation. The oil could be exchanged for food and other necessities, and in time, the desert might develop into a local population center of very high density. This is essentially what happens in cities, which exchange manufactured goods, technological know-how, and various services for food, commodities, and other needed materials. If, instead of oil, water were discovered and could be made available locally, the surrounding desert might be made to bloom; and intensive agriculture might also permit the establishment of a higher population density than prevails in Tahiti. This, in fact, happens around oases.

However, we cannot be optimistic about the prospects for intensive agriculture in the tropics, where the soils will not, with present technology, support intensive agriculture and high densities of people. Possibly some of these areas, through the development of a "tree culture," with shade-loving vegetables beneath the trees, could successfully support more people than they do now. But the suggestion that all land areas can be made to support population densities as great as those of such European countries as the Netherlands is misleading, for two reasons. First, Europe is blessed with very favorable soils and climate, which are not equalled in the tropics, where most poor countries are located. Second, Europe is by no means self-sufficient in food. Even Denmark, an exporter of dairy products, eggs, and meat, must import huge quantities of oilseed cakes and grain to support the livestock. Denmark imports more protein per person than any other country—240 pounds per year. This is three times the average annual protein consumption of each Dane! Measured against food needs and production, Europe is already overpopulated. The continent is also a consumer of nonrenewable resources that are largely imported from other areas, and it also has serious population-related pollution problems.

Relative to resources, then, optimum population is not a simple figure to establish. The size and location of the land area and its possibilities for exchange with other areas must be considered. In addition, the question of how long the population is to be maintained is important. An area must be considered overpopulated if it is being supported by the rapid consumption of nonrenewable resources. It must also be considered overpopulated if the activities of the population are leading to a steady deterioration of the environment. In other words, when we are dealing with the concept of optimum population, we must consider the relationship of human numbers to the carrying capacity of the environment, viewed over both the short and the long term. Taking into account present population densities and the other factors involved in carrying capacity, we arrive at the inescapable conclusion that, in the context of man's present patterns of behavior and level of technology, *the planet Earth, as a whole, is overpopulated.*

Biochemist H. R. Hulett of the Stanford University Medical Center, in considering the possible size of an optimum population, has made some interesting calculations that bear on the question of the degree of overpopulation. He assumed that the average United States citizen would not consider the resources available to him to be excessive. He then divided estimates of the world production of those resources by the American per capita consumption. On this basis, Hulett concludes: ". . . it appears that (about) a billion people is the maximum population supportable by the present agricultural and industrial system of the world at U.S. levels of affluence." Hulett's estimate means that, even ignoring depletion of non-renewable resources and environmental deterioration, the population of the Earth is already almost three billion people above a reasonable optimum.

This does not mean that in certain ways some areas of the Earth may not still be underpopulated. For instance, if more people lived in Australia now, that country might be able to afford a better surface transport system and extend paved roads across the continent. Australians would also be in a better position to develop and utilize their mineral and energy resources. But, unhappily, even though a larger population could well live there, the "frontier philosophy" is even more rampant in Australia than in the United States in terms of environmental deterioration and agricultural overexploitation. Thus Australia may be considered overpopulated already in relation to its long-term ability to feed its people, even though the continent is too thinly populated in terms of highway construction and economic development.

Regardless of such examples of present "underpopulation," it is clear that in dealing with population problems we must focus on the Earth as a whole, because it has become a single, closed-loop feedback system as far as human activities are concerned. Air pollution is a global problem, resource depletion is a global problem, food shortage is a global problem, chlorinated hydrocarbons are a global problem, and thus an excessive population in one area of the world creates problems for all other areas.

Evolution and Human Reproduction

The urge toward maximizing the number of children successfully reared has been fixed in us by billions of years of evolution, during which our ancestors were fighting a continual battle to keep the birth rate ahead of the death rate. That they were successful is attested to by our very existence, for, if the death rate had overtaken the birth rate for any substantial period of time, the evolutionary line that led to modern man would have become extinct. Even among our apelike ancestors a few million years ago it was still relatively difficult for a mother to rear her offspring successfully. Most of her children died before they reached reproductive age. The death rate was near the birth rate. Then another factor, cultural evolution, was added to biological evolution. The two kinds of evolution, operating together, resulted in a trend toward larger brains.

Human brain size was eventually limited by the ability of women to carry and deliver large-headed infants without themselves being immobilized. Consequently, more and more brain growth was concentrated in the period after birth. Although this resulted in a longer period of postnatal helplessness for the infants, presumably this was less of an adaptive disadvantage than further pelvic expansion of the mothers would have been.

The long period of helplessness of the human infant had many effects, most of which center on the mother's problem of caring for and protecting the infant. Presumably a selective premium was placed on keeping the father with the family group, and an essential step in that direction was the elimination of the short, well-defined breeding season characteristic of most mammals. Year-round sexuality and the development of strong mother-offspring and father-mother bonds (pair-bonds), which led to the evolution of family groups, may be traced at least in part to increased brain size. These are, of course, the essential ingredients of what mankind has developed into the vast, varied, complex, and pervasive social phenomenon that is sometimes referred to in our society simply as "sex." This social phenomenon affects the way we raise our children, our family structure and ideals, our sexual mores, and the roles and relative status of the two sexes and their relationships both within and outside the family, to mention only some of the more obvious manifestations. Sex in this sense is not simply an act leading to the production of offspring, but rather it is a cultural phenomenon penetrating into all aspects of our lives, including our self-esteem and our choice of friends, cars, and leaders. It is tightly interwoven with our mythologies and history, and it influences our views of nearly everything.

Many plants and animals reproduce without any sort of sexual process. Biologically, sexual reproduction evolved not only as a mechanism of reproduction, but also as a mechanism that provided variability. In many organisms the basic sexual function is to provide the genetic variability that permits natural selection, and sexual processes occur at different stages in the life cycle than do reproductive processes. Most of the vertebrates have two differentiated sexes and generate variability in the process of producing reproductive cells. In these animals, and in man, sex (in the restricted biological sense) and reproduction are closely associated. Just as "biological sex" evolved not only to promote reproduction but to provide variability, "cultural sex" evolved not only to promote reproduction, but primarily as a cultural device to protect the social structure of the family. An essential function of copulation in human beings is to strengthen and maintain the pair-bond; cultural sex reinforces and protects this function in society. Understanding these points makes it easier to evaluate many arguments raised against birth control on the basis of emotional ideas about the "natural" function of sex. Furthermore, a grasp of the cultural importance of sex brings home the difficulty of changing the reproductive habits of a society, since attempts to do so may be perceived by the society as an assault on the very basis of its culture.

The Natural Environment of Man

In addition to the evolutionary origins of man's attitudes toward reproduction, we must consider what kind of environment man is best adapted to. What size groups does he feel most comfortable in? How important is solitude for the well-being of the human psyche? Is the color green an important component of the environment of *Homo sapiens*? Such questions have been the subject of extensive speculation, but they are exceedingly difficult to answer. In theory, for instance, natural selection could change certain human characteristics dramatically in 6 to 8 generations—in only about 200 years (although this would involve a very large portion of the population not reproducing in each generation). But other characteristics may be so ingrained in the human genetic-developmental system that they would be impossible to change without much longer periods of genetic readjustment, or the changes might even be so traumatic as to lead to extinction. To give an analogy, one may, by selection, experimentally create a strain of fruitflies that is resistant to DDT in 6 to 8 generations, presumably as a result of some minor changes in enzyme systems or behavior. It seems unlikely, however, that any number of generations of selection would produce a fruitfly able to fly with one wing; in fact, an attempt to produce such a change by artificial selection would probably lead to extinction of the experimental population.

Some biologists feel that mankind's evolutionary history has been such that the present environments to which he is subjecting himself are essentially asking him to "fly with one wing." This general viewpoint has been expressed by three biologists at the University of Wisconsin, H. H. Iltis, P. Andrews, and O. L. Loucks. They feel that mankind's genetic endowment has been shaped by evolution to require "natural" surroundings for optimum mental health. They write:

> Unique as we may think we are, we are nevertheless as likely to be genetically programmed to a natural habitat of clean air and a varied green landscape as any other mammal. To be relaxed and feel healthy usually means simply allowing our bodies to react in the way for which one hundred millions of years of evolution has equipped us. Physically and genetically, we appear best adapted to a tropical savanna, but as a cultural animal we utilize learned adaptations to cities and towns. For thousands of years we have tried in our houses to imitate not only the climate, but the setting of our evolutionary past: warm, humid air, green plants, and even animal companions. Today, if we can afford it, we may even build a greenhouse or swimming pool next to our living room, buy a place in the country, or at least take our children vacationing on the seashore. The specific physiological reactions to natural beauty and diversity, to the shapes and colors of nature (especially to green), to the motions and sounds of other animals, such as birds, we as yet do not comprehend. But it is evident that nature in our daily life should be thought of as a part of the biological need. It cannot be neglected in the discussions of resource policy for man.

There is little consensus between cultures or even within our own culture on what sort of an environment best provides an optimal "quality of life." In addition, there is virtually no experimental evidence on how varying such factors as the density of the population, or levels of noise, or the amount of green in the environment may alter human behavior. We do know from the systematic observations of anthropologist Edward T. Hall that peoples of different cultures have different perceptions of "personal space." It is not clear, however, how much such differences are attributable to the perception of crowding as opposed to the actual tolerance of crowding. For instance, do the residents of Tokyo feel uncrowded at densities that might make residents of Los Angeles feel intolerably crowded, or are the Japanese merely better able to tolerate the crowding, even though their perceptions of it may be essentially the same?

We have almost no information on the levels of crowding at which people feel most happy and comfortable and can perform various tasks with the greatest efficiency. We do not know whether high density during one part of the daily routine (at work, for example) coupled with low density at another (at home) would have the same effects as medium density throughout the day. We do not know exactly what role high density plays in the incidence of stress diseases and mental health. We do not know whether density alone can be a contributing cause to riots. People have many opinions about such questions, but we have little solid information on which to base conclusions. Our laboratory, in collaboration with psychologist Jonathan Freedman of Stanford University, has undertaken some preliminary investigations of density effects on human beings. The earliest results suggest that the peoples of the world will have extremely varied views toward the problems of crowding, and very different perceptions of what level of density constitutes a crowded situation. If this conclusion is substantiated (and it certainly conforms to casual observation), it supports the idea that an optimum global population must be small enough to permit considerable local variations in population density.

Generally, however, we must resort to speculation in discussing the psychological and social effects of human crowding. In dealing with a high population density, the Japanese seem to have developed a variety of cultural devices to alleviate the stress. It has been suggested that their very formal and elaborate etiquette may be one mechanism for self-protection against the inevitable frictions of constant human encounter. The Japanese have been relatively crowded for a long time. Around 1870 Japan had some 210 people per square mile. Indeed, because Hokkaido is relatively infertile and inhospitable, the density in many areas is and was much higher. Thus a century ago, Japan had four times the population density of the United States today. In contrast to the Japanese and the Europeans, who also have had high population densities for several generations, people from currently or recently low-density countries (such as the United States or Australia) are likely to have the reputation of being informal and easy-going, or even bumptious and rude. The Japanese are famous for their interest in aesthetic values and respect for nature, which they demonstrate in their lovely gardens. They also successfully create an illusion of space where there is very little in their homes and buildings, a talent that possibly contributes much to domestic serenity.

People in general remain unaware of the influence that population size and density have upon their ways of life and their perceptions of the world. After all, these factors usually do not change drastically in times on the order of a generation or less. When they do change rapidly, as they are doing in some Latin American countries, the result seems more likely to produce disruption than gradual social change. Around 1910 the United States had about half the number of people that it has today. Society then differed from today's in ways that cannot be entirely explained by the processes of industrialization and urbanization, or by such historical events as two world wars and a depression. Such qualities as friendliness and neighborliness, once common in this country and generally esteemed, now seem to exist primarily in rural areas, small towns, and occasional enclaves in big cities. In myriad ways our lives have become more regulated, regimented, and formalistic, a trend that is at least partly due to population growth. If we add another 100 million people in the next thirty-odd years, this trend will certainly continue and will probably even accelerate.

Cultural and social factors, as well as physical limitations, must be a part of a discussion of optimum populations. A standard of living involves more than per capita income, purchasing power, and possessions. "The best things in life are free," an old song tells us, but they may no longer be available to people in overcrowded populations. Population size and density have a strong influence on social arrangements, and it is certainly appropriate to consider what sort of society we would prefer in trying to reach decisions about population size. Do we like a large degree of personal freedom and free and easy manners? Or do we prefer more formality and a high degree of organization?

Certain values conflict with numbers, even though numbers may also be considered a value by many people, such as economists, politicians (who see more votes), and parents of large families. Those who promote numbers of people as a value in itself may fail to consider the cheapness such abundance often brings. One might well ask whether traditional ideals of cherishing human life have not been eroded by our growing population in the last generation or two. There is some sign of this, especially in the way the nation today barely reacts to such tragedies as devastating floods, hurricanes, and airline crashes—a striking contrast to the prolonged sympathy and relief operations evoked by disasters of lesser magnitude before World War II. The growing impersonality of life in our large cities, in which citizens' cries for help are often ignored by bystanders, further supports this view.

The conflict between values and numbers may arise in a choice between having many deprived children or having only a few who can be raised with the best care, education, and opportunity for successful adulthood. The decision is equally valid whether it is made by a family or a society. It is surely no accident that so many of the most successful individuals are first or only children; nor that children of large families (particularly with more than four children), whatever their economic status, generally do relatively poorly in school and show lower I.Q. test scores than their peers from small families. Studies with very young children conducted at Harvard University by three psychologists, Burton L. White, Jerome Bruner, and E. Robert La Crosse, have lent substance to these findings. They have found that children establish their own level of "competence"—ability to cope with their culture—well before school age. This level of competence is strongly correlated with the amount and kind of attention each child receives from his mother during his earliest years. The significance of this in relation to family size is obviously great.

How much do humans really love children? Demographer Lincoln Day of the Harvard School of Public Health suggests that the truth is that Americans, at least, love their *own* children, not their neighbors'. Most adults, in fact, do not ordinarily have much contact with other people's children, and relatively few seek it, unless their occupations bring them into contact with children. Perhaps more opportunities for contact between generations would go a long way toward compensating for large families, when and if a small family norm can be established. The simplest way to provide intergenerational contact is to encourage the development of neighborhoods composed of families of all ages—from newlyweds to senior citizens—and provide communal areas where they can associate. Very structured child-adult relationships have been developed in such social organizations as hippie communes and Israeli Kibbutzim, where all adults in the community come into regular contact with children.

Although human beings are capable of adapting themselves to a wide variety of environments, it is plain that we do much better in some sets of circumstances than others. *Whether we measure adaptive success by how many individuals can survive in a given area or by how many can live healthy, productive, reasonably happy, and comfortable lives is a vitally important point.*

Determining an Optimum

The approach to establishing optimum population sizes relative to resources is straightforward in principle. We must first determine what material standard of living for people is desired and then determine how many people can be maintained at that standard. The minimum size will be determined by the societal complexity necessary for divisions of labor, construction of public works, and so forth. The maximum size will be set by the need to avoid the various unhappy consequences of overpopulation already discussed. It should be noted that the goal expressed in the slogan "the greatest good for the greatest number" is an impossible double maximization. The greater the total number of people, the fewer there will be who can "live like kings" at any given time.

But material standards, as we have seen, are only part of the story. Approaches to optimizing the quality of life should recognize the need for diversity. Population size must be set so that a continuum of density is possible, from crowded cities to utter solitude. People should be able to establish themselves at whatever density makes them feel most comfortable, and strict regulations might prevent great density changes within specified areas. Such a utopian system would require an overall global density considerably below the maximum "base subsistence density." Not only could the rewards for the human psyche be enormous, but some scope would be left for human social and cultural development, including genuine opportunities to create "free societies," without the need to pour all our efforts into solving the elemental problems of survival.

With the passage of time, both technological change and cultural evolution will inevitably change optima. Therefore, all governments, including eventually a world governmental body, must be ready to encourage appropriate population trends just as they now intervene in attempts to produce desired economic trends. In other words, the size of the human population must be brought under rational control, but not with the idea of establishing some sort of permanent optimum. The ideal of an optimum population size must be a dynamic one, in which population size changes in response to human needs. The number of children that couples may have will not simply be the number of children they desire, but will take into account the children's future well-being, as well as social and physical environmental factors. Arriving at ideals of optimum population sizes, however, will involve more than simply avoiding unwanted births. By virtually every standard the world is already overpopulated, and there is considerable evidence that, even if every unwanted birth were avoided, the global population would still grow. In order to achieve population control, extraordinary changes in human attitudes—attitudes produced by eons of biological and cultural evolution—will have to occur. These changes will inevitably trouble men's minds; death control goes with the grain, but birth control goes against it. Changing people's views of birth control and family size to coincide with the goal of a better future for all mankind is one of the greatest challenges humanity has ever faced.

Bibliography

Allen, Durward L., 1969. Too many strangers. *National Parks Magazine,* (August).

Althus, William D., 1966. Birth order and its sequelae. *Science,* Vol. 151, pp. 44–49. Evidence that first-born children are more likely than others to achieve eminence or educational attainment.

Anonymous, 1969. Children: the intelligent infant. *Time,* March 28, p. 56.

Associated Press, 1969. Mother's age and baby's IQ. *San Francisco Chronicle,* Jan. 18. Report on studies in Scotland by Sir Dugald Baird at Aberdeen University, relating children's IQ scores with mother's age and the size of the family.

Dubos, Rene, 1965. *Man Adapting.* Yale Univ. Press, New Haven. Deals with all aspects of the individual's adaptation to his environment.

Enke, Stephen, 1969. Is a stationary U.S. population desirable and possible? Manuscript.

Hulett, H. R., 1970. Optimum world population. *BioScience,* vol. 20, no. 3 (March).

Marshall, A. J. (ed.), 1966. *The Great Extermination.* Heinemann, London. Describes human destruction of Australia's environment.

Morris, Desmond, 1967. *The Naked Ape.* McGraw-Hill, New York. In spite of some errors of fact and interpretation, this is an excellent book for putting man in perspective.

Pines, Maya, 1969. Why some 3-year-olds get A's—and some get C's. *N.Y. Times Magazine,* July 6.

United Press International, 1968. Big family children not bright. *Palo Alto Times,* Nov. 26. Account of speech made by Dr. E. James Lieberman of the Public Health Service's Center for Studies of Child and Family Mental Health.

CHAPTER 9

Birth Control

*"Unlike plagues of the dark ages or contemporary diseases
we do not yet understand, the modern plague of
overpopulation is soluble by means we have
discovered and with resources we possess.
What is lacking is not sufficient knowledge of the solution
but universal consciousness of the gravity of the problem
and education of the billions who are its victims."*

Martin Luther King (1929–1968)
(Speech delivered on receiving the Margaret
Sanger Award in Human Rights, 1966.)

An essential feature of any humane program to regulate the size of the human population, and to achieve the goal of a world optimum, is the control of births. This chapter summarizes present techniques by which birth control may be accomplished and describes some others that are under development. For a review of reproductive anatomy and physiology, see Appendix 5.

History

Many birth-control practices are at least as old as recorded history. The Old Testament contains obvious references to the practice of withdrawal, or *coitus interruptus* (removal of the penis from the woman's vagina before ejaculation). The ancient Egyptians used crude barriers to the cervix made from leaves or cloth, and even blocked the cervical canal with cotton fibers. The ancient Greeks practiced population control through their social system as well as through contraception; they discouraged heterosexual marriage and encouraged homosexual relationships, especially for men. The idea may be distasteful to most of us, but it undoubtedly worked. The condom, or penis sheath dates back at least to the Middle Ages, when it was made of linen, fish skins, or sheeps' intestines. The latter version is still in use today, although it has largely been superseded by the cheaper, more popular, rubber one. Douching. the practice of flushing out the vagina with water or a solution immediately after intercourse, has had a similarly long history in Europe. The widespread practice of withdrawal and a trend toward late marriage are believed to be responsible for the reduction of European birth rates that followed the Industrial Revolution. The simplest, the most effective, and perhaps the oldest method of birth control is abstention; but this method seems to have been favored mainly by older men, particularly unmarried members of the clergy.

Besides the fairly effective methods of birth control mentioned above, a host of others have been tried at various times in various societies, including the use of plants and herbs, chemicals, drugs, saliva and dung from animals, vegetable oils, and even the performance of such rituals as holding one's breath and stepping over graves.

Attempts to limit family size by one means or another appear to be a universal phenomenon. Abortion has a very long history and is believed to be the single most common form of birth control in the world today, despite its illegal status in most countries. Infanticide, which is viewed with horror by prosperous people in industrialized societies, was a rather common practice among the ancient Greeks. Only a century or so ago, it was widely practiced in Europe in an institutionalized, although not entirely socially approved, system sometimes called "baby farming" (Box 9-1).

Infanticide today rarely takes the form of outright murder. Usually it consists of deliberate neglect or exposure to the elements. Among the Eskimos and other primitive peoples who live in harsh environments where food is scarce, infanticide is a fairly common practice, since greater importance must be placed on the survival of the group than on the survival of an additional child. It exists even in our own society, especially among the overburdened poor, although intent might be hard to prove. Certainly "masked infanticide" is extremely common among the poor and hungry in underdeveloped countries, where women often neglect ill children, refuse to take them to medical facilities, and show resentment toward anyone who attempts treatment. According to Dr. Sumner Kalman of the Stanford University Medical Center, the average poor mother in Colombia—where 80 percent of a large family's income may be needed to provide food alone—goes through a progression of attempts to limit the number of her children. She starts with ineffective native forms of contraception and moves on to quack abortion, infanticide, frigidity, and all too often to suicide.

The modern family-planning movement began in the United States and England as an outgrowth of the women's rights campaign. In the beginning it was intended primarily to relieve women of the burdens of too many children, which not uncommonly included a threat to the mothers' very lives. In the early years of this endeavor, men (including members of the medical profession), generally opposed the idea or were indifferent to it. Later, when the economic advantages and the benefits to conjugal and family life became evident, men began to support family planning, and the medical profession developed more modern and effective methods of birth control. Nevertheless, more often than not, the wife still holds the primary responsibility for birth control in the family. This is reflected by the fact that the majority of modern birth-control methods, particularly those used by married couples, are designed to be employed by the woman.

Conventional Methods

Among the so-called conventional methods and devices for birth control are the condom, the diaphragm, and the cervical cap; various creams, jellies, and foams; the douche; and the rhythm system. All of these are intended to prevent the meeting of sperm and ovum. More recent additions to the arsenal include the contraceptive pill and the intrauterine device (IUD). Some of these methods and devices are more effective than others, and each has ad-

---

BOX 9-1   INSTITUTIONALIZED INFANTICIDE IN EIGHTEENTH CENTURY

The following quotation is from George Burrington's pamphlet "An answer to Dr. William Brakenridge's letter concerning the number of inhabitants, within the London bills of mortality," London, J. Scott (1757):

Where the Number of lusty Batchelors is large, many are the merry-begotten Babes: On these Occasions, if the Father is an honest Fellow and a true Church of England-Man, the new-born Infant is baptized by an indigent Priest, and the Father provides for the Child: But the Dissenters, Papists, Jews, and other Sects send their Bastards to the Foundling Hospital; if they are not admitted, there are Men and Women, that for a certain Sum of Money will take them, and the Fathers never hear what becomes of their Children afterwards . . . in and about London a prodigious Number of Infants are cruelly murdered unchristened, by those Infernals, called Nurses; these detestable Monsters throw a Spoonful of Gin, Spirits of Wine, or Hungary-Water down a Child's Throat, which instantly strangles the Babe; when the Searchers come to inspect the Body, and enquire what Distemper caused the Death, it is answered, Convulsions, this occasions the Article of Convulsions in the Bills of Mortality so much to exceed all others. The price of destroying and interring a Child is but Two Guineas; and these are the Causes that near a Third die under the Age of Two Years, and not unlikely under two Months.

I have been informed by a Man now living, that the Officers of one Parish in Westminster, received Money for more than Five Hundred Bastards, and reared but One out of the whole Number. How surprizing and shocking must this dismal Relation appear, to all that are not hardened in Sin? Will it not strike every one, but the Causers and Perpetrators with Dread and Horror? Let it be considered what a heinous and detestable Crime Child-murder is, in the Sight of the Almighty, and how much it ought to be abhorred and prevented by all good People.

vantages and disadvantages that may make it more or less suitable for a particular couple at a particular stage of life. Beyond these contraceptives, for a couple whose family is complete, there is sterilization. For the male especially, this is a simple, harmless procedure that removes the possibility of fathering a child, and has no other effect. In addition to the conventional methods of birth control, certain "folk methods" exist in our culture, which are used mainly by ingenious teenagers. These include douches with soft drinks, and condoms devised from plastic wrapping materials. Despite the ingenuity they reflect, they cannot be recommended, especially the douche. Their effectiveness is unknown, although that of the plastic condom may be quite high.

New methods of birth control are now being developed and tested in laboratories. Hopefully, some of these will be available to the public within the next few years.

THE CONDOM

Many men have learned about the condom in the armed forces, where it is presented to them as a means of avoiding venereal disease. It is also one of the most popular and most effective means of birth control. Usually made of rubber, the condom is a very thin sheath that fits tightly over the penis during intercourse and retains the semen after ejaculation. Its advantages lie in its simplicity of use and its availability. The failure rate is low, especially if the man has been instructed in its proper use. Care is especially required to insure against spillage of semen at the time of withdrawal. Defective condoms are seldom encountered and can be guarded against by inspection before use. Unlike other devices, condoms require no fitting or prescription by a doctor; but many men complain that they interfere with the enjoyment of intercourse by reducing sensation, and by causing an interruption of foreplay in order to apply them.

THE DIAPHRAGM

This device, essentially a rubber cup with a rubberclad rim of flexible spring steel, is designed to fit over the cervix, where it acts as a barrier to sperm. It is inserted into the vagina before intercourse, and is left in place for several hours afterward. Before insertion it is coated on the edges and underside with a spermicidal jelly or cream to prevent any sperm from getting through underneath. A well-fitted, properly used diaphragm is a highly effective contraceptive, but it is relatively complicated to use compared to the condom and some other methods. To ensure a proper fit, it must be prescribed by a doctor, who also instructs the woman about its placement and use. When in position, it cannot be felt, and its use does not in any way interfere with either partner's enjoyment of sexual relations.

THE CERVICAL CAP

Like the diaphragm, the cervical cap bars entrance of sperm into the uterus. It is made of plastic or metal, fits tightly over the cervix, and may be left in place for long periods of time. It need be removed only for menstruation. If properly fitted, the cap is extremely effective. Its main disadvantage lies in the difficulty of placing it correctly.

SPERMICIDAL AGENTS

A variety of spermicidal jellies and creams are available that can be deposited in the upper vagina with special applicators. Although these agents are less effective than the devices discussed above, they have the advantage of being easier to use than mechanical contrivances, and they require neither fitting nor prescription by a doctor.

Foam tablets, aerosols, and suppositories are similar to the jellies and creams, and operate on the same principles. The foam varieties may be more effective than the others, perhaps because they are more thoroughly dispersed in the vagina.

RHYTHM

Also referred to as "periodic abstention," rhythm is the only method of birth control now sanctioned by the Roman Catholic Church. The basic idea is to abstain from sexual relations during the several days each month when a woman might be capable of conceiving. The difficulty is that this period is often hard to determine, particularly in women with irregular menstrual cycles. To avoid conception, the couple must abstain from coitus for at least two days before and one-half day after ovulation. Unfortunately the occurrence of ovulation can only be determined after the event, and not too accurately even then. When ovulation has taken place, the woman's temperature rises about half a degree, and drops again when her menstrual period begins. The time of ovulation must be predicted on the basis of carefully kept records of her previous menstrual and temperature cycles. To allow an adequate safety margin, several additional days should be included both before and after the estimated fertile period. Thus, the period of abstention amounts to a considerable fraction of the month, to the inevitable detriment of the conjugal relationship, especially since the fertile period may be a time when the woman is relatively more receptive to sexual relations. What is worse, the rhythm method is one of the least effective of birth-control methods. Approximately one woman in six has a cycle so irregular that the system will not work at all for her. But the Church claims this is the only "natural" form of birth control, since it requires no mechanical devices or chemical solutions—a claim that neglects the necessary preoccupation with calendars, clocks, thermometers, pencils, and graphs.

THE PILL

The modern steroid oral contraceptive, generally known as "the pill," is the most effective means of birth control known today, other than sterilization. When taken without fail according to instructions, it is virtually 100 percent effective.

The pill is composed of the female hormone estrogen and of progestin, a synthetic substance that is chemically similar to the natural progesterone produced by a woman's ovaries. This combination is believed to act by suppressing ovulation. The pill is taken daily for 20 or 21 days of the 28-day cycle, beginning on the fifth day after the onset of the menstrual period. The steroids may be administered sequentially or in a combined form. In the sequential system, the estrogen is administered alone during the early part of the cycle, with the progestin added only during the latter part. The pills have the effect of regularizing the menstrual cycle to exactly 28 days, even in women who have never had regular cycles before. Moreover, menstrual flow is noticeably reduced, or even occasionally suppressed altogether. Most women consider these effects advantageous.

As is inevitable with any drug, particularly a hormonal drug, there may be undesirable side-effects. Most of these, however, wear off within a few months or can be dealt with by adjusting the dosage or changing brands. Many of them resemble the symptoms of pregnancy, which in a sense is hormonally simulated in the woman's body by the progestin. The most common side-effects are tenderness and swelling of the breasts, weight gain and retention of fluid, nausea, headaches, depression, nervousness and irritability, and bleeding. About one in four or five women taking the pill experiences one or more of these symptoms.

There are some indications that taking the pill for a long time may extend the period of a woman's sexual activity; in other words, a middle-aged woman who is using the pill may be as sexually active as a woman five years younger who is not on the pill. Some women may even find that they have increased libido. This reaction may simply be the result of not having to worry about pregnancy at the time of coitus, or it may have a hormonal basis.

The advantages of an oral contraceptive are obvious, even apart from the advantage offered by its effectiveness. Its use is far removed in time from the act of intercourse, and there are no mechanical devices or chemicals except the pill to deal with. On the other hand, the woman must remember to take it each day, which requires a fairly high degree of motivation. The chances of pregnancy increase with each forgotten pill.

In the course of up to seven years of testing on large numbers of women prior to its release to the public in 1962 in the United States and its use by millions since then, the pill has produced no serious medical problems for the overwhelming majority of women, although the results of using it over an entire reproductive span of 30 years or so are still unknown. Over the short term it is probably no more dangerous than undergoing a pregnancy. Physicians generally do not prescribe the pill for women who have histories of liver disease, cancer, or thromboembolic diseases. Some kinds of liver disease are known to be aggravated by the hormones produced during pregnancy; the pill seems likely to have the same effect.

Whether the pill plays a role in inducing cancer is still unclear. Early results from a study sponsored by Planned Parenthood of New York were inconclusive. They showed that certain "precancerous" changes in the cervix were more common in women using oral contraceptives than in a control group using diaphragms. This difference remained even after various sociological differences between the two groups of women were accounted for. Nevertheless, the possibility remains that a diaphragm may constitute a positive protection against the "precancerous" condition. This condition, although it is known to precede the development of cancer of the cervix, does not always do so. Whether it would lead to cancer in women who use the pill remains unknown. In any case, the precancerous condition is easily and completely curable. Further studies are now under way in an effort to learn whether use of the pill can lead to cancer.

Another possible hazard, thromboembolism, also presents a complicated picture. Research published in England in 1968 revealed that women over the age of 35 who were using the pill had a significantly higher chance (8 per 200,000) of dying of thrombophlebitis (inflammation of veins together with blood clots) or pulmonary embolism (blood clots in the blood vessels of the lungs) than women of the same age who were not using the pill (1 in 200,000). The risk is less than one-half as high in either case for women under 35. In both age groups the risk of death from thromboembolic disease while using the pill is probably about equal to that of death resulting from pregnancy. The estrogen component of the pill appears to be responsible for development of these disorders. The Food and Drug Administration of the United States is currently sponsoring extensive research to find out more about this relationship. Meanwhile, it has required that the labels of the pills warn of possible hazard to women with a history of venous disorders.

Much more time will have to pass and much more data will have to be gathered before definite statements can be made about the risks of cancer and thromboembolism involved in the use of oral contraceptives. We are in somewhat the same position as we were when DDT first came into use. The risks must be weighed against the benefits, and the long-term risks are still unknown. From what we know now, it appears that for most women the benefits outweigh the risks; the latter can be minimized through close supervision by an alert physician. Obviously, continued monitoring of the long-term effects of the pill (or any future hormonal contraceptives) is essential.

THE IUD

The intrauterine device, or IUD as it is generally known, is a plastic or metal object that is placed inside the uterus and left there for as long as contraception is desired. It comes in a variety of shapes, each having its own advantages and disadvantages relative to the others. The most commonly used include the loop, the ring, the spiral, and the bow (Fig. 9-1). Exactly how these devices work is uncertain, but one possibility is that they prevent or disrupt the implantation of the embryo after conception. Another possibility is that they may interfere with fertilization by stimulating the ovum to travel very rapidly through the fallopian tubes. That the presence of a foreign body in the uterus would act to prevent pregnancy has been known for a long time, and such devices have been used in animal husbandry. Only the most recently developed forms, made of plastic or flexible steel, have been considered reliable and safe enough to be used widely for humans.

The advantages for the user are several; the primary one is that once in place the IUD can be forgotten. There are no pills to remember, no

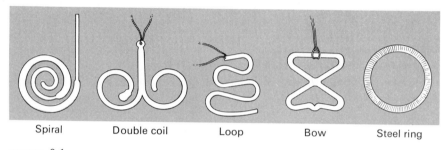

| Spiral | Double coil | Loop | Bow | Steel ring |

FIGURE 9-1
Various forms of IUDs.

contraceptive materials to deal with. This is a great advantage for an individual whose lack of motivation, educational background, or financial resources would make other forms of birth control unreliable or beyond her means. The device costs only a few cents. It must be inserted and subsequently checked by a physician, or a paramedical person.

About 10 percent of women spontaneously expel the device, sometimes without knowing that they have. This tendency varies greatly with age and also with the number of children previously borne. Young women with no children are most likely to expel it; women over 35 with several children are least likely. Expulsion is most likely to occur during the first year of use and the rate sharply declines thereafter.

For the woman who can successfully retain the IUD, it is a highly effective contraceptive, though the pill is more so when properly used. The pregnancy rate varies somewhat with size and type of IUD, and is higher among young women (as it is under any conditions.) The risk of pregnancy drops considerably after the first year of use and continues to drop for succeeding years.

Many women have to remove the IUD because of such side effects as bleeding and pain. Some bleeding and discomfort are usual for a short time after insertion; but when these symptoms continue or are excessive, it is best to remove the IUD. Such problems usually disappear immediately after the device is taken out. Less frequently, the IUDs may be associated with pelvic inflammation, though there is some question whether the device is primarily responsible or only aggravates a pre-existing condition. There is no evidence that IUDs lead to the development of cancer. In very rare cases perforation of the uterus occurs. This happens most often with the bow-shaped device, and there is some evidence that it happens during insertion.

The IUD in its present stage of development is probably most suitable for women over 30 who have completed their families; they are least likely to have a birth control failure, to have problems with side effects, or to expel the IUD.

The various methods of birth control are compared in Table 9-1. The ef-

TABLE 9-1
Failure Rates of Contraceptive Methods

Method	Pregnancy rates for 100 woman-years of use	
	High	Low
No contraceptive	80	80
Aerosol foam	—	29
Foam tablets	43	12
Suppositories	42	4
Jelly or cream	38	4
Douche	41	21
Diaphragm and jelly	35	4
Sponge and foam powder	35	28
Condom	28	7
Coitus interruptus	38	10
Rhythm	38	0
Lactation	26	24
Steroid contraception (the "pill")	2.7	0
Abortion	0	0
Intrauterine contraception (averages) Lippes loop (large) 0–12 months	2.4	
12–24 months	1.4	

SOURCE: After Berelson et al., *Family Planning and Population Programs,* University of Chicago Press, 1966.

fectiveness of techniques is calculated on the basis of 100 woman-years— that is, the number of women per hundred who will become pregnant in a one-year period while using a given method. Among 100 women using no contraception, 80 can expect to be pregnant by the end of one year. The failure rates are based on actual results, no distinction being made whether the method failed or the individuals were careless in using it. The lower rates are generally achieved by highly motivated individuals under close medical supervision.

Sterilization

For couples whose families are complete and who wish to rid themselves of concern about contraceptives, sterilization is often the best solution. This procedure can be performed on either partner, but it is much simpler for the male. A vasectomy takes only fifteen or twenty minutes in a doctor's office. The procedure consists of cutting and tying off the vas deferens, thus making it impossible for sperm to be included in the ejaculate (although the absence of the sperm may only be detected by microscopic examination).

The female's operation, called a salpingectomy or tubal ligation, is more complicated, involving an internal surgical operation with the usual attendant risks. The abdomen must be opened under anesthesia and a section of the fallopian tubes cut and removed so that the ova cannot pass through. This operation is best done right after the birth of a baby, when the tubes are in a relatively accessible position. A new method, involving an approach through the vagina, is now being used by some doctors, and may prove to be superior and safer.

Contrary to the beliefs of many people, sterilization does not in any sense end one's sex life. Vasectomy is *not* castration. The hormonal system is left intact, and sperm are still manufactured by the body; they are simply prevented from leaving it. Sexual performance, including orgasm and ejaculation, is normally unchanged. In the few cases in which psychological problems develop, they usually are found to have grown out of previously existing disturbances. In many cases, psychological improvement is reported as worry over unwanted children ends.

The same is true for the female; her hormones still circulate, ova are still brought to maturity and released, the menstrual cycle goes on. All that is changed is that her ova never reach the uterus, nor can sperm travel up the fallopian tubes. Adverse psychological reactions to this operation are extremely rare.

Many individuals hesitate to take so final a step as sterilization. Although in actual practice only a very small percentage of sterilized people ever ask to have the operation reversed, many want some assurance beforehand that it can be done. For men, successful reversal of the operation can now be achieved in 50 to 80 percent of cases. New methods of sterilization, notably one in which plastic plugs are inserted into the vas deferens, show promise of being virtually 100 percent reversible. The woman's operation can be reversed in 52 to 66 percent of the cases, but women are even less likely than men to request restoration of fertility.

Sterilization is perfectly legal in the United States, although it is restricted in Utah and Connecticut to cases of "medical necessity." Nevertheless, in most places it is difficult for an individual to find a doctor who is willing to perform these operations. Why the medical profession should be so demonstrably reluctant is obscure. The obstacles to sterilization in one major city, San Francisco, are clear from the following passage in a letter from Mary Morain of the Association for Voluntary Sterilization:

> As Board member of the Association . . . I get weekly calls from people asking where they can find a doctor who will give them permanent birth control. The women are faced with a community-wide quota system by which medical committees in hospitals will not give a doctor permission to 'tie their tubes' unless of a certain age with a certain number of children. In San Francisco the *most liberal* standard is this: one must have had five children if one is under thirty, four children if thirty to thirty-four, three children if thirty-five and over. . . . The men have often been sent from pillar to post trying to find a doctor who will do a vasectomy for them.

She goes on to mention the substantial "number of cases where couples want no children and for good reason." For these people it is virtually impossible to find help. There is more:

> As it is we are forcing parenthood on the unwilling. This is even more striking in the County hospitals, many of which will not sterilize a woman no matter how many childen she has had, and of most importance, no matter how much she begs for it.

Population groups at Stanford and elsewhere receive appeals from individuals who have been unsuccessful in finding a doctor who would perform a vasectomy. Through medical connections, lists of local doctors who will perform the procedure have been assembled, and are made available to people who need them. A nationwide organization, the Association for Voluntary Sterilization, is working to make vasectomy and salpingectomy more widely and readily available.

Apparently many doctors are motivated by a fear of lawsuits over sterilization. Attorney General Thomas Lynch of the state of California reportedly interpreted the performance of vasectomy as an "assault," regardless of whether the customary release was signed by the patient. This resulted in the withdrawal by insurance companies of insurance coverage for doctors who perform vasectomies. The fact remains that no lawsuit over sterilization has ever been won in a case where a release had been signed. At last report the policy has been changed and the availability of vasectomies in California should improve, as insurance is now obtainable. It is possible to protect doctors by law against such suits over sterilization, although Virginia, Georgia, and North Carolina are the only states that have made such protection available.

In July 1969 the California District Court of Appeals ruled that "nontherapeutic surgical sterilization was legal in this state where competent consent has been given." The decision was rendered in the case of a couple who desired no more children than they had, but the husband had been denied a vasectomy by a hospital. This decision may lead to more humane hospital policies relative to sterilization.

Abortion

In most of the world, induced abortion is illegal. Where it is legal, it is often permitted only under rather strictly defined conditions. Nevertheless, abortion is believed to be the commonest form of birth control in all parts of the world, even in countries where modern contraceptives are readily available.

Abortion is the arrest of a pregnancy in the early stages. The medically approved method of inducing abortion is through a simple operation known as dilation and curettage (scraping) of the uterus, which removes and destroys the fetus. This is preferably done no later than the 12th week of pregnancy. After the 16th week the procedure is considerably more complicated, and abortion then is ordinarily resorted to only if the pregnancy seriously endangers the mother's life. Doctors in the Soviet Union have developed a newer, evidently safer method, involving the use of a vacuum device in place of curettage. This device is also being generally used in eastern European countries and possibly in mainland China.

When performed under appropriate medical circumstances by a qualified physician, abortion is safer than a full-term pregnancy, but if it is delayed beyond the 12th week, the risks of complications or death rise considerably. Similarly, the risks increase when the abortion is illegal, the amount of increase depending upon the circumstances. These may range from self-inducement with a knitting needle or—almost equally dangerous—unsterile help from untrained or semitrained people to reasonably safe treatment by a physician in a hotel room or a clandestine clinic. In the United States, as in many parts of the world, bungled illegal abortions are the greatest single cause of maternal deaths, accounting for about 45 percent of them.

Abortion is practiced in some form in all societies today, and there are records of it throughout history. Disapproval of the practice originated with the Judeo-Christian ethic, yet abortion was not made illegal until the nineteenth century, when it was outlawed on the grounds that it was dangerous to the mother, as it was in those days before sterile medical techniques. Today, even in the countries with the most liberal abortion laws, a woman must go through the legal procedure of applying for and receiving official sanction before she can have her abortion. This is the situation in China, Japan, and several countries in eastern Europe, where abortion is essentially available on request. Rumania and Bulgaria, alarmed at very low birth rates, which were due at least in part to the ease of obtaining an abortion, have recently tightened their regulations. Hungary's abortion rate now is higher than its birth rate, which suggests that it must be the primary method of fertility control in that country. The U.S.S.R., after several post-revolution population policy changes, now has liberal abortion policies, but does not advertise the fact. Until 1968, the U.S.S.R. did not permit the use of the pill. Now the pill is being used on an experimental basis only, but eventually it will probably be available to all women who want it.

Scandinavian countries, and, since 1968, England, have fairly liberal abortion policies, allowing it under a wide range of medical, psychological, and social conditions. However, it is by no means simply granted on request.

At the beginning of 1969, most of the United States, virtually all of Latin America, most of Asia, and southern and western Europe still had very restrictive abortion laws. It was allowed, if at all, only when the mother's life was threatened. However, this situation may change rapidly in the next few years. India is now seriously considering legalizing abortion, and some other countries may follow suit, either to ease their population pressures or to put an end to the tragic deaths from botched illegal abortions.

In the U.S., ten states had moderated their abortion laws by the end of 1969. These new laws permit abortion in cases where bearing the child presents a grave risk to the mental or physical health of the mother, where the pregnancy is a result of incest or rape, and where (except in California) there is a substantial likelihood that the child will be physically or mentally defective. To obtain an abortion, a woman usually must submit her case to a hospital reviewing board of physicians, a time-consuming and expensive process. Although the laws were relaxed to reduce the problem of illegal abortions, hospital boards in general have interpreted the changes in the law so conservatively that they had had little effect. The number of illegal abortions per year in the U.S. has been variously estimated at between 200,000 and 2 million, with one million being the most often quoted figure. This amounts to more than one abortion for every four births. There are estimated to be 100,000 illegal abortions per year in California; in the first six months after passage of the "liberalized" law there were just over 2,000 legal ones. The figures are similar for the other states.

Illegal abortions can probably be obtained in every country in the world. They are most prevalent where laws are most restrictive. In Italy, where contraceptives are strictly prohibited, the abortion rate is estimated to be nearly equal to the birth rate. Many of these are self-inflicted or accomplished with the aid of an untrained but sympathetic friend. When a woman with hemorrhage is brought to a hospital, she is automatically given tetanus and penicillin shots. She will never admit having had an abortion; under Italian law she has committed a crime and could be sent to prison. Death is estimated to result from about 4 percent of Italian abortions. Some years ago, in a confidential survey of 4,000 married women of all classes, all admitted to having had abortions, most of them not once but many times. The pill is now available on prescription for "medical reasons," and a family planning clinic has opened in Rome. It is to be hoped that this new availability of birth control will have an effect on the appalling rate of medically unsupervised abortions.

In France, contraceptives can be purchased, but their advertisement and the dissemination of information about them are prohibited. Those women pregnant with an unwanted child who cannot afford to visit a Swiss clinic abort themselves in secret, concealing their action even from their husbands. If things go wrong, they often wait too long before seeking medical help for fear of being found out. The result is that France has an even higher rate of death and permanent injury than would exist if help were sought promptly.

Illegal abortion is rampant in Latin America. Contraceptives, though legally available, are actually obtainable only by the rich in most places. The poor and ignorant, who make up the bulk of the population in most Latin American countries, are generally unaware of the existence of birth control other than by ancient folk methods, and could not afford modern methods even if they knew of them. There are exceptions to this where governments and volunteer organizations such as Planned Parenthood have established free birth control clinics. Although these help, they as yet reach only a small fraction of the population. In areas where hunger and malnutrition are widespread, a failure of primitive birth control methods leaves women with no alternative but to practice equally crude forms of abortion.

Bungled abortions are estimated to account for more than 40 percent of hospital admissions in Santiago, Chile. In that country, an estimated one-third of all pregnancies end in abortion. For South America as a whole, some authorities believe that one-fourth of all pregnancies end in abortion. Other estimates are that abortions outnumber pregnancies brought to term.

The greatest obstacles to freely available, medically safe abortion in most countries are the Roman Catholic Church and other religious organizations that consider abortion as immoral. The crux of the Catholic argument is that the embryo is, from the moment of conception, a complete individual with a soul. In the Catholic view, induced abortion amounts to murder. Catholics also oppose abortion on the grounds that it will encourage promiscuity— exactly the same reason given in Japan for banning the pill and the IUD. There is no evidence to support either point of view on promiscuity, but even if there were an increase it would be a small price to pay for a chance to ameliorate the mass misery of unwanted pregnancies.

Many Protestant theologians hold that the time when a child acquires a soul is unknown and perhaps unimportant. They see no difficulty in establishing it at the time of "quickening," when movements of the fetus first become discernible to the mother; or at the time, around 28 weeks, when the infant, if prematurely born, could survive outside its mother's body. To them, the evil of abortion is far outweighed by the evil of bringing into the world an unwanted child under less than ideal circumstances.

To most biologists, a three-month fetus is no more a complete human being than a blueprint is a complete building. The fetus, given the opportunity to develop properly before birth, and given the essential early socializing experiences and sufficient nourishing food during the crucial early years after birth, will ultimately develop into a human being. Where any of these is lacking, the resultant individual will be deficient in some respect. From this point of view, a fetus is only a *potential* human being, with no particular rights, certainly none that should be asserted before those of its mother and/ or previously born siblings. An abortion is clearly preferable to adding an additional child to an overburdened family or an overburdened society, where the chances that it will realize its full potentialities are slight. Indeed, if a fetus had a choice, it might prefer *not* to be born to such a life. The argument that a decision is being made for an unborn person who "has no say" is often raised by those opposing abortion. But unthinking actions of the very same people help to commit future unheard generations to misery and early death on an overcrowded planet. One can also challenge the notion that older men, be they medical doctors or celibate clergymen, have the right to make decisions whose consequences are borne largely by young women and their families.

There are those who claim that free access to abortion will lead to genocide. It is hard to see how this could happen if the decision is left to the mother. A mother who takes the moral view that abortion is equivalent to murder is free to bear her child. If she cannot care for it, placement for adoption is still possible.

Few people would claim that abortion is preferable to contraception, if only because the risk of injury to the mother is usually greater. But large and rapidly growing numbers of people feel that abortion is vastly preferable to the births of unwanted children, especially in an overpopulated world. Until a far more effective form of contraception than we now have is developed, abortion will remain a common method of birth control when contraceptives fail.

Attitudes on abortion have changed before, and they can reasonably be expected to change again in the future. Indeed, polls taken in the United States indicate that the attitudes of Americans changed significantly between 1965 and 1967 (Table 9-2). These polls revealed that within a period of

TABLE 9-2
Increase in Approval of Abortion

	Percentage approval	
Reason	*1965*	*1967*
Woman's health endangered	87	86
Victim of rape	52	72
Pregnancy due to incest*	—	69
Possibility of deformed child	50	62
Woman unmarried	13	28
Can't afford child	11	25
Child unwanted	8	21

SOURCE: *Data from Studies in Family Planning,* no. 30 (supp.), The Population Council, 1968.
* Not surveyed in 1965.

only two years, approval of abortion for each of seven reasons but one (to save the mother's life, which already had more than 85 percent approval) rose by an average of 15 percentage points during the two years. But less than 30 percent of those polled approved of abortion for such social reasons as not being married, or not wanting or not being able to afford another child. A poll taken early in 1969 asked a slightly different question: Should an abortion be available to any woman who requests one? In apparent contradiction to the earlier opinions, more than half those interviewed said yes. Although they did not approve of abortion except for the more serious reasons, such as danger to the mother, rape, incest, or the possibility of a deformed child, the majority apparently felt that mothers should be free to make their own decisions.

In a democratic country such as the United States, there is good reason to question the legality of denying women the right of access to abortion. The

American Civil Liberties Union (ACLU) raised this question late in 1968, taking the stand that present laws infringe women's civil liberties, and more recently that they are unconstitutional because they are based on Roman Catholic dogma. The ACLU maintains that judgments on the morality of abortion "belong solely in the province of individual conscience and religion." At about the same time, the American Public Health Association's governing council and the Planned Parenthood Federation both made public announcements in favor of completely unrestricted access to abortion.

The female half of the world's population has already cast its silent vote. Every year perhaps one million women in the United States, and countless millions in the rest of the world, make their desires abundantly clear by seeking and obtaining abortions, more often than not in the face of society's disapproval and of very real dangers and difficulties.

Possibilities for the Future

Many possible ways of interfering with the reproductive process have yet to be explored; some of the most promising of these are under investigation in laboratories or are being tested clinically in humans. Within the next few years a variety of new methods of birth control should become available for general use. Some of the methods currently being developed show considerable promise as practical approaches for population control in underdeveloped countries, where only the simplest and cheapest methods are likely to result in a substantial lowering of birth rates. Most of the new contraceptives are designed for women, and are extensions of the research that produced the pill.

PROGESTIN

Among the developments most likely to prove useful soon are the various forms of low, continuous dosages of the steroid progestin. Unlike the high dosage of progestin combined with estrogen in the present pill, the low dosages do not suppress ovulation. Exactly how the progestin does act is still uncertain, but it appears to be potentially as effective a contraceptive as the pill. It is known to alter the consistency of the mucus of the cervical canal, a change that may prevent the penetration of the uterus by the sperm; it affects the lining of the uterus in a way that may prevent implantation; and it also may cause the ovum to travel too rapidly down the fallopian tubes. It is possible that all three of these factors may operate to prevent conception.

The use of progestin alone has the advantage of avoiding some of the more dangerous aspects of the pill, such as the increased risks of thromboembolism and liver diseases that seem to be associated with the estrogen component. But some side effects do appear. Some women have complained of headaches and dizziness. A more serious drawback seems to be a tendency toward irregular bleeding and amenorrhea (absence of menstruation).

Very large study programs involving thousands of women are now being carried out with two forms of low dose progestins: a mini-pill, taken daily with no "time off" to keep track of; and intramuscular injections at three-month or six-month intervals. The latter method is being used in an extensive testing program at the University of Chile Medical School in Santiago. In cases where irregular bleeding and amenorrhea occur, the researchers there have been able to control both problems by administering very small "accessory" doses of estrogen for 5 to 7 days each month.

The newest way of administering progestin is the "time capsule," which can be implanted under the skin by a hypodermic needle. The material of which the capsule is made—a silicone rubber known as Silastic—releases the steroid at a constant rate over a long period of time, potentially as long as 25 or 30 years. Its effect is completely reversible by removal. The time capsule was scheduled to be tested on humans beginning in 1969, and it should be generally available within a few years if it proves successful.

Progestin administered in low dosages in any of the three ways discussed above shares with the progestin-estrogen pill the advantages of high effectiveness and convenience of use, and has the additional advantages of being far less complicated to use (especially the implanted capsule) and avoiding the hazards of estrogen. It is quite likely that all these forms will be considerably less expensive, at least by the time they can be used in large quantities. If the problems of irregular bleeding and amenorrhea can be satisfactorily solved, and if long-term testing does not turn up some new and unanticipated difficulty, progestin holds considerable promise as an agent for effective population control.

THE MORNING-AFTER PILL

"Morning-after" birth control consists in taking a substantial oral dose of estrogens within a few days after coitus. Pregnancy is prevented, but the woman usually feels quite sick for a day or two. This method is still being clinically tested, but is available in some medical centers in the U.S.

NONSTEROID CHEMICAL METHODS

A variety of chemicals are in the process of being tested on laboratory animals, in the hope of finding some that will not have the drawbacks of the steroid compounds. But since many seem to act by influencing some part of the natural hormone system, it is not too surprising that similar side-effects have occurred in association with some of them. Nevertheless, these possibilities, which have only begun to be investigated, deserve careful examination.

At least one folk-method of contraception is being looked into. A South American weed, *Stevia rebaudiana,* has traditionally been used by the Indians in Paraguay as a contraceptive. Each day the women drink a cup of water in which the powdered weed has been boiled. Experiments with rats have indicated a reduction in fertility of from 57 to 79 percent compared with a control group, with low fertility lasting up to two months after withdrawal of the drug. Undoubtedly many such folk-methods are known in various human cultures. Some of them may be quite effective and might prove adaptable to the urgent need for population control, particularly in underdeveloped countries.

METHODS FOR MEN

Attempts to find steroid or other chemical forms of contraceptives for men have so far been remarkably unsuccessful. Usually these are aimed at reducing or interfering with spermatogenesis. Several of them have proven to be incompatible with the consumption of alcoholic drinks, a serious drawback in most societies. When progestins were administered to volunteers, spermatogenesis was suppressed, but so was the production of the male sex hormone testosterone.

A nonsteroid chemical derived from the manufacture of dynamite is now being tested in rats. So far no untoward side-effects have shown up, and the chemical seems to have no effect on sexual behavior or desire, nor to interfere with spermatogenesis. But somehow the sperm are rendered incapable of fertilizing the ova.

Two removable mechanical devices, now only in the experimental stage, hold promise as means of reversible sterilization. One, invented by an Indian doctor, consists of a clip that can be attached to the vas deferens. The other is a plastic plug that can be inserted in the vas deferens. Not only could these new devices be used as temporary contraceptives, but they also seem to satisfy the objections to sterilization from those who fear taking an irreversible step.

In the light of the current world population situation, it is clear that research on means of birth control has been neglected for too long. Although some promising projects and possibilities for birth control have come out of recent research, it is obvious that we are still several years away from having the means at hand to help make significant rapid reductions in the birth rates among uneducated and unmotivated populations. Progress in research is further being hampered in the U.S. and some other DCs by the stringent regulations imposed on human research by such agencies as the Food and Drug Administration. In the U.S., a minimum of 8 to 10 years of testing is required before a new contraceptive agent can be released for human use. Since DC laboratories are the best equipped and funded for such research, some change in regulations will be needed if they are to make a substantial contribution to contraceptive technology in time.

Recently a high Indian official expressed the opinion that only the need for a really simple, cheap, effective birth control method stands in the way of a breakthrough in controlling births in India. Perhaps he is overly optimistic, but the DCs must nevertheless bend every effort toward aiding the population control efforts of India and other UDCs through research and logistical support in the field.

Bibliography

Aldridge, Leslie, 1968. Why they quit the pill. *McCalls,* Nov. A somewhat sensational discussion of problems with the pill.

Anonymous, 1968. A non-steroid "pill"? *New Scientist.* Feb. 1, p. 232. Some potential developments in birth control.

Anonymous, 1968. Emboli and "the pill"—FDA study seeks answers. *Medical World News,* Dec. 6.

Anonymous, 1968. IUDs challenge status of the pill. *Medical World News,* Sept. 20.

Anonymous, 1968. Sterilization fears seem unfounded. *New Scientist,* May 16.

Berelson, Bernard, et al., 1966. *Family Planning and Population Programs.* Univ. of Chicago Press, Chicago. Contains some information on the various birth control methods and their application in different countries.

Djerassi, Carl, 1969. Prognosis for the development of new birth-control agents. *Science,* vol. 166, pp. 468–473 (24 Oct.).

Editorial, 1968. Voluntary male sterilization. *Journal of the American Medical Association,* vol. 204, no. 9.

Gilmore, C. P., 1969. Something better than the pill. *New York Times Magazine,* July 20.

Goodhart, C. B., 1965. Criminal abortion in the USA. *Eugenics Review,* vol. 57, no. 2, p. 98.

Goodhart, C. B., 1966. How many illegal abortions? *New Society,* 10 Nov.

Guttmacher, Alan F., 1966. *The Complete Book of Birth Control.* Ballantine Books, New York. Revised. Clear description of all presently used methods of birth control.

Hardin, Garrett, 1961. *Biology: Its Principles and Applications.* Contains a good account of human reproductive physiology.

Hardin, Garrett, 1966. The history and future of birth control. *Perspectives in Biology and Medicine,* vol. 10, no. 1 (Autumn). Contains some interesting historical data.

Hardin, Garrett, 1967. Birth control—the prospects. *Medicine Today,* vol. 1, no. 4 (Oct.). Discussion of recently developed contraceptive methods and abortion.

Hardin, Garrett, 1968. Abortion—compulsory pregnancy? *Journal of Mar-*

riage and Family, vol. XXX, no. 2. Discussion of abortion from a biologist's point of view.

Huldt, Lars, 1968. Outcome of pregnancy when legal abortion is readily available. *Current Medical Digest,* vol. XXXV, no. 5 (May), pp. 586–594.

International Planned Parenthood, 1967. *Victor Fund Report,* no. 6, Summer. Some data on abortions.

Kalman, Sumner M., 1967. Modern Methods of Contraception. *Bulletin of the Santa Clara County* (California) *Medical Society,* March.

Kalman, Sumner M., 1969. Effects of oral contraceptives. *Annual Review of Pharmacology,* vol. 9, pp. 363–378. A good discussion of the hazards associated with the pill.

Kistner, R. W., 1969. What the pill does to husbands. *Ladies Home Journal.* January.

Lader, Lawrence, 1966. *Abortion.* Beacon Press, Boston.

Lader, Lawrence, 1969. Non-hospital abortions. *Look,* Jan. 21.

Lader, Lawrence, 1969. Why birth control fails. *McCalls,* Oct.

Lasagna, Louis, 1968. Caution on the pill. *Saturday Review,* Nov. 2.

Loraine, J. A., and E. T. Bell, 1968. *Fertility and Contraception in the Human Female.* Livingstone, Edinburgh. A relatively technical treatment.

Lowe, David, 1966. *Abortion and the Law.* Pocket Books, New York.

Monroe, Keith, 1968. How California's abortion law isn't working. *New York Times Magazine,* Dec. 29.

Moody, Howard, 1968. Protest. *Glamour,* April. A Protestant view of abortion.

Peel, John, and Malcolm Potts, 1969. *Textbook of Contraceptive Practice.* Cambridge Univ. Press. Fairly technical.

Pilpel, Harriet, 1969. The right of abortion. *Atlantic,* June. The ethical and legal problems of abortion.

Pincus, G., 1966. Control of conception by hormonal steroids. *Science,* vol. 153, pp. 493–500. Based on early studies with the pill.

Planas, G. M., and Joseph Kuć, 1968. Contraceptive properties of *Stevia rebaudiana. Science,* vol. 162, p. 1007. Exploring a folk method of birth control.

Schwartz, Herman, 1967. The parent or the fetus? *Humanist,* July–August. A discussion of legal and ethical aspects of abortion.

Schwartz, Richard A., 1968. Psychiatry and the abortion laws: an overview. *Comprehensive Psychiatry,* vol. 9, no. 2 (March), pp. 99–117.

Szasz, T. S., 1966. The ethics of abortion. *Humanist,* Sept.–Oct.

The Population Council, *Studies in Family Planning.* A monthly series. Many contain evaluations of birth control methods.

Tietze, Christopher, and Sarah Lewit, 1969. Abortion. *Scientific American,* vol. 220, no. 1 (Jan.). Good general discussion, including some public opinion survey results.

Viel, Benjamin, 1969. The social consequences of population growth. PRB Selection No. 30 (Oct.). *Population Reference Bureau.* Washington.

Wood, H. Curtis, Jr., 1967. *Sex Without Babies.* Whitmore Publishing Co., Philadelphia. A complete review of voluntary sterilization.

World Health Organization, 1966. Basic and clinical aspects of intrauterine devices. *Technical Report,* no. 332.

World Health Organization, 1967. Biology of fertility control by periodic abstinence. *Technical Report,* no. 360. A study of the rhythm method.

World Health Organization, 1966. Clinical aspects of oral gestogens. *Technical Report,* no. 326. Slightly out-of-date analysis of the pill.

Zañartu, J., 1968. A new approach to fertility control: long-acting injectable progestogens. *Advances in Fertility Control,* vol. 3, no. 3 (Sept.).

Zanetti, L., 1966. The shame of Italy. *Atlas,* Aug. On the abortion problem in Italy.

CHAPTER 10

Family Planning and Population Control

"A common stratagem of those who wish to escape the swirling currents of change is to stand on high moral ground."

John Gardner
Self-Renewal; The Individual and the Innovative Society, 1964

What is being done in the world today to limit human population size? This chapter considers possible ways in which today's efforts could be converted to genuine population control. Considerable emphasis is placed on family planning programs, since these are now the only programs in existence that claim to have as a goal the regulation of human numbers. However, *family planning and population control are not synonymous.*

Family Planning in the DCs

At the time of the industrial revolution in England an early advocate of limiting the size of families through contraception was labor leader Francis Place. Realizing that a limited labor pool would be likelier to win high wages and better working conditions from employers than would a plentiful supply of workers, Place set forth his views in writings that reached large numbers of people. His original treatise, *Illustrations and Proofs of the Principle of Population,* was published in 1822. It was followed by a series of handbills that urged birth control in the interest of better economic and physical health and also described various contraceptive methods. Additional books on birth control appeared both in England and the United States during the 1830's and continued to circulate until the 1870's, when legal attempts were made to suppress them in both countries. The attempt failed in England, but in the United States the "Comstock Law" was passed by Congress in 1873. It forbade the dissemination by mail of birth control information, classing it with "obscene literature." Many states also passed laws against birth control literature, and in 1890 its importation was outlawed.

America's heroine in the family planning movement was Margaret Sanger, a nurse. She has described the incident that triggered her commitment to what became a lifelong cause. In 1912, she and a doctor were called to attend a mother of three who had performed an abortion on herself and had very nearly died. After some weeks of care the woman recovered, but the doctor warned her that another abortion would kill her. The woman understood, and asked the doctor how she could prevent another baby. The doctor's reply was: "You can't have your cake and eat it too, young woman. There's only one way. Tell Jake to sleep on the roof." Three months later the woman was dead of another self-induced abortion.

Within a very few months Margaret Sanger was publishing articles on contraception. Her objective was to free women from the bondage of unlimited childbearing through birth control and her efforts thus became a part of the women's emancipation movement. Although she was prosecuted for her writings, the charges were dropped. In 1916 she opened the first birth control clinic in Brooklyn. This time Mrs. Sanger was arrested and spent time in jail. As a result of her case, however, court decisions subsequently permitted physicians to prescribe birth control in New York for health reasons. These were the first of many such decisions and changes in the laws of various states that ultimately permitted the sale and advertisement of contraceptive materials and the dissemination of information about birth control. The last such court decision was made in 1965, when the Supreme Court ruled that the Connecticut statute forbidding the use of contraceptives was an unconstitutional invasion of privacy. The following year the Massachusetts legislature repealed the last of the Comstock Laws.

Margaret Sanger and others who joined her rapidly growing birth control movement (then known as the Birth Control League) led the fight for these legal changes and for support from medical, educational, health, and religious organizations. In time, clinics were established throughout the United States, and their activities were expanded to include premarital and preparenthood counseling, assistance for sterile couples, and reproductive research. These additional services are still a part of most family-planning programs, even in underdeveloped countries. In 1942 these expanded interests were reflected when the organization changed its name to the Planned Parenthood Federation.

Counterparts to Margaret Sanger existed in many other countries: Dr. Aletta Jacobs in Holland, Dr. Marie Stopes in England, and, later, Mrs. Elise Ottesen-Jensen of Sweden and Lady Dhanvanthis Rama Rau of India.

These women, like Mrs. Sanger, were motivated by concern for the health and welfare of mothers and children, and their campaigns emphasized these considerations.

Concurrently, intellectual organizations concerned primarily with population size, known as Malthusian Leagues, were also promoting birth control. They were active in several European countries, but after World War I, when European birth rates had dropped substantially, their Malthusian concerns seemed to lose relevance and the movement died out.

The birth control movement in the United States was at first opposed by the medical profession. As the health and welfare benefits of family planning became apparent, the medical profession moved to a position of neutrality, and in 1937 the American Medical Association (AMA) finally called for instruction on contraception in medical schools and medical supervision in family planning clinics. In 1964 the AMA recognized matters of reproduction, "including the need for population control," as subjects for responsible medical concern.

Religious opposition to the birth control movement was initially even stronger than medical opposition. The Roman Catholic Church still opposes "artificial" methods of birth control, but Planned Parenthood clinics cooperate in teaching the rhythm method to Catholics who request it. Acceptance of birth control has come gradually from the various Protestant and Jewish groups after their initial opposition; complete sanction was given by the Anglican (Episcopal) Communion in England and the United States in 1958, by the Central Conference of American Rabbis (Reform) in 1960, and by the National Council of Churches in 1961.

Birth rates in America and Europe had already begun to decline, as a result of the demographic transition, long before the establishment of the first birth control clinics. Nevertheless, the Planned Parenthood movement, particularly in the United States, probably deserves some credit for today's relatively low birth rates. It has also played a great role in increasing the availability of contraceptives and birth control information. This has been accomplished not so much through the clinics, which never reached more than a small fraction of the population, but through the removal of restrictive laws, the development of medical and religious support, and the creation of a social climate in which birth control information can circulate freely.

In 1965 some 85 percent of married women in America had used some method of birth control; 26 percent had used the steroid pill. This represents virtual saturation, since most of the remainder were subfertile, pregnant, or planning to use contraceptives only when their families were complete. Catholic women in the sample showed a level of usage of "artificial" contraceptives nearly as high as that of non-Catholic women. Ten years earlier, well over half of the contraceptive users employed condoms or diaphragms, the two most effective methods then available.

Europe presents a surprisingly different and diverse picture. *Coitus interruptus* has been given the major credit for lowering birth rates during the demographic transition, with abortion also playing an important role. In most of Europe, both East and West, *coitus interruptus* seems still to be the most widely used method, followed by rhythm and the condom. Among Western European countries, only in England and Scandinavia do contraceptive devices approach being as well-known and readily available as they are in the United States. Even in those countries the condom is the most commonly used device, and withdrawal is much more commonly practiced than it is in America. Planned Parenthood groups exist in France, Belgium, and the Netherlands in a quasi-legal status, hampered by laws restricting the dissemination of information and materials. Birth control is entirely illegal in Italy, Spain, Portugal, and Ireland, although Italy has recently legalized the pill, for "medical purposes" (presumably to combat the high illegal abortion rate), and condoms have been available "for disease prevention."

The Soviet Union and Eastern European countries distribute contraceptives through government maternal health clinics, with the intent of reducing the abortion rate. There is evidence that this policy has succeeded in some countries, as it has for example in Japan. The pill, which is currently being introduced there, will probably accelerate this trend away from dependence on abortion for birth control.

Throughout its history, the emphasis and primary concern of the family planning movement has been the welfare of the family; it has stressed the economic, educational, and health advantages of well-spaced, limited numbers of children. Its policy has been to provide information and materials for birth control in volunteer-staffed clinics for the poor, serving any interested client. Once the movement was established, little effort was made to recruit clients until the 1960's, beyond the routine promotion that accompanied the opening of a new clinic. For the United States this policy was apparently adequate; this nation is overwhelmingly committed to family planning. Within the next few years, family planning services will doubtless be extended to the remaining estimated 3.5 to 5 million women in low-income groups to whom they have not previously been available, either through private agencies or through local or federal government welfare programs.

Family Planning in the UDCs

In 1952 Mrs. Sanger, Mrs. Ottesen-Jensen of Sweden, Lady Rama Rau of India, and others in the birth control movement joined to form the International Planned Parenthood Federation, a federation of the already established national groups. By the end of 1968, the IPPF had grown to include organizations in 54 countries, 36 of them UDCs. Many of these organizations, notably those in India and Pakistan, operate with funds provided by their own governments. Others are supported by the international organization, which in turn receives funds from private sources and, more recently, from government grants. These grants have come from the United States, Sweden, Denmark, Norway, the Netherlands, and Britain.

In response to rising alarm during the 1950's over the population explosion in underdeveloped countries, several other organizations in the United States began to be involved in population research and overseas family planning programs. Among these were the Ford Foundation, the Rockefeller Foundation, the Population Council, the Population Reference Bureau, and the Population Crisis Committee. The 1960's brought a great proliferation of family planning programs in UDCs (Table 10-1) assisted or administered

TABLE 10-1
Family Planning in UDCs

Size of population (in millions)	Have an official family planning policy and/or program, or major governmental involvement	Are doing something official in family planning, or limited governmental involvement	Are doing nothing official in family planning
400 & more	China (1962?) India (1952, reorganized 1965)	———	———
100–400	Pakistan (1960, reorganized 1965)	Indonesia	
50–100	———	———	Nigeria Brazil
25–50	Turkey (1965) United Arab Republic (1966) South Korea (1961)	Mexico Philippines Thailand	Burma
15–25	Iran (1967) Colombia (1967) North Vietnam (1964)	———	Ethiopia Congo South Vietnam Afghanistan
10–15	Morocco (1966) Taiwan (1964) Ceylon (1967)	Peru Nepal	Sudan Algeria Tanzania North Korea
Less than 10	Malaysia (1966) Kenya (1966) Chile (1966) Tunisia (1966) Hong Kong (c1960) Dominican Republic (1967) Honduras (1965) Singapore (1966) Jamaica (1966) Trinidad & Tobago (1967) Mauritius (1965)	Venezuela Cuba Nicaragua Costa Rica Barbados	Africa—31 countries Asia—12 countries Latin America 9 countries

SOURCE: Berelson, *Studies in Family Planning no. 39,* (supp.) The Population Council, 1969.

by one or another of these organizations, or by government-sponsored ones from other countries, such as Sweden. Some federal agencies in the United States, such as the Agency for International Development (AID), have begun to assist such programs also. So far these are the only programs that have been brought into action against the population problem in UDCs (except possibly in mainland China).

Characteristically, family planning programs begin with knowledge, attitude, and practice (known as KAP) surveys, which are designed to ascertain the extent of knowledge about and level of practice of birth control, and what attitudes exist toward the idea in the "target population." In most UDCs, few people know anything about birth control (often, only about 10–20 percent of the adult population), and knowledge is mainly restricted to withdrawal. Only a fraction of those who know about birth control practice it. But among people interviewed in surveys, including those previously ignorant of birth control, interest is high, especially in couples with three or more children. Knowledge, practice and interest are related to economic and educational levels, just as they are in DCs. All are higher in urban than in rural populations, although often not as much higher as one might expect. There is considerable variation from one country to another, but it is a fairly typical experience that when family planning clinics are opened in areas where a high degree of interest and willingness to learn has been indicated, the clientele turns out to be much smaller than expected. People often say one thing, and then do another, and it is difficult for surveys to correct for this. The problem may be especially serious if the interviewer is perceived as a social superior by the person interviewed, in which case answers may be slanted in an attempt to please the interviewer. Tables 10-2 and 10-3 give figures on family sizes desired in both UDCs and DCs.

Family planning programs in UDCs are usually carried out through clinics that are either independent or work in cooperation with maternal and child health agencies, and in some countries mobile units are used to carry workers and equipment to remote villages. Unlike the traditional planned parenthood organizations in DCs, these programs actively recruit clients, employing specially trained field workers for this purpose and utilizing whatever form of mass communication and promotion seems effective. These may include pamphlets and circulars, advertisements in public transportation, billboards, radio and newspaper announcements, or plays and skits produced by traveling troupes. In India an elephant is taken from village to village, and is used to pass out pamphlets and contraceptives.

The propaganda would be familiar to Americans, though perhaps some of the methods of disseminating it would not. The primary emphasis is on preventing the "unwanted child," and the program makes the greatest effort to reach women who already have at least three children. Such women are usually most receptive to the idea of birth control; furthermore, their proven high fertility makes them statistically likely to have several more children if they do not use contraceptives.

Family planning programs generally offer a variety of birth control methods, including sterilization, although the latter has only been used or promoted on a large scale in India and Pakistan. The most popular method in Asia has been the IUD, although it has proven to be less ideal than it first appeared. Fewer than 50 percent of the women fitted with IUDs still wear them two years later. Malnutrition may contribute to this high discontinuance rate by increasing the tendency to bleed after insertion. This is just one example of how conditions brought on by overpopulation can hinder population control. Great efforts have been made by the family planning workers to

TABLE 10-2
Desired Family Size Compared to Birth Rate

Area	Date	Size sample	Average number of children desired	Percentage desiring: 4 or more	5 or more	1969 birth rate
Austria	1960		2.0	4		17.4
W. Germany	1960		2.2	4		17.3
Czechoslovakia	1959	3,192	2.3			15.1
Hungary	1958–1960	6,732	2.4	13	6	14.6
Great Britain	1960		2.8	23		17.5
France	1960		2.8	17		16.9
Japan	1961	2,753	2.8	22	8	19
Switzerland	1960		2.9	22		17.7
Puerto Rico	1953	888	3.0	19		26
Italy	1960		3.1	18		18.1
Norway	1960		3.1	25		18.0
Netherlands	1960		3.3	39		18.9
U.S.A.	1960	2,414	3.3	40	15	17.4
Ceylon	1963	302	3.2	25	12	32
Jamaica	1957	1,368	3.4–4.2	48	19	40
Colombia	1963		3.5			45
Turkey	1963	5,122	3.5	42	25	46
South Africa (white pop.)	1957–1958	1,022	3.6	54	10	
Taiwan	1962–1963	2,432	3.9	62	22	29
Thailand	1964	1,207	3.8	54	26	46
Pakistan	1960	2,086	3.9	65	26	52
Chile	1959	1,970	4.1	58	26	33
Canada	1960		4.2	70		18.0
India	1952–1960	5,909	3.7–4.7	57–63	25–34	43
Indonesia	1961–1962	2,208	4.3	66	36	43
S. Korea	1962	1,884	4.4	77	44	41
Ghana	1963	637	5.3	88	56	47
Philippines	1963	7,807	5.0	71	53	50

SOURCE: Data from *Studies in Family Planning no. 7*, Population Council, 1964. Birth rates from 1969 World Population Sheet, Population Reference Bureau.

reduce the rate of discontinuance by warning women in advance of probable minor complaints and assuring them that they are not serious enough to warrant removal of the IUD. Many who expel IUDs spontaneously are re-fitted, and those who cannot tolerate them are offered the pill, sterilization, or some other alternative.

Clinic staffs include doctors (usually gynecologists), nurses, midwives, and occasionally social workers. A few programs also employ anthropologists to advise the staff personnel on the best approach to villagers. Midwives are often used as field workers and/or medical workers within the clinic, although

TABLE 10-3
Desired Family Sizes of Women in Seven Latin American Cities

Latin American Cities	Average number of children wanted	1969 birth rate of country
Bogota, Colombia	3.6	45
Buenos Aires, Argentina	2.9	23
Caracas, Venezuela	3.5	41
Mexico City, Mexico	4.2	43
Panama City, Panama	3.5	41
Rio de Janeiro, Brazil	2.7	38
San Jose, Costa Rica	3.6	45

SOURCE: Data from Berelson et al., *Family Planning and Population Programs.* Univ. of Chicago Press, 1966.

some problems have resulted from employing them. In some countries, midwives see family planning as a threat to their incomes from child delivery, as well as from illegal abortion, in which some are also profitably involved.

Besides offering contraceptives, the family planning programs in the UDCs, like the older ones in DCs, provide counseling services for marriage, parenthood and child-spacing, and assistance for subfertile and sterile couples. Women's discussion groups are often organized in villages to interest wives in birth control. Advice on nutrition and child care may be included in the discussions partly because these subjects will help attract women to the family planning program, and partly because the dissemination of this information supplements the program's child welfare goals.

Some hope of increased effectiveness in reaching younger women early in their reproductive lives is held out by the idea of introducing family planning to them immediately after the birth of their first child in the maternity hospital. Pilot studies of this approach in both DCs and UDCs have brought promising results, although to be effective this program may require special personnel in the hospital who do nothing else. Attempts to have regular hospital doctors and nurses add to their other duties the teaching of family planning to their maternal patients have failed. Doctors and nurses, especially in UDCs, are generally overworked already, and they simply have no time for one more function. In addition, they are often not particularly motivated in favor of family planning.

With the single exception of India, no UDC had an official family planning policy prior to 1960. India's began in 1952, but for the first decade it was not strongly supported. Most of that time was spent with surveys, pilot projects, and experiments with the rhythm method. In 1965 the program was completely reorganized, and a much more vigorous effort is now under way, using considerably stronger measures than are employed in most such programs. These include the establishment of clinics (associated with maternal health facilities were possible), temporary camps, and mobile units, all accompanied by a very active education campaign to promote small families. Vasectomy and the IUD are the most-used methods, although female sterilization and traditional contraceptives are available. Men who accept vasectomies, and any individual who persuades a man to have one, are paid small fees. Railway stations are often used as vasectomy clinics in place of hospitals, partly because they attract large numbers of people and partly because Indians traditionally regard hospitals as a place to die. Legalized abortion is being seriously considered. In addition, a program of active research and development of new contraceptive methods, including an investigation of folk methods, is being carried on.

But India has run into some problems with her policies, particularly in rural areas. Aside from the monumental logistic difficulty of taking family planning to every village, a good deal of resistance has been met in some places, which has even led occasionally to riots and the destruction of camps and mobile units. This resistance results in part from the existence of three other active medical traditions in India—ayurvedic, unani, and homeopathic—besides Western medicine. So far the family planning program has been implemented only through Western medicine, a circumstance that naturally results in resentment and opposition from the others. This opposition has begun to show itself in a drop in the vasectomy rate from lack of candidates.

Pakistan's program was established in 1960, but, as in India, the active, large-scale phase did not begin until 1965. Hong Kong's program also began in 1960. Taiwan and South Korea began large-scale operations in 1964, although both programs had been started sooner, Taiwan's without government support. Seventeen other countries had started serious family planning programs by the end of 1967, and eleven more were making preliminary steps in that direction.

The earlier and more vigorous programs have made considerable progress in terms of reaching a large proportion of the reproductive population. Yet, as reflected by current birth and growth rates, they show remarkably little progress toward fulfilling their own rather modest short-term goals of birth-rate reduction (Table 10-4). Taiwan and South Korea have shown some drop in birth rates since the programs were initiated, but birth rates in both countries had begun to decline before then. How much of the recent decline is due to the family planning program is extremely hard to determine, as the administrators of the programs themselves admit. Although neither country has made any effort to propagandize in behalf of small families, there is some evidence that the activities of the family planning program may have stimulated interest in this direction. This is shown by the increasing acceptance of birth control among women in the younger age group and those with few children.

Taiwan and South Korea may, within a few years, give us some measure of the potential effectiveness of family planning for reducing population growth in UDCs although both started with some advantages over most other UDCs. Taiwan, and to a lesser degree Korea, were fairly highly urbanized (for Asia), relatively literate, beginning to industrialize, and had governments favorable to the idea of family planning programs. In addition,

TABLE 10-4
Family Planning Effects Measured Against Goals

Country	Program begun	Birth rate per 1000 Goal*	Birth rate per 1000 1969†	Growth rate in percent Goal*	Growth rate in percent 1969†	Population of married couples Target** (millions)	Population of married couples Protected (percent)
India	1965	40 to 25 (in 10 years)	43	—	2.5	90	5.4 (1968)
Pakistan	1965	40 to 50 (by 1970)	52	—	3.3	—	—
S. Korea	1962		41	2.9 to 2.0 (1962–71)	2.8	3.8	30 (1968)
Taiwan	1963	36 to 24 (by 1973)	29	3.02 to 1.86 (1965–73)	2.6	1.8	38 (1968)
Ceylon	1967	33 to 25 (in 8–10 years)	32	1.6 (by 1976)	2.4	—	—
Turkey	1965		46	3.0 to 2.0 (by 1972)	2.5	—	—
Singapore	1966	30 to under 20 (in 5 years)	27		2.5	0.3	40 (1968)
Malaysia	1966		36	3.0 to 2.2 (by 1987)	3.1	1.2	3 (1968)
Dominican Republic	1967	48 to 40 (by 1972) to 28 (by 1978)	49	3.4 to 2.7 (by 1972)	3.4	—	—
Morocco	1966	50 to 45 (by 1973)	46	—	3.0	—	—
Trinidad & Tobago	1967	38 to 19 (by 1978)	38	—	2.4	—	—

* Data on birth and growth rate goals, which have been set by the national family planning programs, are from Berelson, *Studies in Family Planning*, no. 39 (supp.), 1969.
† Data for 1969 birth and growth rates are from the Population Reference Bureau.
** The "target population" is the number of married couples in the reproductive ages (15–44). The "protected population" refers to the percentage of the target population which is sterilized or using some form of contraception. Data from *Studies in Family Planning*, 1965–68.

birth rates in both countries had already begun to decline, indicating a desire for birth control among the people.

Hong Kong and Singapore are also considered to have successful family planning programs, although neither could by any means be considered a typical UDC. Nor has either come close to controlling its population growth, though both have birth rates well below the average for Asia. Both are island countries, are overwhelmingly urban, and have fairly high literacy rates and well-organized medical services. Apparently the need to limit population when it is confined to small islands is as obvious to citizens as to the government, and progress in lowering birth rates may be more easily achieved under these special conditions.

Attitudes and Birth Rates

Unquestionably the single most important factor in a country's reproductive rate is the motivation of the people toward the regulation of family size. The strength of the desire for a small family is critical. If a couple is determined not to have more than two children, they usually will not, regardless of whether or not there is a birth control clinic down the street. Conversely, if the motivation is weak, the practice of birth control is likely to be a sometime thing, although the motivation often grows with the number of children in the family.

The overriding importance of motivation is made clear by the example of Europe, where the family planning movement has had relatively little influence, particularly in Catholic countries. The continent as a whole has the lowest birth rates of any comparable area in the world, and most European countries have had low birth rates for at least two generations. The population of Europe is growing at considerably less than 1 percent per year (0.8 percent): only Albania, Rumania, and Iceland have growth rates that exceed 1.2 percent. This remarkable record has been and is being accomplished largely in the absence of modern contraceptives! Both information and devices are completely banned in several countries, and they are seriously restricted in several others. Yet the birth rates are just as low in these countries as in neighboring countries where information and devices are generally available and in moderately wide use. *Coitus interruptus* is known and practiced everywhere, especially where birth control is restricted, and is generally backed up by abortion, either legal or illegal, depending on the country. In one way or another, most Europeans manage to avoid having children they do not want.

Studies in various countries with different levels of development and different population densities show that people usually have the number of children they say they want. In general, families in DCs tend to fall slightly short of their goals; in UDCs they tend to exceed them. But, even if reproductive goals were always perfectly achieved, each country's growth rate would probably be very little changed. Surveys show (Table 10-1) that the average number of children wanted per family varies from 2.0 to 3.3 in

European countries; in the U.S. it is currently 3.3. By contrast the average in most UDCs varies between 3.5 and 5.5. Given the death rates characteristic of DCs, it would require an average of only 2.3 children per married couple over the long run to result in a steady population size. It is therefore obvious that population growth cannot be stopped merely by preventing the births of unwanted children.

A great many socioeconomic factors affect the reproductive goals of individuals and of a society. Among these are the general education level, the degree of urbanization, the social status of women, the opportunities open to women for employment outside the home, and the costs of raising and educating each child. Other factors, such as the average age at marriage (especially of women), the degree of tolerance for illegitimate births, or the usual length of time of breast-feeding, can directly affect the fertility rates.

Family planning programs in general make no effort to influence these factors, as demographer Kingsley Davis has pointed out. At most, they try to influence people by emphasizing the economic and health advantages of small families. Government officials, economic advisors, and many demographers tend to believe that the process of economic development will automatically bring about the higher levels of education and urbanization that lead to the desire for fewer children and in turn cause a demographic transition in UDCs. Family planning has therefore been introduced in some countries where extremely high population growth rates were impeding the rate of economic development. This is a step in the right direction, but unfortunately this great faith in the possibilities of industrial development, the demographic transition, and the prevention of unwanted children too often encourages governments in these countries to relax under the illusion that their population problems are being solved.

A demographic transition would at best merely reduce growth rates to the level of those of the DCs, and thus cannot be expected to solve any country's population problem. In most UDCs, lack of resources and overpopulation will combine to prevent sufficient development for a demographic transition to occur. From all points of view the demographic transition is no solution.

If vigorous family planning programs had been initiated just after World War II when death control and the ideas of economic development were introduced in UDCs, the population problem might be of much more manageable dimensions today. But it plainly would still be with us. Even if the strongest feasible population control measures were everywhere in force today, the time lag before our runaway population growth could be appreciably slowed, let alone arrested, would still be discouragingly long. For UDCs it would be at least a generation or two before the population ceased to expand, unless catastrophe intervened, because of the age structure of their populations.

Population Growth in the United States

Some people seem to believe that in order to stop growth rates there should be no reproduction at all. Actually, to reduce the 1968 United States birth rate of 17.4 per 1,000 population (higher than most European countries) to a level where it would ultimately balance the death rate (at about 13 per 1,000) would require less of a reduction than took place between 1957 and 1967. During that decade, the United States birth rate fell from 25.3 to 17.8. Reduction of the birth rate to about 13 per 1,000 would eventually stabilize the population—even though the current death rate is 9.6—because such low birth rates would within a few decades change the age structure of the population. The average age of the population would rise from the present 28 to about 37, and with a greater proportion in the older age classes, the death rate would rise significantly.

Of course the projected rise in the number of women of reproductive age (15–44) during the 1970's means that to achieve such a low birth rate there would have to be a substantial reduction in the fertility rates of that segment of the population. The 1967 fertility rate was 87.6 births per 1,000 women of reproductive age, down from a peak of 122.9 in 1957. The

TABLE 10-5
Percentage of Ever-married United States Women,
55 to 59 Years Old in 1960, by Numbers of Live Births

Number of children	Percentage all women ever married	Children per 100 women
0	17.5	0
1	16.5	16.5
2	19.7	39.4
3	14.4	43.2
4	10.3	41.2
5 & 6	11.0	60.5
7 and over	10.6	94.6
	100	295.4

SOURCE: Data from *1960 Census of the United States.*

lowest fertility rates ever achieved in the United States were 76 to 79 births per 1,000 women of reproductive age during the Depression years of 1933–1939.

Looking at it another way, if the average size of the American family were shifted downward by about one child, from 3.3 to 2.25, the growth rate of the United States population would eventually be reduced to zero.

Economist Stephen Enke has calculated a possible distribution of family sizes that would achieve the desired replacement rate. The data in Table 10-5 show the childbearing performance of women whose families were complete in 1960. Enke assumes that many of these women who were childless or had only one child probably wanted more. With the medical assistance available today, sterile and subfertile couples probably would have more children than was possible a generation ago. Under Enke's scheme, 50 percent of married women would have 2 children, which might be considered the norm or the ideal. Some 10 percent might have only one child and 5 percent remain childless. Above the norm, 30 percent might have three children, and another 5 percent more than three, with an average of five. Obviously, this plan still allows for a few large families, but the vast majority of families would have one, two, or three children. Childlessness and large families both would be much rarer than they were a generation or two ago, as can be seen by comparing the Enke distribution with that of Table 10-5.

Poverty, Race, and Birth Control

The entrance of the United States government into the field of birth control through the extension of family planning services to the poor has aroused a controversy quite out of proportion to its potential effect on the national birth rate. The majority of poor people are not Negroes, nor are the majority of Negro families poor—about 30 percent of Negro families were below the poverty level in 1967. But Americans, both black and white, tend to see the two terms as synonymous. This is one reason for the bitterness of the controversy.

Birth rates are higher among the poor and among nonwhites (Negroes, Orientals, and American Indians) than they are among the nonpoor and among whites. In the United States population as a whole, high birth rates are strongly associated both with economic and educational levels. The poorest and least educated have the highest birth rates, with nonwhite families at this level having about one-third more children than comparable whites. Above the poverty level, this difference diminishes, and college-educated nonwhites have fewer children than their white peers. Among nonwhite poor, after a generation away from the farm, the reproductive difference also disappears.

Some of the truth behind the saying, "The rich get richer and the poor get children," is revealed in the fact that large families tend to be poor. About 42 percent of American families with more than 5 children are poor, whereas only 10 percent with 1 or 2 children are poor. Furthermore, large families are far likelier to remain poor, especially if they are headed by a woman.

Although there is conflicting evidence regarding desired family sizes among the poor, several surveys conducted in the 1960's indicate that they wish to have only slightly more children than do middle class couples, and nonwhite couples in most socioeconomic classes want fewer children than comparable whites do. This is especially true among the younger couples in their prime childbearing years.

At the same time, the incidence of unwanted children among the poor and near-poor in the 1960's was estimated to be as high as 40 percent. For nonpoor couples the incidence was about 14 percent. The reasons for this disparity between desires and actual reproductive performance appear to lie less in the lack of knowledge of contraceptives than in the availability of effective ones. The poor who do use birth control tend to use less reliable methods than do members of the middle class.

Because poor people cannot usually afford contraceptives, and because no family planning information or services were provided through welfare health services until the late 1960's, most poor people were until then deprived of effective methods of birth control. There is some dispute about whether the number of women in need is about 2 million or as high as 5 million, but the experience of the Planned Parenthood clinics and those hospitals and public health centers that have offered birth control services suggests that the need and the demand are both great. Whatever the total number of women in need, this help for the poor is long overdue.

Despite the tendency of black militants to regard the provision of birth control to the poor as a policy of genocide against Negroes, it should be emphasized that the government's present program is basically a welfare program, intended to benefit the poor, and poor children in particular. In this connection it is unfortunate that the government has chosen to label it as a "population control" measure, which it is not; rather, it is a logical extension both of the family-planning movement and of the welfare program.

Although many middle-class Americans favor population control for others, especially the poor, they must realize that it is really their own excessive reproduction that accounts for most of the United States population growth rate. Furthermore, the middle class and the wealthy are responsible for the high rate of consumption and pollution, which are the most obvious symptoms of overpopulation in the United States.

Population Control

Population control is the conscious regulation of population size by society. Given the threat to our environment and the menace this represents to our already failing ability to provide food enough for today's population, it is clear that the human population cannot afford *any* further growth, and will soon have to decline. Whatever lands may remain available that seem capable of supporting larger populations than they do now are more than counterbalanced by the vast areas that are grossly overpopulated. In an overpopulated world, no country can have the right to indulge itself in a high growth rate. Since the human population of the world is truly a single interdependent community, such behavior by any country could reasonably be regarded as irresponsible and a threat to all the rest.

No nation has yet adopted as a goal the reduction of its population growth rate to zero, let alone a reduction in absolute population size. In fact, governments in many UDCs—especially in Africa, where the death rate is still well above the average DC level—are hotly pursuing a high birth rate in the belief that their countries need more people in order to develop! (The role of population growth relative to economic development is discussed in Chapter 12). These countries, needless to say, generally do not even have official family planning programs (Box 10-1). As an example of this thinking, in November 1969, Luis Echeverria Alvarez, presidential nominee in Mexico, announced his opposition to officially sponsored birth control programs, saying, "I don't know whether the birth control pill is effective . . . What I do know is that we have to populate our country and that we have to have faith in our youth and our children."

BOX 10-1   POPULATION POLICIES AROUND THE WORLD

Africa

In general, among past and present colonial countries in Africa, family planning on a private basis has long been available in English colonies but not in colonies of Catholic countries such as France, Belgium, Spain, Italy, and Portugal. Several former English colonies now have national family planning policies, although they may be promoted only for welfare reasons. See Table 10-1 for details of UDCs with family planning programs. A few former French colonies are beginning to relax their prohibitions and at least to allow the sale of contraceptives in drug stores. The Portuguese colonies remain pronatalist and strongly opposed to birth control. Many of the North African countries are initiating family-planning programs.

In South Africa and Rhodesia the dominant European populations have traditionally practiced birth control. These countries are now trying to extend family planning services to their African populations, but only unofficially through private agencies. At the same time, however, South Africa is tending to encourage larger families in its white population.

The belief that more people are needed for development is common among African nations south of the Sahara. Concern about migration is often greater than concern about the high birth rates. Ghana, for example, has one of the highest average reproductive aspirations in the world, 5.3 children per couple; the country has a high birth rate (47) and a strongly pronatalist government.

Many African countries still have death rates that are higher than 20 per thousand, and some are even more than 30. A number of demographers and family planners believe that interest in population control will remain low until the death rates have been substantially reduced. Ways must somehow be found to change this point of view so that birth rates may be lowered *along with* death rates.

Asia

Asia presents a widely diverse picture in regard to population policies. At one extreme, India and Pakistan are pursuing strong family planning policies accompanied by some social measures, while several of the smaller countries have still shown no interest in population policies. Mainland China has established strong population policies, largely as a part of other social programs. The effectiveness of these is not known. For political reasons, during the 1950's China did not actively encourage birth control, but the enforced segregation of the sexes in communes must have had an effect on the birth rate. Since the early 1960's a strict policy of late marriage (minimum age 25 for women and 30 for men) has been enforced. The two-child family is strongly promoted, with a space of 3 to 5 years between births. Voluntary sterilization for men who have had two or three children is also encouraged. Birth control methods are apparently widely available; so is legal abortion, probably utilizing the Russian vacuum device. As is typical of Communist countries, women are fully employed outside the home, given limited maternity benefits, and provided with child care.

Japan, the only fully industrialized country in Asia, reduced her birth rate rapidly to DC levels after World War II largely by legalizing abortion. A policy of encouraging the use of birth control methods has since reduced the abortion rate without changing the birth rate. The social policy, which was promoted through massive educational and communications programs, very strongly discourages having a family with more than two children.

North America

Neither Canada nor the United States has an official government population policy, except in respect to immigration. The U.S. government provides some family planning services to the poor through public welfare agencies, and it is engaged in extending these services. There has been some activity in Congress towards legislation which would define and promote antinatalist policies for the future. There has also been a trend toward liberalizing abortion restrictions in the various states. Since 1967, foreign aid agencies have been permitted to include family planning assistance in their programs.

In July 1969, President Nixon proposed the creation of a commission on population growth and the American future, responsible for inquiry and recommendations in the three areas of demographic development, resource utilization, and the probable effects of population growth on the activities of government at all levels. He also called for expansion of the government's activities in reproductive research and the provision of family planning services to the poor.

Latin America

Latin America as a region, despite having the highest population growth rates in the world, has been among the most reluctant to accept a need for population control. This is probably in part due to the influence of the Roman Catholic Church, but there is also a widespread belief at least in South America that the continent still contains vast untapped resources of land and minerals, that the answer to all problems is development, and that more people are needed for development. Furthermore, Latin American politicians tend to view American proposals regarding birth control with considerable suspicion. Some seem to believe we are trying to impose a new and subtle form of imperialism. Economists and many politicians have come to accept family planning agencies only on health and welfare grounds and as a means of reducing the horrendous illegal abortion rate. In a few cases they are beginning to realize that the galloping population growth rate is swallowing all the economic progress each year, leaving a per capita rate of progress of zero or even less.

Some of the poorest, most overpopulated, and fastest-growing countries, such as Haiti and El Salvador, have no official population policies.

Europe and U.S.S.R.

Western European countries generally have no official population policies, although birth control is almost universally practiced. Sweden is an exception in that there is an official policy for sex education in schools including birth control, a moderately liberal abortion policy, family planning services as part of the national health organization, and a program to assist other family planning programs abroad. England also provides family planning services and abortions through the health service.

Most Catholic countries ban birth control in some degree, but late marriages, high rates of illegal abortion, and other *subrosa* methods of birth control keep the birth rates down.

Eastern European countries and the Soviet Union provide family planning and abortion through their health services, although Communist ideology officially calls for pronatalist policies. Discouragement of early marriage, an emphasis on training and education, and the full outside employment of women supported by child-care facilities, also undoubtedly contribute to the low birth rates.

Oceania

Australia and New Zealand have historically regarded themselves as underpopulated. Consequently their policies have been pronatalist and pro-immigration. There is evidence that these policies are currently being re-evaluated as the public becomes aware of the world population problem. In any case, as former English colonies, both countries have long had family planning groups and access to contraceptives. Their birth rates are well within the usual DC range.

Before any really effective population control can be established, the political leaders, economists, national planners, and others who determine such policies must be convinced of its necessity. Most of the measures that might be effective have never been tried, because they are considered strong and restrictive and they run counter to traditional attitudes. In many countries these measures may not even be considered until massive famines, political unrest, or ecological disasters make their initiation imperative. In such emergencies, whatever measures are economically and technologically expedient will be the likeliest to be imposed, regardless of their political or social acceptability.

We should long ago have begun exploring, developing, and discussing all possible means of population control. But we did not, and time has nearly run out. Measures that may seem totally unacceptable today to the majority of people at large or to their national leaders may be seen as very much the lesser of evils only a few years from now. It must be remembered that even family planning, easily justified on humanitarian grounds alone, and economically feasible for even the poorest of countries, was generally considered totally unacceptable as a government policy only ten years ago.

Bernard Berelson of the Population Council has analyzed and rated several proposed population control measures according to these criteria: technological, political, administrative, and economic feasibility; ethical acceptability, and presumed effectiveness. Most of the proposals that might be expected to be effective were rated relatively unacceptable on one basis or another. Abortion, for example, was considered low in political and ethical acceptability, uncertain in administrative feasibility, but technically and economically feasible. Compulsory fertility control was rated low on all counts except economic capability. But even such mild measures as incentive programs and tax policies favoring small families were rated moderately low or low in political and economic feasibility, and uncertain in their effectiveness. Berelson's analysis is useful, although his conclusions may have been influenced by his long commitment to family planning. Nevertheless, all of these criteria are certainly susceptible to change. Promising methods that are not now technologically possible should be developed, so that they might be available if and when the need for them arose. Generous assistance from developed countries could remove many economic and lack-of-personnel objections for UDCs. Moral acceptability is very likely to change as conditions change in most societies. The struggle for economic development in the UDCs is producing considerable social upheaval, which will particularly affect such basic elements of society as family structure. Radical changes in family structure and relationships are inevitable, whether population control is instituted or not. Inaction, attended by a deterioration in living conditions, will bring changes everywhere that no one could consider beneficial. Thus, it is beside the point to object to population control measures simply on the grounds that they might change the social structure or family relationships.

Rather than resisting social change, modern communications methods and educational techniques can be used to help develop constructive attitudes and accelerate desirable trends. Trained and sympathetic personnel—for example, social scientists familiar with local cultures and the techniques of introducing change—can work effectively on these problems. Setting up communications centers, training behavioral and other scientists, and supporting technicians and social workers abroad could be major contributions of the DCs to population control efforts.

The moral objections to population control often seem to exist primarily in the minds of political or religious leaders. With regard to abortion, for example, women around the world are plainly unimpressed by the moral objections. The precise number of abortions performed each year is not known, but a U.N. Conference on Abortion in 1965 estimated that there are about 30 million abortions per year (as opposed to about 120 million births). Attitudes toward abortion have been shown to change considerably in a very short period of time.

Measures for Population Control

Among proposed general approaches to population control are family planning, the use of socioeconomic pressures, and compulsory fertility control. Maximum freedom of choice is provided by family planning, which allows each couple to plan the number and spacing of their children. But family planning alone should not be regarded as "population control," because it does not include consideration of optimum population size for the society. Although population growth may be slowed or stopped by family planning where individual motivation favors low birth rates and planning is for relatively few children, family planning in other areas may equally well result in average family sizes too large to produce the desired population growth, stability, or decline.

The use of abortion and voluntary sterilization to supplement other forms of birth control can quite properly be included as part of family planning. These methods can be made available at costs everyone can afford. Objections have been raised to the idea of including abortion in family planning programs on the grounds that UDCs lack the trained personnel and medical facilities to carry it out. Even England, since liberalizing her abortion laws, has had some difficulty along this line. But the answer to this problem might lie in the use of the vacuum device developed in the U.S.S.R. (Chapter 9); it may reduce or even eliminate the need for hospital recuperation, and probably could be operated by a trained midwife. Certainly its use should be investigated as a possible back-up method for all countries.

An extension of family planning might be a first step toward population control. Although many DCs may have very nearly achieved saturation with this voluntary approach, there is a good deal of room for action in the UDCs. Family planning programs can provide the means of contraception, and through their activities and educational campaigns can spread awareness of the idea of birth control among the people. These programs should be expanded throughout the underdeveloped world as rapidly as possible, *but other measures should be instituted immediately as well.* Additional programs beyond family planning will unquestionably be required in order to halt the population explosion. The important distinction between *family planning* and *population control* must be recognized and given emphasis in all birth control programs.

SOCIOECONOMIC MEASURES

Population control through the use of socioeconomic pressures to encourage or discourage reproduction is the approach advocated by, among others, demographer Kingsley Davis, who originated many of the following suggestions. The objective of this approach would be to influence the attitudes and motivations of individual couples. An important part of such an approach would be a large-scale educational program to persuade people of the advantages of small families, to themselves and to society. Information on birth control, of course, should accompany such educational efforts. Programs of this kind should be offered in schools and should also be communicated to adults through a variety of appropriate media, both directly and indirectly. Such an educational campaign is one of the first measures that could be adopted in all countries, UDC or DC, and used at least until its efficacy could be evaluated in terms of other efforts and objectives.

As United States taxpayers know, the federal government uses economic pressure in its present income tax laws to encourage marriage and child-bearing. The provisions in our tax laws that do this are based on pronatalist attitudes that are no longer appropriate. Tax laws should now be adjusted to favor (instead of penalize) single people, working wives, and small families. Perhaps they should even penalize large families that have incomes above certain levels. One suggestion, which has obvious psychological advantages, would be to offer more realistic income tax deductions for the first two children (say $2,000 each) and no deduction for additional children. Tax measures in the United States and other countries might include marriage fees, taxes on luxury baby goods and toys, and removal of family allowances, where they exist.

Measures like these would clearly be applicable only in countries that have reached a stage of development where a substantial portion of the population is affluent enough to pay taxes, and where tax collection is reasonably honest and effective. Tax measures of this sort have the advantage of shifting the burden of supplying government services more onto the shoulders of those large families who produce the need for them; and at least this can be done for large *affluent* families. Tax measures in general can be designed to reinforce the idea that population growth is no longer desirable.

Another suggestion related to taxation is that the amount of free education available to a family might be limited to 24 years, enough to put two children through high school. This proposal, however, along with one that would limit maternal benefits, has the potential disadvantage of heavily penalizing children (and in the long run society as well). The same criticism may be made of some other tax plans, unless they can be carefully adjusted to avoid denying at least minimum care for poor families, regardless of the number of children they may have.

A somewhat different approach might be to provide incentives for late marriage and childlessness. Possibilities include paying a bonus to a first-time bride who is over 25 (or to her parents, in countries where bride prices and arranged marriages are customary); a bonus could also be given to couples after five childless years or to men who accept vasectomies after their wives have a given number of children. Lotteries open only to childless adults have also been proposed. Sociologist Larry D. Barnett has calculated the cost of annual fees, based on a percentage of annual income that could be paid to couples who have no more than two children until the wife reaches the age of 45. For example, the cost (based on 5 percent of the annual income up to an income ceiling of $20,000 and calculated on the expected United States population for 1975), would be some $9 billion for that year. Barnett concludes that the savings in pollution and other costs would justify the expenditure.

Adoption can be encouraged through subsidies and simplified procedures; particularly as a measure to satisfy couples who have a definite desire for a son or daughter. Further research on sex determination should be pursued for a similar reason. Too many families have additional children in an attempt to have a son, if they have only daughters, or to have a daughter if they have only sons. A special kind of social security could be provided for aging adults who have had few or no children who might support them in their old age.

There are many possibilities in the sphere of family structure, sexual mores, and the status of women that can be explored, as Kingsley Davis and sociologist Alice Taylor Day have suggested. With some exceptions, women have traditionally been allowed to fulfill only the roles of wife and mother. Anything that can be done to diminish the emphasis upon these roles and provide women with equal opportunities in education, employment and other areas is likely to reduce the birth rate. Any measures that postpone marriage, especially for women, would also help to encourage a reduction in birth rates. Outside interests, besides employment, can also be cultivated, and social life could be planned around these outside interests or the couple's work, rather than exclusively within the neighborhood and family. Adequate care for preschool children should be provided at low cost, and in fact, it could provide an important source of employment for women. Provision of child care seems more likely to encourage employment outside the home with concomitant low reproduction than to encourage reproduction. The deplorable lack of good doctors and medical services in many parts of the United States could be overcome by actively recruiting and training more women as doctors and other needed specialists. In the Soviet Union more than half of the doctors are female. Women represent a large, relatively untapped pool of intellectual and technical talent in the United States; tapping that pool effectively could help to control our population and also provide many other direct benefits to society.

Social pressures on both men and women to marry and have children must be removed. As Stewart Udall has observed in his book, *1976: Agenda for Tomorrow.* "All lives are not enhanced by marital union; parenthood is not necessarily a fulfillment for every married couple." If society were convinced of the need for low birth rates, no doubt the stigma that has customarily been assigned to bachelors, spinsters, and childless couples would soon disappear. But alternative life-styles should be open to single people, and perhaps the institution of an informal, easily dissolved "marriage" for the childless is one possibility. Indeed, the fact that many DC societies already seem to be evolving in this direction suggests that fully developed societies may produce such arrangements naturally. In UDCs, they might be encouraged deliberately, as the status of women changes.

Although free and easy association of the sexes might be tolerated, illegitimate childbearing could be strongly discouraged. One way to carry out this disapproval would be to insist that all illegitimate babies be put up for adoption. If the mother really wished to keep her baby, she would be obliged to go through adoption proceedings, which might remain more difficult for single people than for couples. Abortion for illegitimate pregnancies might also be required, either as an alternative to placement for adoption or as the only choice, depending on the society.

Somewhat more repressive measures have also been proposed. Whether their effectiveness would counterbalance their social disadvantages is questionable, but at least they should be discussed. These proposals include limiting paid maternal leave (common in many countries) to two children, or reducing it with each child after the first; assigning public housing without regard for family size; and removing dependency allowances from student grants or military pay. The idea behind these is the observation that people in the past have voluntarily controlled their reproduction most stringently during periods of great social and economic stress and insecurity, such as the Depression of the 1930's.

INVOLUNTARY FERTILITY CONTROL

The third approach to population control is that of involutary fertility control. Several coercive proposals deserve serious consideration, mainly because we may ultimately have to resort to them unless current trends in birth rates are rapidly reversed by other means. Some coercive measures are less repressive or discriminatory, in fact, than some of the socioeconomic measures that have been proposed.

One idea that has been seriously proposed in India is to vasectomize all fathers of three or more children. This was defeated not only on moral grounds but on practical ones as well: there simply were not enough medical personnel available even to start on the eligible candidates, let alone deal with the new recruits added each day! Massive assistance from the developed world in the form of medical and paramedical personnel, and/or a training program for local people, might put such a policy within the realm of possibility, although it still would not be very popular. But probably India's government will have to resort to some such coercive method sooner or later, unless famine, war, or disease takes the problem out of its hands. There is little time left for educational programs and social change, and the population is probably too poor for economic measures (especially penalties) to be effective.

A program of sterilizing women after their second or third child, despite the greater difficulty of the female operation, might be easier than trying to sterilize the fathers. At least this would be the case in countries where the majority of babies are born in maternity hospitals and clinics, and where the medical corps is adequate. The problem of finding and identifying eligibles for sterilization would be simplified in this way.

The development of a sterilizing capsule that can be implanted under the skin and removed when pregnancy is desired opens another possibility for coercive control. The capsule could be implanted at puberty and might be removable, with official permission, for a limited number of births. Various approaches to administering this system have been offered, including one by economist Kenneth Boulding of the University of Colorado. His proposal is to issue to each woman at marriage a marketable license that would entitle her to a given number of children. Under such a system the number could be two if the society desired to reduce the population size slowly. To maintain a steady size, perhaps one out of three couples might be allowed to have a third child if they purchased special tickets from the government or from other women, who, having purchased them, decided not to have a child or found they had a greater need for the money. Another idea is that permission to have a third child might be granted to a limited number of couples by lottery. This system would allow governments to regulate more or less exactly the number of births over a given period of time.

Of course a government might require only implantation of the capsule, leaving its removal to the individual's discretion but requiring reimplantation after childbirth. Since having a child would require positive action (removal of the capsule), many more births would be prevented than in the reverse situation. Certainly unwanted births and the problem of abortion would both be entirely avoided. The disadvantages, besides any moral objections, include the questionable desirability of having the entire female population on a continuous steroid dosage, with the contingent health risks, and the logistics of implanting capsules in 50 percent of the population between the ages of 15 and 50.

Adding a sterilant to drinking water or staple foods is a suggestion that, initially at least, seems to horrify people more than most proposals for involuntary fertility control. Indeed this would pose some very difficult political and social questions, to say nothing of the technical problems. No such sterilant exists today. To be acceptable, such a substance would have to meet some rather stiff requirements. It would have to be uniformly effective, despite widely varying doses received by individuals, and despite varying degrees of fertility and sensitivity among individuals. It would have to be free of dangerous or unpleasant side-effects, and have no effect on members of the opposite sex, children, old people, pets, or livestock.

Botanist Richard W. Schrieber of the University of New Hampshire has proposed that a sterilizing virus could be developed, with an antidote available by injection. This would avoid the problem of finding an appropriate staple food or adjusting doses in water supplies, but it might present some other difficulties. Not the least difficulty might be the appearance of a mutant virus immune to the antidote.

Physiologist Melvin Ketchel, of the Tufts University School of Medicine, believes that a sterilant could be developed that would have a very specific action—for example, the prevention of implantation. He proposes that it be used to reduce fertility levels by adjustable amounts, anywhere from 5 percent to 75 percent, rather than to sterilize the whole population completely. In this way, fertility could be adjusted from time to time to meet a society's changing needs, and there would be no need to provide an antidote. Family planning would still be needed for those couples who were highly motivated to have a small family. Subfertile and functionally sterile couples who strongly desire children could be medically assisted, as they are now, or encouraged to adopt.

This plan has the advantage of avoiding those socioeconomic programs that might tend to discriminate against some groups in a society or that might penalize children. It would also involve no direct action against individuals, such as sterilization operations or implanted capsules. In extremely poor and overpopulated countries, such a program would undoubtedly be far more effective and far easier to administer than any of the others, at least until development and educational levels reached a point where people could be affected by small-family propaganda and be influenced by social or economic pressures. The administration of this sort of program would probably also be easier to safeguard against corruption and abuse in favor of some segments of society, although this is likely to be a problem with any form of population control, just as it is with any government program having far-reaching social consequences.

Compulsory control of family size is an unpalatable idea to many, but the alternatives may be much more horrifying. As those alternatives become clearer to an increasing number of people in the 1970s, we may well find the public in many countries *demanding* such control.

Population Control and Attitudes

No form of population control, even the most coercive and repressive, will succeed for long unless individuals understand the need for it and accept the idea that humanity must limit its numbers. Therefore, the ultimate key to population control lies in changing human attitudes concerning reproductive behavior and goals in all societies. Achieving this throughout the world would be a gigantic task even if it became the world's first-priority goal, as many believe it should be.

But human survival seems certain to require population control programs, at least in some places, even before the necessary changes in attitudes can be brought about in the population. In fact, the establishment of such programs might in itself help to convince people of the seriousness of the population problem.

Most of the population control measures discussed here have never been tried; we know only that their *potential* effectiveness may be great. The socioeconomic proposals are based on knowledge of the sort of social conditions that have been associated in the past with low birth rates. We need to know more about all peoples' attitudes toward human reproduction; we need to know how these attitudes are affected by various living conditions, including some that seem virtually intolerable to us. Even more, we need to know what influences and conditions will lead to changes in these attitudes in favor of smaller families. How can we convince a poor Pakistani villager or a middle-class American that the number of children his wife bears is of crucial importance not just to himself and his family but also to his society? How can we make everyone care?

Bibliography

Adams, E. Sherman, 1969. Unwanted births and poverty in the United States. *The Conference Board Record,* vol. VI, no. 4, pp. 10–17.

Anonymous, 1968. A limit to "wanted" babies? *Medical World News,* Dec. 6.

Anonymous, 1969. Family planning campaign—the Louisiana story. *U.S. News and World Report,* July 28, pp. 55–7. Account of family planning program for the poor.

Barnett, Larry D., 1969. Population policy: payments for fertility limitation in the U.S.? Manuscript. An analysis of the economics of such a program.

Berelson, Bernard, et. al., 1966. *Family Planning and Population Programs.* Univ. of Chicago Press, Chicago. Basic information on family planning programs.

Berelson, Bernard, 1969. Beyond family planning. *Science,* vol. 163, pp. 533–543. An evaluation of proposed means of population control and an affirmation of the value of family planning programs.

Best, Winfield, and Louis Dupré, 1967. Birth control. *Encyclopedia Brittanica.* Interesting account of the history of the planned parenthood movement.

Blake, Judith, 1969. Population policy for Americans: is the government being misled? *Science,* vol. 164, pp. 522–29. Raises some important questions relative to proposed family planning policies for the poor.

Campbell, Arthur A., 1966. White-nonwhite differences in family planning in the United States. *Health, Education & Welfare Indicators* (Feb.). U.S. Dept. of Health, Education and Welfare.

Davis, Kingsley, 1965. Some demographic aspects of poverty in the United States. *In* Margaret S. Gordon (ed.), *Poverty in America.* Chandler Publishing Co., San Francisco.

Davis, Kingsley, 1967. Population policy: will current programs succeed? *Science,* vol. 158, pp. 730–739, One of the most important papers on socio-economic means of population control; excellent.

Day, Alice Taylor, 1968. Population control and personal freedom: are they compatible? *The Humanist,* Nov.–Dec. Contains some excellent ideas in the socio-economic realm of population control measures.

Enke, Stephen, 1969. Is a Stationary U.S. Population Desirable and Possible? Manuscript.

Frederiksen, Harald, 1969. Feedback in economic and demographic transition. *Science,* vol. 166, pp. 837–847. An overly optimistic discussion of the possible benefits of death-control in motivating people to have smaller families in UDCs.

Guttmacher, A. F., 1966. *The Complete Book of Birth Control.* Ballantine Books, New York. Contains some history of the family planning movement.

Harkavy, O., F. S. Jaffe, and S. M. Wishnik, 1969. Family planning and public policy: who is misleading whom? *Science,* vol. 165, pp. 367–373. A reply to Judith Blake's article by the family planning establishment.

Hauser, Philip M., 1967. Family Planning and population programs. *Demography,* vol. 4, no. 1. Critical review of Berelson's book on family planning, raising some pertinent questions on the approach of family planning as a solution to the population problem.

Hill, Adelaide C., and Frederick S. Jaffe, 1966. Negro fertility and family size preferences: implications for programming of health and social services. *In* Talcott Parsons and Kenneth B. Clark (eds.), *The Negro American.* Houghton Mifflin Co., Boston.

Ketchel, Melvin M., 1968. Fertility control agents as a possible solution to the world population problem. *Perspectives in Biology and Medicine,* vol. 11, no. 4 (Summer). Discussion of fertility reducing agents which could be administered impartially to all members of a society.

Lelyveld, Joseph, 1969. Birth curb drive slowing in India. *New York Times,* April 20. Details decline in India's sterilizing program.

McElroy, William D., 1969. Biomedical aspects of population control. *BioScience,* vol. 19, no. 1, pp. 19–23 (Jan.). More on the population control controversy; another strong vote for more effective action.

Newman, Lucille F., 1968. Family planning: an anthropological approach. Paper presented at the International Congress of Anthropological and Ethnological Sciences, Tokyo, Sept. 6. Raises some pertinent points relative to attitudes and reproductive behavior.

O'Brien, Fr. John A., 1968. *Family Planning in an Exploding Population.* Hawthorne Books, Inc., New York. A progressive Catholic point of view.

Potter, R. G., R. Freedman, and Lien-Ping Chow, 1968. Taiwan's family planning program. *Science,* vol. 160, pp. 848–853.

Smith, Mary, 1968. Birth Control and the Negro woman. *Ebony,* March.

The Population Council, *Studies in Family Planning.* A monthly series. An excellent account of family planning programs around the world.

Social, Political and Economic Change

The ecological constraints on population and technological growth will inevitably lead to social and economic systems different from the ones in which we live today. In order to survive, mankind will have to develop what might be called a steady state. The steady state formula is so different from the philosophy of endless quantitative growth, which has so far governed Western civilization, that it may cause widespread public alarm.

René Dubos
Science, 14 November, 1969

A change in the attitudes of individuals is the key to population control and to many other measures necessary for the amelioration of the population-environment crisis. Such change is possible. For example, former President of the United States Dwight D. Eisenhower said in 1968: "Once, as president, I thought and said that birth control was not the business of our Federal Government. The facts changed my mind . . . I have come to believe that the population explosion is the world's most critical problem." Changes in our social, political, and economic institutions are also essential. Our problems cannot be solved by destroying our existing institutions, however; we do not have the time or the wisdom to dismantle them and put them back together again in better ways. But these institutions must be successfully altered—and soon—or they and we will not survive. Whether significant changes in attitudes and institutions can occur fast enough to affect mankind's destiny is an open question.

No one is more acutely aware than we are of the difficulties and hazards of trying to criticize and comment constructively on such broad areas of social relevance as religion, education, economics, legal and political systems, and the psychology of individuals and societies. We believe, however, that in order for people to translate into effective and constructive political action what is now known about the roots of the crisis, new, far-reaching and positive programs must be undertaken *immediately*.

Therefore, in this chapter and the next we depart from the realm of relatively hard data in the physical, biological, and social sciences and embark on an exploration of the many other areas of human endeavor which are critically important to a solution of our problems. In doing so we are making the assumption that many reforms are essential. The dangers of making the opposite assumption are beautifully set forth in the following quotation from biologist Garrett Hardin's article, "The Tragedy of the Commons" (*Science, 1968*):

> It is one of the peculiarities of the warfare between reform and the status quo that it is thoughtlessly governed by a double standard. Whenever a reform measure is proposed it is often defeated when its opponents triumphantly discover a flaw in it. As Kingsley Davis has pointed out, worshippers of the status quo sometimes imply that no reform is possible without unanimous agreement, an implication contrary to historical fact. As nearly as I can make out, automatic rejection of proposed reforms is based on one of two unconscious assumptions: (i) that the status quo is perfect; or (ii) that the choice we face is between reform and no action; if the proposed reform is imperfect, we presumably should take no action at all, while we wait for a perfect proposal.
>
> But we can never do nothing. That which we have done for thousands of years is also action. It also produces evils. Once we are aware that the status quo is action, we can then compare its discoverable advantages and disadvantages with the predicted advantages and disadvantages of the proposed reform, discounting as best we can for our lack of experience. On the basis of such a comparison, we can make a rational decision which will not involve the unworkable assumption that only perfect systems are tolerable.

Religion

Within the theological community, at least in the Western world, there has recently been a heartening revolution in thought and action on human problems in which the quality of life in urban areas, environmental deterioration, and the population explosion have become predominant concerns. Protestant, Catholic, and Jewish clergymen have come more and more to the forefront of public activities in the struggle for human rights, often at great personal sacrifice and risk. For example, Father John A. O'Brien, a distinguished Professor of Theology at Notre Dame University in Indiana, has edited an excellent book, *Family Planning in an Exploding Population,* and he has also been a leader in criticizing Pope Paul VI's 1968 encyclical, *Humanae Vitae,* which condemns the use of contraceptives. Commenting on this encyclical in an article in the January 1969 *Reader's Digest,* Father O'Brien said, "Since the decision is bound to be reversed by his (Pope Paul's) successor, it would be far more honorable, proper and just for the Pope to rescind it himself." Thousands of other Catholics, from Cardinals to common men, have spoken out against the encyclical, which has caused immense anguish among Catholics, millions of whom have followed their consciences and used contraceptives, usually after a period of intense soul-searching. Bishop C. Kilmer Myers, of the Episcopal Diocese of California, has established an Ad Hoc Metropolitan Planning Group which is deeply concerned with the problems of population and environment. The Social Ministry of the Lutheran Church in America has a highly enlightened policy on population. The numbers of socially concerned clergymen are increasing, and there is every reason to believe that their involvement in population-related problems will continue to grow.

Religious leaders may help to overcome cultural taboos related to population control through an emphasis on the quality of human life rather than on its quantity. Protestant, Catholic, and Jewish theologians have been active in promoting sex education in our schools, and at least Protestant and Jewish theologians and lay people can actively promote the enactment of more liberal abortion laws. Except for the Roman Catholic Church, all major Western religious groups have by now officially sanctioned "artificial" contraception, and even though the Catholic hierarchy has not changed its official policy, many enlightened Catholic clerics no longer condemn the use of these methods.

In general, then, there is reason to hope that organized religion can become a powerful force in working toward population control, especially as the suffering caused by overpopulation becomes more widely recognized. The influence of the present Pope's position seems likely to decline as the older members of the hierarchy retire or die and are replaced by administrators more in touch with humanity and modern times. Elderly Catholic economist Colin Clark could still, in 1969, claim on a television program that India would, in a decade, be the most powerful country in the world because of her growing population! He could also write (*Los Angeles Times,* Nov. 9, 1969) that "Population growth, however strange and unwelcome some of its consequences may appear at the time, must be regarded, I think, as one of the instruments of Divine Providence, which we should welcome, not oppose." Such support of outdated dogma among conservative Catholics, especially in governments, still helps to block effective attacks on the population problem both by Catholic countries and by the United Nations. But the new look in Catholic attitudes is typified by those of Catholic biologist John H. Thomas who in 1968 wrote to San Francisco's Archbishop Joseph T. McGucken: "The Church must affirm that the birth rate must soon be brought in line with the death rate—i.e., a growth rate of zero. This is the responsibility of all people regardless of race or religion. The Church must recognize and state that all means of birth control are licit . . . [it] must put its concern for people, their welfare, and their happiness above its concern for doctrine, dogma, and canon law . . . It is time that the Church stop being like a reluctant little child, always needing to be dragged into the present."

The possible role of non-Western religious institutions in the population crisis is more problematical than that of Western religions. For example, within the Islamic religion there is no organized, deep involvement in social problems, although Islamic scholars have recently tried to find religious justification for birth control practices in countries hard-pressed by exploding populations. There are at least 500 million Moslems in the world (roughly half the number of Christians), more than 95 percent of whom live in Africa and Asia, with high concentrations in such problem areas as Indonesia and the Indian subcontinent. Pakistan, with its aggressive family planning program, has made it clear that Moslem countries can take a rational view of their population problems and can make a vigorous attempt to solve them without religious conflict. In the foreseeable future, however, it seems unlikely that Islam will become a positive force for population control.

Much the same can be said of Buddhism, which—if we include as Buddhists those who also subscribe to Shintoism, Taoism, and Confucianism —has perhaps 700 million adherents, almost all in Asia. Since in Asia the barriers to population control and the potential for supporting it both seem to be much more connected with local conditions than with religion, it seems unlikely that changes in the religion will have any substantial effect on population policy.

Similarly, it is hard to picture Hinduism, as an entity, becoming a force in population control. More than 99 percent of the 450 million or so Hindus live in Asia, mostly in India. Like Buddhism, it is a rather heterogeneous, relatively "unorganized" religion. There is still considerable "religious" opposition to population control among Hindus, perhaps based more on medical beliefs and local superstitions than on religious conviction.

For those in the Western world who are interested in population control, one of the best courses of action seems to lie in working with the already established religious groups and using modern methods of shaping attitudes. In the non-Western world, the relative fragmentation of religious groups, their lack of organization and their psycho-social traditions would seem to limit their immediate effectiveness on population control policies.

In the United States, the unorthodox but constructive and quasi-religious attitudes expressed by members of the so-called "New Left" and the "hippie" movements may well help save our environment. The hippies especially have borrowed many religious ideas from the non-Christian East, including Zen Buddhism, the rewards of close personal relationships, spiritual values, a reverence for life, and an abhorrence of violence in any form. The members of both these groups of young people share a disdain for material things, a fascination for nature, and an interest in what might be called an ecological way of life. These attitudes on the part of members of the New Left are the antithesis of those of the old left of socialism and communism, which resemble Judeo-Christian attitudes regarding the exploitation of nature. Many people in our society are horrified at these new attitudes, which go against some cherished religious, political, and economic beliefs, and are, quite properly, appalled by the actions of some individuals in these groups. It would, however, be a good idea for those of us who are neither hip nor members of the New Left to pay attention to some of their ideas, whether or not we approve of their dress and general behavior. Those questioners of the status quo may not have the answers, but at the very least they are asking some important questions. Here is what Professor Lynn White, a Christian churchman, has to say: "Both our present science and our present technology are so tinctured with orthodox Christian arrogance toward nature that no solution for our ecologic crises can be expected from them alone. Since the roots of our trouble are so largely religious, the remedy must also be essentially religious, whether we call it that or not."

The Conservation Movement

The fascination and profound emotions—essentially religious feelings—aroused in many of us by wilderness areas, wildlife, and beautiful natural scenery are not easily explained to others who do not share them. Disparate beliefs and attitudes are obvious every time those interested in conservation find themselves defending aesthetic values against those who are equally dedicated to "progress." For many years now people in the conservation movement have fought individually and in groups to halt the extinction of rare animal species and the destruction of the last vestiges of the primitive areas of the Earth. Largely through the efforts of such organizations as the Sierra Club, the Audubon Society, and the Nature Conservancy in the U.S., and these and similar organizations in other countries, many of these efforts have been successful. It is becoming clear, however, that in the long run the conservation movement as a whole has been fighting a losing battle.

Perhaps the most obvious reason the battle is being lost is that conservation is a one-way street. Essentially each organism or place conserved remains in perpetual jeopardy. Each gain is temporary, but each loss is permanent. Species cannot be resurrected; places cannot be restored to their primitive state. Consequently, even if the conservationists were evenly matched against the destroyers, the battle would probably remain a losing one. But, of course, the battle has been far from even. Powerful economic interests and government agencies, pushed by population pressures, have promoted the development of practically every last inch of the United States, by building dams in the Grand Canyon, driving roads through the remaining wilderness areas, cutting the last of the primeval forests, drilling for oil on the northern slope of Alaska, and so on. It is a tribute to the conservationists, past and present, that any of our primitive areas remain unspoiled. Political and financial power tend to be arrayed against conservation, and, as people increase and resources dwindle, the situation seems bound to deteriorate further. In many parts of the world the situation is worse than in the United States; in a few it is better.

There are encouraging signs that a new thrust is appearing in the conservation movement. Growing numbers of people are beginning to realize that conservation is a global problem, that in the long run it is not enough to preserve a few isolated treasures such as a grove of redwood trees. If global pollution causes a climatic change, the grove cannot long survive. Many conservationists now realize that if the growth of the human population is not stopped and the deterioration of the planetary environment is not arrested, *nothing* of value will be conserved. They are now also beginning to recognize that *Homo sapiens* itself is an endangered species.

It seems likely that conservation groups will become more militant, and more united—at least in their global concerns. While the important local battles must continue to be fought, more general programs of public education and political action should become predominant. It is no longer necessary to plead for conservation on aesthetic or compassionate grounds only. The preservation of the diversity of life and the integrity of the ecological systems of the Earth are absolutely essential for the survival of man.

Education

In the United States and around the world there clearly has been an almost total failure to prepare people to understand and make decisions relating to the population-environment crisis. The universities, which should be leading the way in education, have been too conservative and compartmentalized. Unfortunately, most human problems do not fall neatly into such academic categories as sociology, history, economics, demography, psychology, or biology; and the solutions to these problems require the simultaneous application of the best ideas from many academic disciplines. Our failure to provide a multidisciplinary education explains the optimism of many physical scientists, economists, technologists, and others relative to the environmental crisis. Their kind of optimism is exemplified by a statement made by physicist Gerald Feinberg, who wrote, in 1968, that "Most of our immediate problems will be solved in a relatively short time by the march of technology and the worldwide spread of those aspects of Western culture that are responsible for our high living standards."

There are many examples of such naive optimism mixed with cultural chauvinism. The illusion that the "green revolution" will save mankind from starvation illustrates a faith in science and technology characteristic of the "well-informed" layman. This faith is all too often shared by academicians who have little insight into biology and into what is involved in agriculture and agricultural development in poor countries. Ignorance of the environmental consequences of population expansion leads many social scientists to underrate the significance of population growth in the DCs. For instance, Bernard Berelson of the Population Council believes that "the problem is most urgent in the developing countries, where rapid population growth retards social and economic development." He apparently sees only the localized and short-range advantages of the exploitative and environment-destroying behavior of the developed countries, and does not understand the consequences of attempting to spread this sort of behavior to the UDCs by trying to "develop" them in a similar fashion.

Many of the solutions put forth by technological optimists are based on ignorance of ecology, demography, anthropology, and so forth. Those who see a panacea in nuclear agro-industrial complexes are simultaneously required to ignore, among other things, economics, the scale of the problem, the state of reactor technology, the potential ecological damage, and an entire spectrum of political and social problems. Those few scientists who still propose migration (to Australia or to other planets) as a solution to the population problem, or who would accommodate our surplus people in concrete cities floated on the sea, simply need remedial work in arithmetic.

Finally, our educational system has seriously straightjacketed the economic thinking of most of our citizens to the point where they are mesmerized by the axiomatic "good" of growth. The thrall in which growth for its own sake holds our "educated" citizens was beautifully exemplified by a statement made on December 2, 1969, by John A. Carver, Jr., a member of the Federal Power Commission. He claimed that Americans would be in "a race for their lives" in order to meet electrical power "needs" up to the year 2000. He foresaw a need for four times the 1970 power generation facilities by 1990—"the equivalent of 670 Hoover Dams," and called for a compromise with environmental quality in order to meet that need. Naturally his solution is to be found in nuclear power plants. Carver, like many technologists, is evidently incapable of considering the obvious alternative to supplying more power—namely, *regulating demand*. Promoters of increased power consumption also seem unaware that Europeans do not appear to be "racing for their lives," even though European per capita electric power consumption is far less than half that of North America.

One would think that these educational problems could be relatively easily solved at the university level, and indeed they might be. Unfortunately, universities are quite determined to perpetuate their medieval structures. Nevertheless, the possibility of loosening the rigid departmental organization does exist, even though the rate of movement in this direction is now very slow. Stanford University, with the help of the Ford Foundation, has developed an interdisciplinary undergraduate curriculum in Human Biology with the express purpose of avoiding the trap of disciplinary myopia and of preparing students to attack pressing human problems. Some other colleges and universities are also instituting interdisciplinary programs of various sorts. Such reforms, however, must accelerate rapidly if universities are to contribute in any significant degree to the increase of mankind's chances for survival.

Perhaps the greatest hope for action in our universities and colleges lies with the students. The current group is much more mature and socially aware than the students of a decade ago, and most of them are determined to change our society for the better. Many are actively working for political and social revolutions, and even though the behavior of some of them has been reprehensible, few have approached the level of irresponsibility manifested by some of their elders, including certain political leaders and other public figures. Consider, for example, a statement made in 1969 by Senator

Richard Russell of Georgia: "If we have to start over again with another Adam and Eve, I want them to be Americans, and I want them on this continent and not in Europe." Moreover, of course, these young activists have yet to create an abomination remotely on a par with segregation, America's regressive tax system, or the Vietnam War. In our opinion and that of many colleagues, the majority of the most exciting and progressive changes in higher education during the late 1960's have had their roots in student activism. We hope that these young people may produce equally salutary changes in society as a whole.

To a large extent college students today have a more realistic view of the world than their parents because they do not see it through the rose-colored glasses which were constructed for older generations by society and the educational system. Those who matured just before World War II were young during a time when personal financial insecurity was an overriding consideration for much of the population. Today's students grew up in an era when, for most, financial security could be taken for granted. They grew up in a time of unprecedentedly rapid change. Moreover, they have had the world brought into their homes through the medium of television, and they have been forced into a global outlook by global threats to personal safety. These students are change-oriented, concerned about other people, and they think about subtle problems that involve all of mankind. That they show such concern should not be viewed as anything but a hopeful sign.

Although the educational system below the college level is in some ways less resistant to change, it is similarly inadequate in preparing people for the realities of the world crisis. In some of the better school systems, however, there are signs that this may be changing—sometimes due to the initiative of the students themselves. Even junior high school students in some areas have demonstrated their concern for environmental deterioration through various activities. Many teachers are beginning to encourage interest in population and environment, with or without administrative support.

A serious problem in many countries is a lack of adequate sex education. We face a population problem and a venereal disease epidemic in the United States, and yet powerful groups in the United States are determined to keep the "facts of life" from our young people. No subject is more likely to bring out a mob of angry parents than the thought of injecting the most innocuous sex education curriculum into a school, even if the program is endorsed by educators, psychiatrists, and clerics of all faiths. Some of these parents in our sex-saturated society even claim that a straightforward description of sexual intercourse, of the sort that should be perfectly acceptable reading for any child, is part of a communist plot to destroy our youth! This is a vicious cycle, with a minority of ignorant and disturbed parents fighting to guarantee that their children grow up equally ignorant and disturbed.

There are, of course, serious barriers to reasonable sex education in schools, churches, and in the home. One is a lack of training for potential teachers who need a thorough understanding of the subject. The second is the nearly ubiquitous feeling that sex education must be tied up with a series of moral judgments. In the face of massive ignorance and our current crisis, however, it is difficult to construct an argument against three basic aspects of sex education in the schools. First, children must be thoroughly informed about the anatomy of sex organs and the physiology of sex and reproduction. Second, they must be taught the difference between "sex" and reproduction and about the methods of contraception. Third, they should be informed of the dangers of venereal disease.

These straightforward factual matters are easy. Introducing the student to the role sex plays in society, the attitudes toward it in different religious and social groups, attitudes towards contraception, illegitimacy, marriage, divorce, virginity, and sex-as-just-plain-good-fun must be handled with great care and by specially trained teachers. But the cycle of the blind leading the blind, that of embarassed and uninformed parents "educating" their children, must be broken somehow. One way in which school systems have successfully introduced sex education programs is to give parents a preview of the material. The parents are invited to evaluate the program; in fact, one purpose is to educate *them*. Such preparations of the adult population would seem essential to avoid perpetuating ignorance. A sex education program has been initiated in West Germany for grandparents, who often care for children while parents work. Perhaps sex education should be compulsory for all American adults with preschool children.

Finally, our educational system is failing to produce the ecologists, agricultural and other technicians, social scientists, paramedical personnel, and similar specialists needed to help solve the pressing problems of the world, especially in the UDCs. Indeed, at the moment there is a "brain drain" problem. Trained personnel from the UDCs, especially medical doctors, are attracted to the United States and other DCs. Even more serious is the fact that many individuals from the UDCs who are educated in the DCs do not wish to return to their homelands. Although some DCs, notably the Soviet Union, virtually force a return, most do not. One relatively humane solution to this problem would be for the DCs to establish and help staff more training centers within the UDCs. This should have the additional benefits of training local people to work on problems of local significance, and of familiarizing visiting faculty members from the DCs with those problems.

The Legal System

Perhaps the greatest potential for reversing environmental deterioration in the United States and bringing our population under control lies in the utilization of our legal system. A law may be defined as a "rule of conduct for a community prescribed by a governing authority and enforced by sanction." The sanction enforcing a law may be either a reward or a punishment. For instance, to control agricultural production the government might pay a subsidy for not raising crops (a reward) or jail a farmer who raises crops (a punishment). Where a government wishes to induce an affirmative action, a promised reward is often more effective than the threat of punishment. In the United States, constitutional questions involving due process, equal protection, and so forth are more likely to arise where punishment, rather than reward, is involved. Bonuses for not having children would certainly raise fewer constitutional questions than jail for over-reproducers.

Law is also sometimes defined as custom. In a sense, legislators, policemen, and judges are merely social instruments for enforcing customary behavior. Historically they have also helped to create custom by defining acceptable conduct. This has been especially true of legislators and is becoming increasingly true of judges. The new problems of local and global overpopulation and pollution clearly require new rules of conduct and new customs: in short, new laws. Just as the ancient laws relating to trespass had to be modified by the courts and by the legislatures to handle the new circumstances created by automobiles and airplanes, new devices must now be developed for dealing with pollution and population pressure. The laws of our free enterprise system are failing to meet the needs of everyone everywhere as long as they *permit unrestricted reproduction and pollution.* We are today witnessing increases in violence and disorder in the United States partly because the legal system has not changed fast enough in response to changing needs. Such symptoms may be just a small taste of what is to come if our legal system does not promptly take cognizance of the population-environment crisis.

POLLUTION: NUISANCE

Fortunately there are many legal precedents that permit society to attack polluters legally. Under Common Law (the law generally applicable in Britain and her ex-colonies) and under Civil Law (the law generally applicable throughout the rest of the Western world) the concept of nuisance has for centuries permitted some of the coercive powers of government to be brought to bear on those who create excessive smoke, noise, odor, filth, and the like. In some jurisdictions access to sunlight and even an attractive view are among aesthetic values protected by public administrators. Public administrators, however, have not been notable for their diligence in complaining about local businesses. Private nuisances can be stopped by individual citizens who go to court and obtain injunctions to stop them. Private citizens may receive money damages for the injury caused them by the nuisance.

Existing nuisance laws present a number of difficulties. First, the nuisance doctrine generally serves only to protect rights associated with real property. As things now stand, a private nuisance can be stopped only by a person occupying adjacent or nearby property. Even in the most enlightened jurisdictions, little if anything can be done to protect people in the vicinity who do not own or occupy property.

Second, the nuisance doctrine requires that a complainant show a causal relationship between the condition he is complaining about—for example, smoke or noise—and a direct injury to himself. Generally he has to show that this condition is *the* cause of the injury. Obviously, if each of several polluters contributes a little to the overall problem, the nuisance doctrine is not much help. On the other hand, there is some authority for the proposition that if a suit is filed against all the persons who are contributing to the nuisance, it is up to them to show to what extent each has contributed. Thus there have been successful cases involving river pollution in which *all* contributors to upstream pollution have been sued.

Third, the nuisance doctrine is applied only if in the eyes of the court the polluter is causing more harm than he is doing good. Unfortunately it has been held by many courts that a so-called lawful business (paint manufacturing, for example) cannot constitute a nuisance. Today there is an increasing public tendency to recognize the dangers from pollution, and, in balancing these against economic considerations, to require businesses to do whatever a court or an administrative agency may think is economically reasonable. The fact that the economic interests of the polluters are taken into consideration by our governmental authorities often leads to spurious arguments based on the notion that restrictions would foster unfair competition: "We cannot compete with the Jones Company if we cannot spray our crops with DDT." The answer to the argument of course is: "We will stop the Jones Company too." Often the best way of avoiding unfair competition arguments is to pass legislation that affects an entire industry. For example, if a law were passed prohibiting the manufacture of *all* persistent insecticides (for instance, all those with a half-life of more than two days under average field conditions), the chemical companies would very quickly lower prices on those that met the requirements and would develop new ones which also break down rapidly.

Fourth, under the nuisance doctrine, a single public-spirited individual can do very little to stop an industrial polluter. The individual cannot rely on injury to other individuals as an argument in trying to stop the pollution. Normally, he can collect damages only for the injury he himself has suffered. He will not be able to get an injunction against further injury unless the direct injury to himself outweighs the countervailing economic interests of the polluter.

The serious defects in the existing nuisance laws might make it appear that they will not really assist in controlling pollution, but this is not so. With some relatively minor adjustments these laws could be made very effective. These are among the changes that must be made: (1) expand the nuisance doctrine to include people who are hurt by the pollution but who do not necessarily occupy nearby property; (2) permit individuals to bring actions not only on their own behalf, but also on behalf of all other individuals in similar circumstances who are being damaged by pollution; (3) permit recovery of punitive damages (damages in excess of the dollar value of the injury suffered) in cases where the polluter could have avoided some or all of the pollution; (4) organize public-spirited scientists so that they might become a more readily available source of testimony. The real value of the nuisance laws is that they provide an existing framework within which to elaborate newer and more restrictive rules of conduct without also requiring the development of previously unrecognized rights and duties.

POLLUTION: TRESPASS

Another ancient legal doctrine, that of trespass, can also assist in stopping pollution. According to law, if you hit another man with your fist or with your automobile, or if you hike over another man's land, you have committed a trespass. Trespass is both a crime (a public offense) and a tort (an individual, private injury).

For many years there have been metaphysical arguments concerning what constitutes a trespass—for example, whether it is necessary to be able to see whatever hits you or falls on your land. It has been said that rays of light cannot constitute a trespass, and in the past not even smoke could constitute a trespass. However, the old idea that it was necessary to be able to see, feel, and even weigh the offensive object is going out of style. The decision in one California case permitted recovery of substantial damages for lung injuries sustained by a motorist who drove through invisible chemical fumes emitted by a nearby factory.

One serious defect in applying the trespass laws to the control of pollution is that the most an individual can recover are his own damages, which are generally limited to the monetary value of the individual's private injuries. In one case, however, the Oregon Supreme Court permitted a private individual to collect punitive damages in addition to his actual personal damages. The court reasoned that some private wrongs are so evil that the wrongdoer should be punished as well as be forced to pay for the actual injury he has caused the complainant. Punitive damages have long been recognized in our legal systems. If industries guilty of pollution were assessed for punitive damages more often than they are, private individuals would be given more incentive to initiate law suits against them. This possibility would provide industries with an economic motive to stop their pollution.

Like nuisance laws, the trespass laws could be made much more effective merely by permitting an individual to sue for the value of the injuries sustained by *all* individuals similarly situated. Such suits are called class actions, and the individual represents not only himself, but also all others similarly situated or in the same class as himself. There exists ample authority for class actions in other circumstances. For example, a stockholder has long been able to bring a class action on behalf of all stockholders against a corporation or its officers or directors. Today, there is evidence that trespass laws will increasingly be used in what are essentially class actions against polluters. The suits against the Union Oil Company by the State of California and by individuals in connection with the famous 1969 oil leak in the Santa Barbara Channel are class actions.

POLLUTION: LEGISLATION AND ADMINISTRATIVE AGENCIES

In addition to putting pressure on polluters through the courts, there is the vast and fertile field of legislation and administrative law. State and federal legislatures could easily stop pollution if they wished to do so. The courts would find no constitutional objections to any reasonable legislative limitations on the activities of polluting industries—for example, requirements that effluents be purified, reduced, or eliminated. The courts could even sustain statutes that would put certain corporations out of business.

There are two difficult problems in getting effective legislative action. First there is the notion that if a higher governmental authority (for example, the United States Congress) enacts a law regulating a certain kind of activity, it has pre-empted the field and a lesser governmental authority (for example, a state) cannot enact legislation dealing with the same subject. This has led the tobacco and automobile industries to push for federal regulation in order to avoid the enactment of more restrictive state laws. There is no easy answer to this problem. A national economy does require national standards, and it would be extremely difficult for the automobile manufacturers to satisfy 51 different statutory schemes to regulate automobile pollution. Yet some local problems are so severe that they require more drastic solutions than should be applied to the country at large.

The second difficulty with legislative action is that legislators are often not cognizant of new problems, and some are notoriously at the beck and call of established pressure groups, such as the automobile manufacturers and the oil industry. Furthermore, in those situations where the legislature has taken action, the action has generally consisted of setting up regulatory agencies like the Food and Drug Administration, the Federal Trade Commission, or the Federal Communication Commission. Such agencies in time tend to become dominated by the industries they are intended to regulate; ultimately the foxes wind up minding the chickens. Nevertheless, as public pressure grows, we can hope for more results from legislation and from regulatory agencies than we have seen in the past.

An action program to control pollution would require changing the law through the courts, the legislatures, and the administrative agencies. Laws should be enacted to tax polluters, the tax being based on the amount of pollutants released. At the same time, tax deductions could be granted for the costs of developing and installing pollution-control devices. If such relatively nonpunitive steps do not produce the desired results, then statutes forbidding the release of pollutants and permitting the prosecution of violators as felons should be enacted. Laws are needed now to prohibit the use of certain substances (for example, tetraethyl lead in gasoline and such persistent insecticides as the chlorinated hydrocarbons). In some cases, as discussed in the section on economic change, laws should be passed that would spread the burden of responsibility for reducing and eliminating pollution.

To initiate such an action program will require the efforts of many individual citizens. Letters must be written to legislators, to industries, and to news media. Boycotts must be organized. Lawsuits must be instituted against polluters. Individuals with special expertise, particularly scientists and lawyers, must spend the time and effort required to cooperate in bringing lawsuits.

A beginning in scientist-lawyer cooperation has been made by an organization known as the Environmental Defense Fund (EDF). This group, composed primarily of biologists and attorneys, has been going into the courts and appearing before state agencies in an effort to stop the use of DDT. They succeeded, for instance, in using the courts to stop DDT spraying in Suffolk County, Long Island, and, as a result of the publicity accompanying an unsuccessful EDF suit, more than 50 cities in Michigan decided to stop DDT spraying. In an adversary-style hearing before the Wisconsin Department of Resources, completed in early 1969, the EDF was able to demolish the flimsy case of those attempting to defend the continued use of chlorinated hydrocarbons. Faced with the certainty of cross-examination, many of the scientists who usually defend the petrochemical industry were noticeably absent from the witness chair (although not from the public press). The final decision in the Wisconsin case is not known at this writing; if it is decided not to ban DDT, then the case almost certainly will be carried to the Supreme Court. The EDF, originally a shoestring operation, is everywhere gaining the admiration and support of scientists and others interested in survival. It should serve as a model for similar groups. Another group that has organized to work against both environmental deterioration and overpopulation is composed of students in ten law schools around the U.S. These students had in 1969 already initiated local actions against development plans and were planning an attack on anti-abortion laws both through legislation and the courts.

The legal machinery and the legal notions necessary to control pollution do exist. Slight changes in the legal notions and diligent application of the legal machinery are all that is necessary to induce a great reduction in pollution in the United States.

POPULATION

Although there is considerable legal precedent for governmental regulation of pollution, there is very little precedent to permit the control of reproduction. What little authority there is tends to prohibit or restrict the government from taking population control measures. For example, the argument has been made and accepted that sterilization constitutes a cruel and unusual punishment, and laws have restricted the dissemination of birth control information and devices and have outlawed abortion.

Our legal system is seriously out of date relative to population policy. Our laws and our customs, as embodied in our religious, social, and legal institutions, still reflect the requirements of a nation seeking to fill a frontier. Laws that prohibit or restrict the widest use of birth control, that restrict abortion, that grant tax favors to the heads of large families; indeed, all laws that tend to encourage people to have children should be replaced with laws that encourage people to have few or no children.

Some people—respected legislators, judges, and lawyers included—tend to view the right to have children as a fundamental and inalienable right. Yet neither the Declaration of Independence nor the Constitution mentions a "right to reproduce," nor is there mention of such a right in the Magna Carta or in the U.N. Charter. In fact, there is no basis for a sacrosanct status for the "right" to have children. From the standpoint of legal theory that so-called "right" is really no more than a *privilege,* and there is therefore no reason why we cannot regulate its exercise.

Nor is the privilege to have children so personal that its regulation cannot be exercised by the State. The number of children a woman may have should not be solely a matter of her private concern; it should be a matter of profound *public* concern. Furthermore, the law has long regulated other highly personal matters. It can, for example, prevent a woman from having more than one husband. Why should it not be able to prevent her from having more than two children?

The legal argument has been made that the First Amendment provision for separation of Church and State prevents the United States government from regulating family size. The notion is that family size is God's affair and no business of the State. But the same argument was made against the taxation of church property, prohibition of polygamy, compulsory education of children, and many similar measures that have been enacted. Churches can be and are taxed, polygamy has been outlawed, and even the Amish have to send their children to public school. From a legal standpoint, the First Amendment argument against family size regulation is devoid of merit.

In addition to the justifications based on limited resources and considerations of the quality of life, there are other reasons relevant to accepted legal doctrines that would justify the government in exercising control over the birth rate. It is accepted that the law has as its proper function the protection of each person. A legal restriction on the right to have more than a given number of children could easily be based on the needs of the first children. Some studies have indicated that the larger the family, the less likely the children are to realize their potential levels of achievement. Certainly there is no question that children of a small family can be better cared for and better educated than children of a large family, income and other things being equal. The law could properly say to a mother that, in order to protect the children she already has, she can have no more. It is also accepted that the law has as its proper function the protection of individuals and the maintenance of order in the country. Continued population growth would make the maintenance of order increasingly difficult.

Any laws passed must meet certain standards. They must apply equally to all and they must apply in a way that is reasonably calculated to produce a socially desirable goal. Certainly laws concerning population regulation that satisfy these standards can be drafted and enforced.

Assuming that the State can regulate reproduction and can pass laws to encourage people to have fewer children or to penalize them for having too many children, what specific regulations could be written? What kinds of laws might be passed? Here are a few possibilities:

1. Tax laws could be revised, and new laws could be passed that would provide incentives for late marriage and small families, as discussed in Chapter 10.

2. A federal law could be passed forbidding doctors, except for medical reasons, to refuse to perform abortions or sterilization operations, or to provide contraceptive information. If these procedures conflict with a doctor's own convictions he should be required to refer patients to doctors who will do what is requested.

3. Laws could be passed requiring that federally supported birth control clinics be opened in all suitable localities, and federal funds could be used to subsidize contraception, abortion, and sterilization.

4. A federal law could make sex education mandatory in all public schools, including instruction about contraception.

5. Federal laws could be passed to simplify adoption procedures and subsidize adoption.

6. If such relatively uncoercive laws should fail to bring the birth rate under control, laws could be written that would make bearing a third child illegal and that would require an abortion to terminate all such pregnancies. Failure to obtain the abortion could be made a felony, as could aiding and abetting over-reproducers. Stiff fines and other penalties could be established, carefully adjusted so that the innocent child would not be penalized for his parents' illegal activities. At the moment there might be little public support for such laws, but if the social and environmental situations are permitted to deteriorate much further popular support might develop rapidly. Already there has been considerable talk of forcibly suppressing reproduction among welfare recipients (perhaps by requiring the use of contraceptives or even by involuntary sterilization). This may sadly foreshadow what our society might do if it wakes up too late. One would hope that population size can be controlled in the United States without resort to such distasteful and socially disruptive measures.

Business, Industry, and Advertising

Although legal and legislative action are essential to the solution of pollution problems in the U.S., it is to be hoped that American industries will not wait to be coerced into responsible behavior. In fact, a few industries have already taken the initiative for cleaning up their effluents, and some of these have found it possible to make a profit from pollution by-products. Such unexpected bonuses will not be possible in most cases, of course. Tax incentives and pollution clean-up subsidies from the government may be necessary where costs are high (see section on Economic and Political Change).

Meanwhile, many industrial organizations are exploring technological methods for dealing with various kinds of pollution; indeed, new companies are appearing whose entire business is pollution abatement or waste disposal of one sort or another. On the preventive side of the coin, environmental consulting firms have begun to appear. Their business is to advise communities and businesses in planning development with the least possible damage to the environment and the most benefit to the human inhabitants. These trends and others, such as research on recyclable or biodegradable containers, should certainly be encouraged.

A reorientation of businessmen's and consumers' values is in order. Resources of all kinds are limited, but Americans behave as though they were not. The neglected virtues of economy and thrift must be restored to the pedestals that they once occupied in this country; that they still occupy in other countries. American consumers have been conditioned by advertising to buy gaudy or gimmicky packages, to accept "planned obsolescence," and to want specialized gadgets (such as electric can-openers) that do only one job efficiently. The wastefulness of this system can best be appreciated by a visit to the city dump.

Advertising plays a leading role in perpetuating the American system of consumerism. Using the same methods, the advertising industry could play a leading role in reversing the trend. This presumably would require the co-operation of their clients. Along this line, it is interesting that in the late 1960's many advertisements began to appear featuring various companies' efforts at pollution abatement. This concern over the corporate image with respect to pollution is no doubt a necessary first step. It is to be hoped that the public will encourage pollution-conscious businesses and that the businesses themselves will do more about pollution abatement (or better, prevention) than merely to advertise it.

The advertising industry can do much more than it has so far to encourage their clients to promote products with stress on such qualities as durability, economy, and versatility. For example, automobile advertising should emphasize economy of purchase and operation, especially low mileage, durability, compactness, comfort (but not roominess), engine efficiency, and low pollution emissions. Advertising that stresses large size and power should be discontinued. The public has to a large degree been educated to want large, overpowered vehicles (for that matter, to want personal vehicles at all) and frequent style changes. Presumably it could quickly be educated to want small, efficient, low-powered vehicles that last a long time, particularly if the connections with smog, traffic congestion, and parking space were made clear.

With such a change, the big three American automobile manufacturers could discontinue their larger, more expensive and powerful models immediately. Indeed, one might well ask why they have not already done so. If the automobile industry does not seize the initiative in developing alternatives to the internal combustion engine and the overpowerful, obsolescent automobile, it may one day discover that it is out of business entirely. Sacrificing the largest models now and diverting talent and money into producing genuinely new vehicle designs, rather than small model changes, might mean the preservation of the industry. It would be too bad if resources were used instead to continue promoting the same old qualities and to resist the regulations and restrictions that will inevitably be imposed.

To return to advertising, beyond cooperating with clients in antipollution promotions, the advertising companies could by agreement refuse to design ads promoting wasteful or polluting products; for example, ads featuring powerful engines in automobiles, or food in throwaway cans and bottles. Opportunities should be taken whenever possible to demonstrate benefits to the environment from the product or the company being promoted.

Advertising agencies can also make a contribution to the population situation by refusing to produce ads featuring large families. There are many other ways to promote heavy-duty washing machines—dormitories, laundromats, boarding schools, and orphanages use them, for instance. In a situation where a family has three children, it could be referred to as a "large family." Women could be featured more often in roles other than homemaker and mother. The convenience of many goods can be stressed more as a value for working women than for the overburdened mother, as they usually are now.

The 1970's will be crucial years for everyone. The business community in the U.S. and around the world is faced with a particularly difficult choice. It can continue to pursue the economic goals of the past decades until either an environmental disaster overtakes us or until governments and the public compel a change, or it can actively initiate new approaches to production and industry, with a view to protecting the environment, preserving limited resources, and, hopefully, truly benefitting mankind.

Medicine

There are some signs that the medical profession in the United States is becoming aware of the seriousness of the population problem and the role that medicine has played in creating it, as well as the role that the profession must play if the problem is to be solved. More and more physicians seem to be aware that medical intervention in lowering death rates must be balanced by intervention in lowering birth rates. Courageous doctors in many areas are openly defying antique abortion laws and risking grave financial loss for performing vasectomies. In many UDCs, especially in India, the medical profession is even further ahead in recognizing the desperate need for population control. Interest in the problems of environmental medicine is on the rise also, and some medical doctors have been at the forefront in sounding warnings (often ignored) about the hazards of air pollution, water pollution, and other environmental threats to public health.

On the debit side, the medical profession as a whole has been tardy in backing even such elementary programs as the repeal of laws limiting the distribution of contraceptive information and the establishment of family planning clinics. Furthermore, medical training has militated against abortion except under extremely limited circumstances, and the record of the profession (in contrast to that of some courageous individual physicians) in the area of abortion reform has been atrocious. Even though a so-called "liberal" abortion law has been passed in California, a substantial portion of the abortions in that state continue to be performed by a single group of doctors. The medical profession should take the lead in abolishing not only the abortion laws but all of the pseudolegal hospital rituals attendant to performing abortions. The history of the medical profession's attitude toward voluntary sterilization is similarly reactionary and "moralistic." Beyond establishing that a patient understands the consequences of sterilization, and will not be physically harmed by the operation, the doctor should have no right to make the ultimate decision as to whether or not an adult should be voluntarily sterilized.

Whether the medical profession in the United States will become a strong force for population control remains to be seen. It has a great potential for helping to solve the population problem, both at home and through technical aid to other countries. It could, for instance, assist in setting up field centers in UDCs, where paramedical personnel could be trained to instruct people in the use of contraceptives and to perform vasectomies and abortions. The American Medical Association (AMA) is an extremely powerful organization and an enormous potential force for good. But, as in some other areas of social reform, the AMA has conspicuously dragged its feet on the population controversy. It should be at the very forefront of a crusade for population control measures, particularly those that pertain to medical practice, such as the repeal of abortion laws, increasing the availability of sterilization, and encouraging the dissemination of birth control information.

Transportation and Communications

We cannot discuss in detail the changes which might occur in the systems that move people and information around this country and around the world. But there has been considerable discussion in the United States about the possibilities for a general conversion from automobiles to mass transportation, an idea that has much appeal. It would, among other things, conserve energy resources and help to mitigate the problems of air pollution. Similarly, the crisis in air transportation and suggested cures received wide publicity late in the 1960's. It seems unlikely that transportation systems in the U.S. and other DCs will change significantly for the better until the public becomes sufficiently fed up with smog, noise, delays, and danger that it is willing to forgo further growth in both population and GNP. Automobiles may be made more smog-free, but until the public rebels against them, their numbers will probably increase rapidly enough to keep the overall smog level dangerously high, while more land disappears under freeways. It seems unlikely that even the obvious first step of greatly reducing the size of cars and their engines will be taken in the near future. Airport noise may get worse for a while, not better, as larger and larger aircraft are used. If and when a transition can be made to a nongrowing population and economy, both the need for business travel and the pressure to build more vehicles and more goods should be reduced; perhaps then these transportation problems could be solved. Hopefully, the kinds of transport problems that now plague the DCs (the U.S. in particular) can be totally avoided in most UDCs.

Unlike the transportation system, the communications system seems to have great potential for instituting change. Television and radio seem to have universal appeal, and with relatively little expenditure could have virtually universal coverage. If human problems are to be solved on a worldwide basis, some means of intercommunication among the peoples of the world must be employed. One possibility would be for the DCs to supply UDCs with large numbers of small, transistorized TV sets for communal viewing in villages. These could provide the information channels for reaching the largely rural populations of the "other world." These channels could provide both a route for supplying technical aid and a means of reinforcing the idea that they are members of a global community.

The problems of supplying the channels of information, however, are easily solved in comparison with the problems of determining what information should flow along those channels and in what format. Ideally, much of the programming ought to be informational, even if presented as entertainment. People in the DCs must be made aware of their resource situations, their polluting activities, and the need for population control at home. People in the UDCs must be made aware of the need for population control and the ways it may be achieved. They also need help in solving many other problems such as increasing their agricultural production and improving public health. Programming should be carefully designed by social scientists and communications experts thoroughly familiar with the needs and attitudes of the audiences in each country or locality. This will be especially important in the UDCs, and especially difficult there because of the lack of trained people and the radical change in attitudes that is required. Control of the communications media should obviously be public, with maximum safeguard against abuses.

The problems of educating the people in the DCs to the problems of population and environment are not as serious, assuming time and space can be obtained in the media. Material can be more straightforward, since in many DCs there is already rather widespread awareness of at least some environmental problems. In the United States a great step forward could be taken by simply requiring that both radio and television assign some of their commercial time to short "spots" calling attention to the problems of population, resources, and environment. This could be justified under the equal-time doctrine that put the anti-smoking messages sponsored by the American Heart Association and the American Cancer Society on TV, which themselves could serve as models for the approach. The FCC might require that networks donate time for ads that would awaken people to the population-resource-environment crisis. Long documentary "specials," whether prepared by the networks or by educational channels, are relatively ineffective. For the most part, they reach only those who are already aware that a particular problem exists. The majority of television viewers want to be entertained; they do not want to hear bad news.

Economic and Political Change

In relation to the population-resources-environment crisis, economics and politics can usually be viewed as two sides of the same coin. A very large number of political decisions are made on an economic basis, especially those relating to environmental problems. John Maynard Keynes wrote in *The General Theory of Employment, Interest, and Money* (1936): "The ideas of economists and political philosophers, both when they are right and when they are wrong, are more powerful than is commonly understood. Indeed the world is ruled by little else." Although the major political division of our time—that between capitalist and communist worlds—is thought to be based on differences in economic ideology, the actual differences are relatively few. In fact, a major cause of humanity's current plight lies not in the economic differences between the two superpowers, but in the economic attitudes that they have in common.

GROSS NATIONAL PRODUCT AND ECONOMIC GROWTHMANSHIP

Economists are not unanimous in their view of economic growth. Paul A. Samuelson wrote in *Economics, An Introductory Analysis* (1967): "The ghost of Carlyle should be relieved to know that economics, after all, has not been a dismal science. It has been the cheerful, but impatient, science of growth." On the other hand, E. J. Mishan states in *The Costs of Economic Growth* (1967): "The skilled economist, immersed for the greater part of the day in pages of formulae and statistics, does occasionally glance at the world about him and, if perceptive, does occasionally feel a twinge of doubt about the relevance of his contribution. . . . For a moment, perhaps, he will dare wonder whether it is really worth it. Like the rest of us, however, the economist must keep moving, and since such misgivings about the overall value of economic growth cannot be formalized or numerically expressed, they are not permitted seriously to modify his practical recommendations." The majority of economic theorists hold Samuelson's view and still tend to be growth-oriented, as do most politicians and businessmen in both DCs and UDCs.

In much of the world—indeed, in all countries with any aspirations towards "modernization," "progress," or "development"—a general economic index of advancement is growth of the gross national product (GNP). The GNP is the sum of personal and government expenditure on goods and services, plus expenditure on investment. More important than what the GNP is, however, is what it *is not*. It is not a measure of the degree of freedom of the people of a nation. It is not a measure of the health of a population. It is not a measure of the state of depletion of natural resources. It is not a measure of the stability of the environmental systems upon which life depends. It is not a measure of security from the threat of war. It is not, in sum, a comprehensive measure of the *quality* of life.

When the standard of living of two nations is compared, it is customary to examine their *per capita* GNPs. Per capita GNP is an especially unfortunate statistic. First of all it is the ratio of two statistics that are at best crude estimates, especially in the UDCs, where neither GNP nor population size is known with any accuracy. More important, comparisons of per capita GNP overestimate many kinds of differences. For instance, a comparison of per capita GNPs would lead to the conclusion that the average American lives almost ten times as well as the average Portugese, and some sixty times as well as the average Burmese. This of course is meaningless, since virtually all services and many goods are much cheaper in the UDCs. Americans pay perhaps five or ten times as much for farm labor, domestic help, haircuts, carpentry, plumbing, and so forth as do people in the UDCs, and the services we get are often of inferior quality. And yet these services, because of the accounting system, contribute between five and ten times as much to our GNP as the same services do to the GNPs of, say, Burma or India. Furthermore, figures on the increase of per capita GNP in UDCs do not take into account such things as rise in literacy rate, and thus may underrate the amount of progress a country has made toward modernization.

Nor does the GNP measure many negative aspects of the standard of living. Although the average Burmese may live only one-sixtieth as well as the average American, the average American may cause a hundred times as much ecological destruction to the planet as a whole.

A serious criticism that can be leveled at the majority of economists is one that applies equally to most people and societies: they accept a doctrine of economic determinism. The myths of cornucopian economics as opposed to the realities of geology and biology have already been discussed, but the problem is much more pervasive than that. Economic growth has become *the* standard for progress, *the* benefit for which almost any social cost is to be paid. This problem in economic thought can be fully appreciated by a perusal of Samuelson's excellent *Economics,* one of the best and most influential textbooks ever written. The book is, of course, oriented towards economic growth. Problems of the growing scarcity of nonrenewable resources are presented only briefly as a problem of underdeveloped countries. The physical limits placed on economic growth by the thermal problems associated with energy consumption are not discussed in the text, nor are the other basic environmental constraints discussed in our earlier chapters. Implicit in the treatment of economic development is the idea that it is possible for 5 to 7 billion people to achieve a standard of living similar to that of the average American of the 1960's. Uninformed technological optimism is explicit or implicit throughout the book.

Nevertheless, Samuelson's book reveals more understanding of population and environment than the writings of many other economists. He does realize that growth of GNP must be "qualified by data on leisure, population size, relative distribution, quality, and noneconomic factors." Furthermore, in a recent *Newsweek* column (October 6, 1969) Samuelson wrote, ". . . most of us are poorer than we realize. Hidden costs are accruing all the time; and because we tend to ignore them, we overstate our incomes . . . Thomas Hobbes said that in the state of nature the life of man was nasty, brutish and short. In the state of modern civilization it has become nasty, brutish and long."

The discussion of the problems of UDCs in Samuelson's text is a model of realism when contrasted with the ideas of such economic conservatives as Milton Friedman of the University of Chicago. Most economists subscribe to the "bigger and more is better" philosophy. The growing mixed economy is something to analyze, improve, and by all means to keep growing. In an article that appeared in the *New York Review of Books,* economist Wassily Leontief of Harvard remarked that ". . . If the 'external costs' of growth clearly seem to pose dangers to the quality of life, there is as yet no discernible tendency among economists or economic managers to divert their attention from this single-minded pursuit of economic growth." That economists have clung to this idea is not surprising. After all, natural scientists often cling to outmoded ideas that have produced far less palpable benefits than have the mixed economies of the Western World. The question of whether a different economic system might have produced a more equitable *distribution* of benefits is not one that Western economists like to dwell on. Furthermore, ideas of perpetual growth are congruent with the conventional wisdom of most of the businessmen of the world; indeed, of most of the world's population. The people of the UDCs naturally wish to emulate the economic growth of the West and they long for "development" with all of its shiny accoutrements. Why should they be expected to know that it is physically and ecologically impossible for them to catch up with us when many of our most erudite citizens are still unaware of that fact?

Perhaps most serious is the common idea that not only is growth of the GNP highly desirable, but that population increase, at least in DCs, *promotes* such growth. However, there are some economists, such as J. J. Spengler, of the University of North Carolina, who have made a point of attacking the idea that population growth is necessary to keep the GNP growing in DCs. Certainly in the DCs there is no perfect correlation between population growth and growth of GNP. As Spengler says, "It is high time . . . that business cease looking upon the stork as a bird of good omen." He points out that a substantial portion of the GNP consists of services, and that these may continue to expand with a static population. Even in such heavily people-dependent industries as transportation, there is considerable room for attracting a greater proportion of the population to the use of the service. For instance, a small percentage of the American population does the major portion of airline traveling, and presumably airlines could grow for several generations even if the population size remained stable.

Population growth, on the other hand, absorbs capital and resources that could be used to increase the average standard of living, and population growth adds to the cost of nonrenewable resources by increasing their scarcity. It is, in fact, almost certain that economic growth in the DCs is, or soon will be, hindered by population growth, just as it is clearly hindered in the UDCs now. In the United States, for instance, there is no need for additional people in the labor force. Rather, there is a need for better training of the existing pool of human resources. In fact the pressure of brute numbers at the younger end of the labor pool is probably a major reason that we stick by a retirement age of 65. Many talented people are removed from the labor force, even though they may still be capable of 10 years or more of productive work and do not wish to be "put out to pasture."

Population growth has undoubtedly lowered the quality of the work force. The post-World War II baby boom is one of the reasons for the present shabby condition of the American educational system. Too much money was needed merely to provide more classrooms, more teachers, and more books, and this money was thus not available for much-needed improvement and modernization of teaching techniques and curricula.

These quality problems have been compounded by another phenomenon associated with population growth: urbanization. Rapid changes in population distribution and composition have all but destroyed many cities. As a result many people who might potentially contribute to the economy do not fulfill that potential. Instead they often become destructive elements, largely out of frustration and feelings of ineffectiveness.

But, whether or not population growth helps to raise the GNP, it is clear that the GNP cannot grow forever. Why should it? As John Kenneth Galbraith points out in *The New Industrial State,* it would be entirely logical to set limits on the amount of product a nation needs, and then to strive to reduce the amount of work required to produce such a product (and, one might add, to see that the product is much more equitably distributed than it is today). But, of course, such a program would be a threat to some of the most dearly held beliefs of our society. It would attack the Protestant ethic, which insists that one must be kept busy on the job for 40 hours a week. It is even better to work several more hours moonlighting, so that the money can be earned to buy all those wonderful automobiles, detergents, appliances, and assorted gimcracks which *must* be bought if the economy is to continue to grow. But this tradition is outmoded; the only hope for civilization in the future is to work for *quality* in the context of a nongrowing economy.

Economist Kenneth E. Boulding has begun to develop an exciting set of economic concepts dealing with the population-resource-environment crisis, by recognizing the existence of biological and physical limitations to growth. In "The Economics of the Coming Spaceship Earth," he described the need to shift from our present "cowboy economy," in which both production and consumption are regarded with great favor, and which is "associated with reckless, exploitative, romantic and violent behavior," to a "spaceman-economy." In the spaceman economy there are no unlimited reservoirs, either for extraction or pollution, and consumption must be minimized. In a classical understatement, Boulding describes the idea that production and consumption are bad things as "very strange to economists." But even economists can change, and perhaps this section on economics can end on an optimistic note. Economists of the next generation may be weaned away from their concentration on perpetual growth and high production-consumption and learn, in Boulding's words, to measure economic success in terms of the "nature, extent, quality and complexity of the total capital stock, including in this the state of the human bodies and minds included in the system."

PERSONAL FREEDOM AND THE QUALITY OF LIFE

"We have had no environmental index, no census statistic to measure whether the country is more or less habitable from year to year. A tranquility index or a cleanliness index might have told us something about the condition of man, but a fast-growing country preoccupied with making and acquiring material things has had no time for the amenities that are the very heart and substance of daily life." Stewart Udall was Secretary of the Interior when he wrote those words. His bold challenge to Americans, expressed in *1976: Agenda for Tomorrow,* has not yet been accepted. Is there any way to break into the present system and persuade our society to weigh economic goals carefully against other possible goals of human existence? Can we proceed with Mr. Udall's urgent agenda? The obstacles are great, since economics and politics are so intertwined, and the various elements of the power structure in the U.S. all want and promote "growth." If there is any chance of getting a reversal of this attitude, it lies in convincing those in power as well as the electorate that their own personal lives and freedom are at stake. More men with dedication and perception must be elected to public office, and ways must be found to convince the present leaders of the nation that population growth and accelerating resource utilization, coupled with environmental decay, are injuring their children and progressively limiting their possible futures. Two points may be made:

1. While the American economy has been growing, freedom has been shrinking. Greater and greater controls must be applied to everyday living, and restrictions will inevitably grow more severe as population increases. The use of automobiles, boats, and private airplanes will become even more circumscribed. The keeping of pets, especially those that are noisy or consume substantial amounts of protein, will be forbidden. Increasingly, access to recreational areas will be strictly rationed. Bureaucracy will continue to grow as the government tries to solve more and more pressing problems with less and less success. Each citizen, assuming that at least an illusion of "democracy" will persist, will have an ever-decreasing say in the affairs of state. For instance, consider what has happened to the average citizen's "say" in the past 150 years. In 1810 each of 52 Senators represented, on the average, about 140,000 citizens. Today each of 100 Senators represents about 2,100,000 Americans—15 times as many! A parallel dilution of representation has occurred in the House of Representatives.

2. While the American GNP has been growing, the quality of life in the United States has been deteriorating. The GNP roughly doubled in the decade 1960–1969. Can anyone claim that the average individual's life

has greatly improved in the same period? Here is a short list of the negative changes that have occurred in the quality of his existence. The air that he breaths has become more foul, and the quality of the water he uses has probably declined. His chances of being robbed or murdered have increased, as have his chances of losing his life in a highway accident or his home or business in a civil disorder. His chances of dying of emphysema, bronchitis, and various kinds of cancer have increased. He must travel further to reach solitude, either on increasingly crowded highways, increasingly shoddy trains, or increasingly delay-prone airlines. His children have a more difficult time being accepted into a first class college than they did in 1960. If he has sons they are more likely to be killed in a war, or to flee the country to avoid being drafted. Can a list of *improvements* twice this long easily be constructed?

We suspect that these arguments will not have the desired effect, even if a great many influential people get the message. To a large extent the political-economic system has a life of its own; it possesses emergent qualities beyond those of the individuals who constitute it. There is no conscious conspiracy on the part of individual military men, businessmen, and government officials to destroy the United States and the world, but the total effect of their actions and those of their counterparts in other governments nonetheless is moving us toward that end. People in groups, be they mobs, university committees, armies, or industrial boards, simply do not behave the way single individuals behave. But basically we must try, by changing the behavior of many individuals, to produce the desired changes in the corporate behavior of the economic and political establishment.

ECONOMICS AND THE POLITICS OF THE ENVIRONMENT

One way in which changes in our economic system might be accomplished would be to develop a new economics of the environment. There is a pressing need to re-examine the way cost-benefit calculations are done in our society. Such calculations are usually made over too short a time span. For example, consider the history of a contemporary housing development. A developer carves up a southern California hillside, builds houses on it, and sells them, reaping the benefits in a very short time. Then society starts to pay the costs. The houses have been built in an area where the native plant community is known as *chaparral*. Chaparral, known to plant ecologists as a "fire climax," would not exist as a stable vegetation type unless the area burned over every once in a while. When it does the homes are destroyed, and the buyers and the public start paying hidden costs in the form of increased insurance rates and emergency relief. Of course, there are hidden costs even in the absence of such a catastrophe. The housing development puts a further load on the water supply and probably will be a contributing political factor in the ultimate flooding of distant farmland to make a reservoir. Perhaps wind patterns cause smog to be especially thick in the area of the development, and as it begins to affect the inhabitants they and society pay additional costs in hospital bills and high life insurance premiums. And, of course, by helping to attract more people into the area, the development helps to increase the general smog burden. Then there are the problems of additional roads, schools, sewage treatment plants, and other community requirements created by the new subdivision. While the builder may have put the roads in the subdivision, increased taxes must pay for increased upkeep on roads in the subdivision area, and eventually for new roads demanded by increasing congestion. Among the saddest phenomena of our time are the attempts by politicians and Chambers of Commerce to attract industry and developers to their areas to "broaden the tax base." The usual result, when the dust has settled, is that the people who previously lived in the area have a degraded environment and *higher* taxes.

In short, the benefits are easily calculated and quickly reaped by a select few; the costs, on the other hand, are diffuse, spread over time, and difficult to calculate. For example, how would one assess the cost of weather modification by pollution, which might result in the death of millions from starvation? What is the value of an ecological system destroyed by chlorinated hydrocarbons or of one death from emphysema?

The disparity between present methods of cost-benefit analyses and the real costs borne by society is even more obvious when the problem of industrial pollution is considered. Here the benefit is usually the absence of a cost. Garbage is spewed into the environment, rather than being retained and reclaimed. The industry avoids real or imagined financial loss by this process (the term "imagined loss" is used because some industries have found that reclaiming pollutants has more than paid for the cost of retaining them). More often than not, however, the industry benefits, and the public pays the short- and long-term costs. Air pollutants damage crops, ruin paint, soil clothes, dissolve nylon stockings, etch glass, rot windshield wiper blades, and so on. Pollutants must be removed, often at considerable expense, from water supplies. People with emphysema, lung cancer, liver cancer, and hepatitis must be given expensive hospitalization. Insurance costs go up. In these, and in myriad more subtle ways, *everyone* pays. These costs are what accountants euphemistically call "external diseconomies," because they are external to the accounting system of the polluter. A persuasive case can be made that these diseconomies far outweigh the benefits of growth. Such a case has been made recently in some detail by economist Ezra Mishan in his book *The Costs of Economic Growth*.

One way to attack external diseconomies would be to require industry to internalize them. They could be forced to absorb the costs by laws prohibiting the release of any pollutants. Profits would have to be added on after *all* costs were paid. Clearly, the only solution is for society to insist on pollution abatement at the source. It would be cheaper in every way to curtail it there, rather than attempt to ameliorate the complex problems pollutants cause once they are released into the environment.

Society, having permitted the pollution situation to develop, should now shoulder some of the burden of its correction. As a theoretical example,

Steel Company X, located on the shores of Lake Michigan, is pouring filth into the lake at a horrendous rate. A study shows that it would cost $2.00 per share of common stock to build the necessary apparatus for retaining and processing the waste. Should the company be forced to stop polluting and pay the price? Certainly they must be forced to stop, but it seems fair that society should pay some of the cost. When Company X located on the lake, everyone knew that it would spew pollutants into the lake, but no one objected. The local people wanted to encourage industry. Now, finally, society has changed its mind; the pollution must stop. But how much should Mrs. Jones of Philadelphia pay for its abatement? Last year Widow Jones put all of her husband's insurance money into 1,000 shares of Company X common stock. It is not reasonable for society to assess her $2,000 to clean up the mess. Alderman Brown, who 30 years ago was instrumental in attracting Company X to the lake, owns no shares at all. He would not have to pay a cent. Clearly society should order the pollution stopped, *and pick up at least part of the bill.* It would be a bargain in the long run. Society is already paying a much higher cost for the pollution. The legal tools for forcing compliance with pollution-abatement decisions are essentially at hand.

The task of cleaning up the environment, however, will not be an easy one. Powerful opposition can be expected from economic interests. Such opposition has already been mounted by the petrochemical industry, whose behavior may foreshadow that of other industries. Ever since the publication in 1962 of Rachel Carson's book *Silent Spring,* which was addressed to the public at large, the petrochemical industry has applied constant political pressure (through friends in Congress and such agencies as the USDA) and has resorted to outright lies about the safety of pesticides in order to avoid regulation. The industry has attempted to discredit responsible scientists who have nothing to sell, but who oppose current patterns of pesticide usage because they have learned through careful and patient study that DDT and related pesticides are not mere killers of insects but threaten the capacity of the Earth to support human life. Desperately worried biologists have attempted, through public education and by going to court, to keep more of these poisons from entering the environment, and concerned conservationists have done what they can. But until 1969 the petrochemical industry was successful in forestalling any effective regulation of its activities.

The industry's tactics were typified by an editorial that appeared in the journal *Farm Chemicals* (January 1968), which not only labeled every biologist critical of current pesticide practice as a member of a "cult" and a "professional agitator," but also claimed that "scientists themselves literally ostracized Rachel Carson, and they will come to grips with this eroding force within their own ranks. Of course, it is not unusual that the character of the scientific community is changing. It may be a sign of the times. The age of opportunism!" This editorial appeared four years after Rachel Carson's death, yet the ghost of this remarkably sensitive and extremely capable marine biologist apparently still haunted those whose products she had found were dangerously polluting the environment.

Unquestionably, some chemists and entomologists attempted to discredit

Rachel Carson. Most of those who did, however, were either employed by the petrochemical industry or were too narrowly trained (as most entomologists are) to appreciate the dangers in the use of such powerful chemicals. Scientists in other disciplines disagreed with her too, but for the wrong reasons: some argued that she was speaking outside of her field of expertise; others charged her with emotionalism. Hundreds of biologists, however, admired her tremendously for awakening the general public to the hazards posed by the use of dangerous chemicals in attempts to increase the production of food.

It is true that there were a few factual errors in *Silent Spring,* but in many ways Rachel Carson *underestimated* the hazards of DDT and other chlorinated hydrocarbons. Nevertheless, she succeeded in awakening the public— and did so in a way that a more "technical" and highly documented book like Robert L. Rudd's *Pesticides and the Living Landscape* could not do. Rudd, a zoologist, came to many of the same conclusions that were presented in *Silent Spring,* but because his book was not addressed to the general public it did not engender the level of attack that was directed toward *Silent Spring.* In our opinion, no biologist has made a greater contribution to mankind in this century than Rachel Carson.

The petrochemical industry is now on the defensive because biologists and other citizens have discovered that there are still some legal remedies against being poisoned, and, through the Environmental Defense Fund, they are using these remedies. It seems unlikely that the reaction of the industry is based on the DDT or chlorinated hydrocarbon issue alone. A more likely reason is apprehension about the precedents which will be set if any or all these chemicals are banned or restricted in use. The industry would prefer to account primarily to the friendly and compliant USDA, not to groups of scientists who are concerned with the ecological effects and long-term dangers to human health caused by their activities. But even the USDA finally seemed to see the handwriting on the wall, as in late 1969 it began to discuss, along with the Department of Health, Education and Welfare and the Department of the Interior, the phasing out of all "nonessential" uses of DDT. It is too early to tell whether this will lead to the necessary, almost total discontinuance of hard pesticides throughout the world—and, of course, even if it does it may be too late. But even this glacially slow and possibly token step is in the right direction.

Defensive reactions similar to that of the pesticide manufacturers can be expected from other industries whose activities contribute heavily to pollution. Representatives of the inorganic nitrogen fertilizer industry have given extensive testimony before Congress which confirmed the belief of biologists that the industry simply cannot (or does not want to) grasp the dimensions of the problems that result from the failure to maintain an adequate supply of humus in the soil.

It is most difficult to protect the environment when economists, industries, and governmental agencies team up to wreak havoc, as in the case of the supersonic transport. The SST is "justified" in the United States largely on the grounds that it is needed economically to protect the balance of payments. President Nixon, in endorsing the SST program in 1969, stated, "I want the United States to continue to lead the world in air transport." The economic penalties which will be incurred from sonic boom damage were probably not included in the administration's consideration of whether to proceed with the project, nor were the psychological and emotional damages that people will suffer, nor the possible effects on the world's climate (which themselves may cause heavy economic damage) of the operation of these high-altitude jets.

If our government is serious about leading the world in air transport, it could ban the building of American SSTs, ban the operation of foreign SSTs over U.S. territory, forbid American travel agents to book passengers on foreign airlines which fly SSTs, and try to persuade other governments to abandon their SST projects. At the same time, real effort could be put into improving air safety, alleviating airport congestion, and improving transportation to, from, and within airports.

The problem of preventing environmental deterioration caused in part by governmental agencies will almost certainly have to be attacked by changes in governmental structure. A start would be the establishment of an Office of Environmental Quality (OEQ) with power to restrain agencies, at least temporarily, that propose destructive projects. A landmark bill of this sort was introduced into the Senate by Senator Joseph Tydings in 1969. The bill would create an OEQ with the power to delay such projects for 180 days. A bill similar in spirit, though somewhat weaker (but perhaps more politically feasible), was introduced into the House by Congressman John D. Dingell of Michigan. The fate of these bills is not known at this writing, but even if one were passed it would only be the first step. In the executive branch, President Nixon in early 1969 established a Cabinet-level Environmental Quality Council, which it is hoped will coordinate the federal fight against environmental deterioration and help establish environmental policies. Whether it will be effective is very doubtful (Box 11-1). In any event ways must be found to block permanently such projects as the SST, and to curb the power of such semiautonomous and frequently destructive agencies as the Army Corps of Engineers.

Ideally a new government Department of Population and Environment should be created which would include the old Department of the Interior, the "Health" functions of the Department of Health, Education and Welfare, the Bureau of the Census (now in the Department of Commerce), a demilitarized "Corps of Engineers," and, most important, a large and powerful Office of Environmental Quality. The OEQ would be charged with constant monitoring of all environmentally critical governmental projects, with special attention being paid to the activities of the Department of Agriculture, Department of Housing and Urban Development, and Department of Transportation. This would be a unique function, since Federal Departments normally do not now exercise control over the activities of other Departments. The DPE would become the most important Department in the government, and well it should be. It would be responsible for establishing and maintaining quality standards for the lives of all Americans, and regulating the size of our population so that such standards can be met. It would be the major center of policy planning relative to the environment, and would carry out a program of public education in that general area. It could coordinate the equivalent of Stewart Udall's ambitious "Project 76," a complete renovation of the American environment,

---

BOX 11-1   ENVIRONMENTAL QUALITY COUNCIL AND COMMITTEE

On May 29, 1969 President Nixon created an *Environmental Quality Council* and a *Citizens' Advisory Committee on Environmental Quality*. The Council is composed of the Vice President and the Secretary of Agriculture, Secretary of Commerce, Secretary of Health, Education and Welfare, Secretary of Housing and Urban Development, Secretary of the Interior, and Secretary of Transportation. Various other officials may participate in the deliberations of the Council as observers. The Science Advisor to the President was designated Executive Secretary of the Council. The Council was charged with advising and assisting the President on matters related to environmental quality, reviewing Federal policies and programs affecting the environment, fostering Federal, State and local cooperation in environmental programs, promoting pro-environment technology, and so forth.

The *Citizens' Advisory Committee* was to consist of a chairman and not more than 14 additional members appointed by the President, and serves to advise the President and the Council.

Laudatory as these first steps toward a rational environmental policy may be, it is evident to those familiar with the functioning of our government that the Council and Committee will be unable even to start to save our environment. We badly need a strong independent agency, responsible only to the President, whose sole mission is to deal forcefully with the problems of population and environment. The Council does not begin to qualify. As Congressman Dingell, a champion of a national policy for the en-

vironment, put it, ". . . a Secretary of Agriculture or Interior or HEW or HUD is so busy with day-to-day problems of administration, handling programs, dealing with Congress, and fighting with the Congress over budgets and the Bureau of the Budget and other executive agencies, that he has very little time to deal with the field."

Congressional hearings on *Environmental Quality* were held in May and June of 1968 by the House Subcommittee on Fisheries and Wildlife Conservation of the Committee on Merchant Marine and Fisheries (the Subcommittee chaired by Congressman Dingell). Testimony at these hearings brought out clearly the need for a much stronger advisory body, unencumbered by departmental commitments. Perhaps the most interesting testimony was that presented by Dr. Lee A. DuBridge, Science Advisor to the President and a talented physical scientist. (It is revealing that, in a society whose most pressing problems are environmental and behavioral, we still draw on the physical sciences for our highest level of advice!). Dr. DuBridge's testimony, a long and unsuccessful attempt to defend the President's Council as adequate, illustrates beautifully the entrapment of a bright and dedicated man in the morass of bureaucracy and interbranch rivalry. His testimony, pp. 355–401 of the published transcript (Series No. 41–6, U.S. Government Printing Office), should be read by all of those interested in the problem of getting the United States government to deal effectively with the current crisis. Indeed, the entire transcript of the hearings is of great interest.

especially that of the cities, in the last quarter of this century. The DPE would encourage the establishment of similar departments in state governments to handle policy planning within states, cooperate in enforcing pollution control, help the USDA train agricultural agents in ecologically sophisticated farming methods, exercise demographic controls, and so forth. With such broad responsibility, a large pool of funds would be needed; the possible sources of such funds are discussed later in this chapter. Furthermore, the DPE would have to be kept carefully under the control of the President and the scrutiny of the public so that it would not be captured by special interests, as most other Federal Departments and Agencies have been.

Needless to say, sundry other changes in our government are needed; as many have recognized, its structure is no longer suitable for the task before it. The fragmentation of responsibility among government agencies makes even less sense than the university departmental structure mentioned earlier. The lack of overall control of environmental matters and the impossibility of dealing with problems in any coordinated way are illustrated by the fact that the area of urban affairs comes under the jurisdiction of the Department of Housing and Urban Development, the Department of Health, Education and Welfare, and the Departments of Labor, Commerce, Interior, Justice, and Transportation, to name just the main ones. It is clear that the Executive branch needs reorganizing, and that substantial changes in the Legislative branch are also called for.

Perhaps one of the most fundamental changes needed is that an upper age limit—of perhaps 65 years—be established for appointed and elected federal officials. The advice of older people who have experience and wisdom could still be sought, but the actual work of running the country in our complex world is simply too great a strain for most older men, especially in an era when instant worldwide communications are capable of putting extraordinary loads of responsibility on individuals. A second reason for age limits is the principle that in a dangerous and rapidly changing world those responsible for making decisions should have a reasonable expectation of having to live with the consequences of those decisions. A 65-year old retirement age might mean the loss of some fine talent, but wise men can always be consulted, and it has become clear that some way must be found to keep the senile out of powerful positions.

The communications problem is especially severe for the President, who must now serve functions previously delegated to ambassadors and military commanders in the field. The time may have come to divide the Executive into two branches, one concerned with domestic matters, the other with international affairs. Each could be headed by a co-president assisted by an executive officer whose role would be an expanded version of that now played by the vice-president. This suggestion may be bad or impractical but it is high time our governmental system was modernized, and serious examination of such problems is urgently required. Some cogent suggestions on upgrading the Legislative Branch may be found in the books listed in the bibliography of this chapter. The Center for the Study of Democratic Institutions has had, under the direction of R. G. Tugwell, an ongoing project designed to produce a modern constitution for the United States. This project deserves much more publicity, and the constitution, now in its 34th draft, deserves wide circulation and study.

It may well be necessary for a new political party to be formed, one founded on the principles of population control, environmental quality, and a stabilized economy. Such a party would be national and international in its orientation, rather than basing its power on parochial issues as our current parties do. In 1854 the Republican party was created *de novo,* founded on the platform of opposition to the extension of slavery. It seems probable that in the 1970's the environmental issue will become even more prominent than the slavery issue was in the 1850's, and the creation of a powerful new party might be possible. It could, indeed, grow out of Zero Population Growth, an organization founded in 1968 to take political action on issues of population and environment.

Obviously such changes as those briefly proposed above will threaten not only numerous politicians of both major parties, but many economic institutions and practices. They are likely to be opposed by vast segments of the Industrial State; by much of the oil and petrochemical industry, the steel industry, the automobile industry, the nuclear power industry, the heavy construction industry, and by many subdividers, the Army Corps of Engineers, the USDA, the AEC, the Chamber of Commerce, to name only a few. Even a cursory knowledge of the pervasive nature and degree of control of these interests leads to the conclusion that the necessary change in attitudes and behavior is extremely unlikely among the individuals and organizations where it would be most helpful. But the name of the game is human *survival,* and each one of us is dealt in, whether we like it or not. These individuals and organizations have an unprecedented opportunity to help everyone win. Will they accept the challenge?

Bibliography

Barach, Arnold B., 1964. *U.S.A. and Its Economic Future.* Macmillan, New York. Semipopular and concise.

Bolling, Richard, 1965. *House Out of Order.* E. P. Dutton, New York. Critique of the House of Representatives by a congressman.

Boulding, Kenneth E., 1966. The economics of the coming spaceship earth. *In* H. Jarrett (ed.), *Environmental Quality in a Growing Economy,* Johns Hopkins Press, Balt. A superb article about making the transition from a "cowboy" economy to a "spaceman" economy.

Cipolla, Carlo M., 1965. *The Economic History of World Population*. Penguin Books, Baltimore.

Clark, Colin, 1967. *Population Growth and Land Use*. Macmillan, London. The author of this book once claimed on a television show that India would be the richest country in the world in ten years or so *because* of population growth! Read his book, paying careful attention to his treatment of environmental problems.

Clark, Joseph S., 1964. *Congress: The Sapless Branch*. Harper & Row, New York. Senator Clark criticizes our moribund legislature.

Dales, J. H., 1968. *Pollution, Property, and Prices*. Univ. of Toronto Press, Toronto. An economist's suggestions for cleaning up our environment.

Enke, Stephen, 1966. The economic aspects of slowing population growth. *The Economic Journal,* vol. LXXVI, no. 301 (March), pp. 44–56.

Enke, Stephen, and Richard G. Zind, 1969. Effects of fewer births on average income. *Journal of Biological Sciences,* vol. 1, pp. 41–55.

Fagley, Richard M., 1960. *The Population Explosion and Christian Responsibility*. Oxford Univ. Press, New York. A Protestant perspective on the population explosion, and a good source of religious attitudes toward population control.

Galbraith, John K., 1967. *The New Industrial State*. Signet, New York. A most interesting, logical and controversial thesis about the nature of the military-industrial-university-government complex.

Gardner, John, 1964. *Self-Renewal: The Individual and the Innovative Society*. Harper & Row, New York. A personal approach to change within the individual and within society.

Hamilton, William F., II, and Dan K. Nance, 1969. Systems analysis of urban transportation. *Scientific American,* vol. 221, no. 1 (July). Problems of urban transport and some possible solutions.

Hardin, Garrett, 1969. *Population, Evolution, and Birth Control* (2nd ed.). W. H. Freeman and Company, San Francisco.

Heller, Walter (ed.), *Perspectives on Economic Growth*. Random House, New York. A compendium of the conventional wisdom of economic growth.

Hilu, Virginia (ed.), 1967. *Sex Education and the Schools*. Harper & Row, New York.

Jacoby, Neil H., 1969. The progress of peoples. *Center Occasional Papers,* vol. 2, no. 4. A most interesting discussion of the problems of development.

Jarrett, Henry (ed.), 1966. *Environmental Quality in a Growing Economy*. Johns Hopkins Press, Baltimore. An interesting collection—see especially the article by Boulding, "The Economics of the Coming Spaceship Earth."

Kozal, Jonathan, 1967. *Death at an Early Age*. Houghton Mifflin, Boston. A devastating examination of one of our educational system's major failures.

Lear, John (ed.), 1968. Science, technology, and the law. *Saturday Review,* Aug. 3. This is one of a series of five essays, all of which are pertinent to the question of the law and our population and environmental problems.

Leonard, George B., 1968. *Education and Ecstasy*. Delacorte Press, New York. A most thoughtful and original book on education. Highly recommended.

Lowe, David, 1966. *Abortion and the Law*. Pocket Books, New York.

Lundberg, Ferdinand, 1968. *The Rich and the Super-rich*. Bantam Books, New York. An eye-opening book for those bedazzled by people's capitalism and the high-school civics class versions of how our government functions.

McKeown, Thomas, 1965. *Medicine in Modern Society*. Allan and Unwin, London.

Mishan, Ezra J., 1967. *The Costs of Economic Growth*. Frederick A. Praeger, New York. An excellent discussion.

Nelson, Bryce, 1967. Scientist and citizen: St. Louis group broadens educational role. *Science,* vol. 157, pp. 903–905. Description of a major effort by scientists to involve the public in the technological decisions of society.

O'Brien, Fr. John A., 1968. *Family Planning in an Exploding Population*. Hawthorne Books, Inc., New York. Statements by scholars inside and outside of the Catholic church, edited by an outstanding Catholic theologian who has strongly disagreed with the Church's stand on birth control.

Pearson, Drew, and Jack Anderson, 1968. *The Case Against Congress*. Simon and Schuster, New York.

Pilpel, Harriet, 1965. Sex vs. the Law. *Harper's Magazine,* January.

Pilpel, Harriet, 1969. The right of abortion. *Atlantic Monthly,* June. The ethical and legal aspects of abortion.

Platt, John, 1969. What we must do. *Science,* vol. 166, pp. 1115–1121. A classification of the urgency of our multiplicity of crises and suggestions on how we might meet them.

Samuelson, Paul A., 1967. *Economics: An Introductory Analysis,* 7th ed. McGraw-Hill, New York. One of the great texts of all time.

Spengler, Joseph J., 1960. Population and world economic development. *Science,* vol. 131, pp. 1497–1502.

Udall, Stewart L., 1968. *1976, Agenda for Tomorrow*. Harcourt, Brace & World, Inc., New York. See especially Chapter 8, "The renewal of politics." Many cogent points made on population, environment, and the quality of life.

CHAPTER 12

The International Scene

*"Let us in all our lands . . . including this land . . .
face forthrightly the multiplying problems of our
multiplying populations and seek the answers
to this most profound challenge to the future
of all the world. Let us act on the fact that
five dollars invested in population control
is worth one hundred dollars invested
in economic growth."*

President Lyndon B. Johnson
Speech to United Nations
June 25, 1965

Assuming the United States makes a start on solving its own serious domestic problems, what might Americans do to help improve conditions for people in the underdeveloped world? To date we have in general done more to worsen their situation than to improve it. We have, since World War II, expanded our economic horizons to the far corners of the Earth, investing many billions of dollars to develop a trade network designed in our own self-interest. Like other powerful nations, we have used economic, political, and military means to maintain this network. Our comparatively small foreign aid programs are far more economic and political in orientation than humanitarian; our resources have been devoted to providing additional material goods for ourselves and to an expensive and dangerous arms race, rather than to the improvement of the lot of our fellow men. It is time that our past performance be re-evaluated and a new set of national objectives be established in relation to the rest of the world.

Latin America and the United States

American relationships with UDCs are exemplified by our behavior toward Latin America. When Sol Linowitz resigned in 1969 as U.S. Ambassador to the Organization of American States, he warned of the possibility of "a series of Vietnams" in Latin America. The same year Governor Nelson Rockefeller, on fact-finding tours south of the border for President Nixon, was greeted with a violence that underlined the Linowitz warning. Rockefeller was, of course, an especially ironic choice since his family's Standard Oil empire is so much a symbol of U.S. economic imperialism. But one does not have to look far for more fundamental reasons for his reception. Population growth in Latin America is proceeding at an average rate of 2.9 percent per year; during the first eight years of the "Alliance for Progress," economic growth only averaged about 1.5 percent per year, a full percentage point below the Alliance target. Latin Americans are, for the most part, living in appalling poverty. Diets are inadequate, infant and child mortality sky-high, and decent houses often nonexistent. If 10,000 houses *per day* were built in Latin America between 1969 and 1979, something on the order of 100 million of our southern neighbors (more than one-fifth of the expected population) would still be inadequately housed at the end of that time.

Latin America's political instability is legendary (Fig. 12-1). Between 1961 and 1969 democratically elected governments have fallen to military coups in Argentina, Bolivia, Brazil, Dominican Republic, Ecuador, Guatemala, Honduras, Panama and Peru. Although land reform is beginning to take place in some countries, most recently in Peru, progress toward a more equitable distribution of what income there is has been slow. Some 10 percent of the people still own 90 percent of the land. Resentment toward the United States is widespread. Although the days when American corporations directly controlled small countries are over, there is a huge reservoir of ill-will remaining from the days when the U.S. openly took what it wanted of the mineral and vegetable wealth of the continent. United States economic exploitation of Latin America is still far from over, but some U.S. companies are now so well behaved that they can serve as examples of benevolence, and have made enormous contributions to their host nations.

In 1969 Latin American governments, meeting at Viña del Mar, Chile, drew up a memorandum presenting their program for improving U.S.–Latin American economic relations. They requested the United States to lower its tariff barriers against Latin American goods, and asked for a preferential market for their manufactured goods. Basically they sought redress for the economic imbalance in which Latin America still gives to the United States more than it receives in return. American aid to Latin America amounted to $11 billion in the first eight years of the Alliance. But profits extracted by U.S. corporations operating in Latin America, interest on American loans, and arrangements in which aid funds must be spent for goods on the expensive U.S. markets (and shipped on U.S. ships) have more than compensated for the aid.

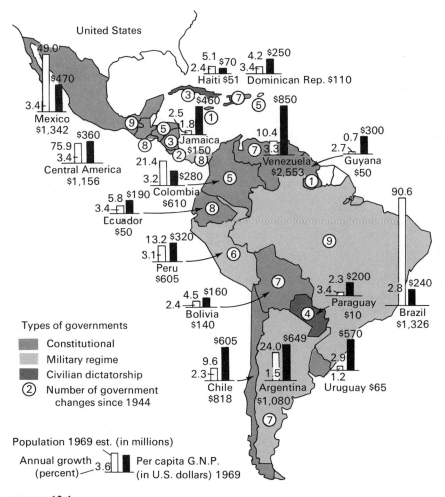

FIGURE 12-1

Latin American Summary: population, per capita gross national product, form of government, number of government changes since 1944, amounts of American investment. [Various sources.]

The announced result of Governor Rockefeller's trip means disappointingly little change in U.S. policies toward Latin America. More equitable economic relations are to be fostered through tariff changes and other means, and the policy of economic "punishment" for governments that nationalize such local industries as copper without compensating to their satisfaction the American companies that developed them is to be abandoned. Whether these changes will be far-reaching enough to counteract to some degree Latin American resentment of economic exploitation remains to be seen; that they can reverse the present exploitative situation is too much to expect. Rockefeller also recommended that the U.S. continue to support all governments that happen to be in power (whether we approve of them or not) and that we sell arms and military equipment to them when requested, a policy which can only contribute to the volatility of the Latin American political situation.

There is little question that American economic interests will be the source of continuing potential trouble with Latin America. Our corporations have an investment of more than $10 billion in the area, much of it concerned with the extraction of nonrenewable resources that are in critically short supply. Major examples are a $2 billion investment in Venezuelan oil, and a $½ billion investment in Chilean copper. As the long-term significance of continued U.S. exploitation of these and other resources becomes clear to Latin Americans, the resulting resentment may be catastrophic for American interests and for the regimes that permit the exploitation.

Development and the Environment

In general the flow of aid from DCs to UDCs has thus far been much too little and too ecologically inept. The United Nations, for instance, declared that 1960–1970 was to be the "Development Decade." Each DC was urged to contribute 1 percent of its GNP to the UDCs during that period. But even that pathetic goal was not achieved. In the calendar year 1967, for instance, United States foreign-aid grants (nonmilitary) totalled 1.8 billion dollars, out of a GNP of 790 billion. That is less than *one-fourth* of the level advocated by the U.N. In addition, the aid that has been given has too often been wasted or has even done direct harm, although some direct benefits have also accrued. We have supplemented our economic aid with military aid, with very limited demonstrable advantage to ourselves or to the average citizens of the recipient countries. A certain amount of economic aid has gone into prestige items—for example, airlines and steel plants, in countries that lack food and housing for their people. But the desire for such "monuments" is understandable in a world dominated by Western economic values.

Even more important has been the ecological incompetence of some development programs, a direct consequence of the environmental nearsightedness which has so long afflicted the politicians and technologists of the DCs. Western technology exported to the UDCs has certainly been a mixed blessing, whether or not that technology has been part of a formal aid program. The consequences of the export of death control technology to the demographic stiuation have been examined earlier, as have such problems as are created by the disastrous export of our pesticide technology to places like the Cañete Valley of Peru. The list, however, runs far beyond this: the misuse of pesticides in Malaysia, the promotion of insects to pest status by irrigation in Israel, the encouragement of schistosomal parasites in Africa, soil deterioration and erosion in many areas, and so forth. In almost every case, great problems could have been avoided or ameliorated if an ecologically sound approach had been taken.

What is perhaps the classic example of misplaced aid in development has been supplied by the Soviet Union. This is the construction of the Aswan High Dam, which may well prove to be the ultimate disaster for Egypt. As is characteristic of much foreign aid, the ecological consequences and social alternatives were not considered in advance. Irrigation from the dam project will not increase food production enough to feed the number of people that will have been added to the Egyptian population during the dam's construction period. In addition, it seems certain that the conversion of some 500 miles of Nile floodplain from a one-crop system of irrigation to a four-crop rotation system will have deleterious effects on the health of that population. The introduction of perennial irrigation creates conditions that are ideal for the spread of certain snails, which are the intermediate hosts of the blood flukes that cause the serious parasitic disease *bilharzia*. Parasitologists expect the Aswan Dam to be the ultimate cause for an explosive outbreak of this disease. Furthermore, the change in the flow of the Nile has had deleterious effects on fisheries in the eastern Mediterranean. It will also have a negative impact on the fertility of the soil of the Nile Delta, since nutrients were previously deposited annually by the Nile flood, which the Aswan Dam will restrain. This problem will be exacerbated by growing several crops a year. Attempts to solve it will undoubtedly include an accelerating use of inorganic fertilizers, with attendant ecological complications.

On the plus side, new fisheries may become established in the Mediterranean and in Lake Nasser (forming behind the dam), it is conceivable that new drugs will help control bilharzia, and technology may be able to maintain yields on the newly irrigated land. But even if most of the problems created by the dam can be solved, two important principles will not be changed. The first is that *all* major development projects are bound to have ecological consequences, which should be carefully evaluated at the time of *planning,* not dealt with haphazardly after the deed is done. The second is that an effort equal to the Aswan Dam project channeled into population control would have benefitted Egypt far beyond the rewards of a totally problem-free dam, especially since in the long run the reservoir behind the dam will silt up and become useless.

Bringing land under cultivation through irrigation has long been recognized as no permanent solution to population-food imbalances. Charles Galton Darwin pointed out that the Sukkur Barrage on the Indus River, diverting water to irrigate 6 million acres of India, did not result in adequate diets for people who were previously hungry. As he put it, "After a few years the effect was only to have a large number of people on the verge of starvation instead of a small number." Population can easily increase enough to overstrain any resource, which is precisely what is happening in Egypt today. In 1969 the birth rate in the United Arab Republic was estimated to be 43, the death rate 15, and the growth rate 2.9 percent (doubling time 24 years). In this context the Aswan Dam project, which required more than a decade to construct and added an equivalent of 2 million acres, one-third of the previously cultivated land, to the arable pool, is a small project indeed. The UAR will have to complete the equivalent of four more

Aswan Dam projects in the next 24 years just to maintain its present inadequate level of nutrition. Worst of all, the propaganda associated with the Aswan Dam has lulled many Egyptians and others into a false sense of security, so that little has been done either to control the population of the UAR or to improve her stagnant agriculture.

Development: A New Approach

As should be apparent by now, the problems of "development" are a complex of population, food, environmental, social, political, and economic problems. Population growth, for instance, is in itself a major barrier to economic development. Goran Ohlin wrote in *Population Control and Economic Development:* "The simple and incontestable case against rapid population growth in poor countries is that it absorbs very large amounts of resources which may otherwise be used both for increased consumption and above all, for development . . . The stress and strain caused by rapid demographic growth in the developing world is actually so tangible that there are few, and least of all planners and economists of the countries, who doubt that per capita incomes would be increased faster if fertility and growth rates were lower . . ."

But although economic problems are important in "development," there are many reasons why most UDCs cannot (and should not) be industrialized along DC lines. The most impressive constraints are probably the environmental ones, especially those associated with pollution, and thermal limits. As one biologist put it, "Just think of what would happen to the atmosphere if 700 million Chinese started driving big automobiles!" But even below these limits it seems highly unlikely that the problems posed by the depletion of nonrenewable resources would permit more than a very limited industrial development of most UDCs, unless, of course, there were some sort of massive de-industrialization of most DCs. The most pressing problem of the UDCs is one of ecologically sensible agricultural development, with supporting facilities for distribution, storage, and marketing—that is, for "semi-development." But as already noted, agricultural development is necessarily connected with general economic improvement; road building, fertilizer production, farm machinery availability, increased demand, etc., are all involved.

If industrialization is not going to occur in the UDCs, how then are they to semi-develop? The answer lies in the DC-UDC relationship. Without a drastic change in DC attitudes and aid patterns, the UDCs are not going to develop in any sense; rather, most are likely to collapse into chaos.

The value of population control in aid programs to UDCs has been studied intensively. Economist Stephen Enke has done much of the analysis, and his conclusions may be summarized in three points: (1) channeling economic resources into population control rather than production growth "could be 100 or so times more effective in raising *per capita* incomes in many UDCs"; (2) an effective birth control program might cost only 30 cents per capita per year, about 3 percent of current development programs; (3) the use of bonuses to promote population control is "obvious in countries where the 'worth' of permanently preventing a birth is roughly twice the income per head." Enke's results are strongly supported by recent computer simulation work by Stanford systems analyst Douglas Daetz, who examined the effects of various kinds of aid in a labor-limited, nonmechanized agricultural society. His results brought into sharp question the desirability of aid programs not coupled with population control programs. They might provide temporary increases in the standard of living, but these are soon eaten up by population expansion. In many circumstances population growth and aid inputs may interact to cause the standard of living to decline below the pre-aid level.

The necessity for population control to permit even semi-development of UDCs is thus plain from practical experience (per capita income gains being small in the face of record population growth) and from economic analysis and computer simulation. The obstacles to UDC development go far beyond this, however. The underdeveloped world today has an entirely different unfavorable demographic situation that differs markedly from that of the DCs during their industrialization. In addition, the UDCs face competition from the DCs if they attempt to compete in international markets for manufactured goods. Most of today's DCs did not have vastly more advanced nations to compete with when they were developing. This is one factor which keeps UDCs in the role of commodity producers, concentrating on the production of agricultural goods and minerals. Furthermore, the UDCs generally lack the cultural traditions which led to industrialization in the DCs. As economist Neil Jacoby of the University of California put it, "development requires a people to choose a new set of philosophical values." The UDCs do, however, have the advantage (or potential advantage) of the accessibility of the technological expertise of the DCs.

There is still considerable debate among economists on technical points of policies relating to development. Tariff and trade policies are especially in dispute, with UDCs arguing strongly for measures to raise prices of their commodities and to obtain trade preferences. These measures have generally been opposed by the DCs, and the United Nations Conferences on Trade and Development (UNCTAD) have generally seen battle lines drawn on a DC-UDC basis. The UDCs claim that there is a built-in bias in world trade and finance in favor of the DCs, and they see in UNCTAD an opportunity to eliminate or even reverse that bias. Also disputed are the roles of colonial history and traditions, the present political decision-making apparatus, land reform, and a wide array of governmental economic policies. Unfortunately, the usual narrow focus on economics characterizes these discussions. For instance, economists often point out that the coffee trade has "enriched" Brazil, ignoring the ecological effects of what Georg Borgstrom describes as the "almost predatory exploitations by the coffee planters." Brazil's dependence on this commodity has not only ruined much of her soil, but is also a major reason why she cannot adequately feed her population today.

The economic and political aspects of UDC development and DC-UDC relationships are extremely complex. But whatever the "answers" are to the disputed policy points, it has become abundantly clear that no solution to the general problem can be found until, in effect, the rules of the game are changed. In our opinion, major changes must occur in the areas of foreign aid, development, and international politics.

FOREIGN AID

The DCs must recognize that their fates are inextricably bound up with those of the UDCs. They must further recognize that their patterns of resource utilization cannot continue, and that dramatic measures must be taken to effect some level of redistribution of the wealth of the world. Recently two scientists, Dr. C. P. Snow of Great Britain and Dr. Andrei D. Sakharov of the U.S.S.R. have made rather similar proposals along these lines. Dr. Sakharov, "father of the Russian hydrogen bomb" and one of the youngest men ever elected to the Soviet Academy of Sciences, expressed his views in an extraordinary document entitled, "Progress, Coexistence, and Intellectual Freedom," which was not published in the U.S.S.R. Among his many proposals is that after the U.S.A. and the U.S.S.R. have "overcome their alienation" they should collaborate in a massive attempt to save the UDCs. This attempt would be financed by a contribution on the part of the DCs of some 20 percent of their national income over a 15-year period to the effort. Lord Snow, an eminent physicist and novelist, supports the suggestion of Academician Sakharov. He recommended that the rich nations devote 20 percent of their GNP for 10–15 years to the task of population control and development of the poor countries. By the scale of the effort, and by its no-strings-attached nature (a substantial portion might be channeled through international agencies), the people of the "other world" might be convinced that the developed countries *do* care. Though there is much suffering today in the UDCs and more is unavoidable, a substantial lowering of DC-UDC tensions could occur if the UDCs felt that help was really on the way. And, of course, the joint DC effort could help to bring about that community of feeling that psychologists regard as so essential to the abolition of war.

SEMI-DEVELOPMENT

A large-scale effort on the part of the DCs will not suffice, however, unless there are basic changes in the value systems related to development. If industrialization of the entire world is neither possible nor desirable, new standards of value will have to be established which will permit *all* peoples to have access to the basic human needs of adequate food, shelter, clothing, education and medical care, regardless of the economic value of their productivity.

The first question asked of any aid project should be: will it benefit the

people or only the government or some special interest group in the beneficiary country? If the project benefits only the latter groups, it should be
rejected unless it can be proved that it will ultimately benefit the general
population in some real and measurable way. Thus a steel mill might be a
poor project for a UDC, even though it might provide employment and
contribute to the economy. A fertilizer plant, on the other hand, would also
provide employment and benefit the economy. Beyond that, it would produce fertilizers for agricultural development, contributing to the country's
ability to raise its food production and feed its population. An example of a
small-scale program aimed at solving one particular problem with a minimum
of outside intervention and social disruption is described in Box 12-1.

As examples of semi-development, Kenya and Tanzania might be semi-
developed as combination agrarian-recreation areas. They, and some other
African nations, can supply the world with a priceless asset: a window on
the past when vast herds of nonhuman animals roamed the face of the Earth.
They could also provide one of the many living stockpiles of organic diversity,
stockpiles which may prove of immense value as mankind attempts to
replenish the deteriorated ecosystems of the planet. These and similar areas
could serve as rest-and-rehabilitation centers for people from the more
frantic industrialized parts of the planet. They would also serve as guaran-
tors of cultural diversity, as areas specifically reserved to permit peoples to
maintain their traditional ways of life. One of the grim dangers facing
Homo sapiens is the continued homogenizing of cultures, the erosion of
mankind's spectacular array of cultural differences. Urbanization, mass communications, and the explosive spread of Western technology and Judeo-
Christian attitudes have already irretrievably reduced this diversity. But
who is to say that one world view is "better" than another, that a British
scientist's way of structuring the world is superior to that of a Hopi Indian,
that a militant Christianity is superior to a gentle Oriental religion, that the
Australian aboriginal view of kinship is inferior to that of a jet-set sophisti-
cate?

So we need a restructuring of our ideals and values. We need to create a
demand for what Aborigines, Eskimos, Kenyans, and Hondurans can supply,
what might be called cultural resources. These priceless resources are in
short supply, they are dwindling rapidly, and they are nonrenewable. A way
must be found to permit these people access to more of the fruits of industrial societies without attempting to industrialize the entire world. At the
moment the trinkets of industrial civilization have the strongest appeal to
the naive, both within and outside of industrial society. If we continue to
train our own people to think of the automobile and color TV as the finest
achievements of mankind, it seems unlikely that the "rising expectations"
of the UDCs will rise above them either. But if we can learn to recognize
and attempt to correct our own gruesome errors, then perhaps the UDCs
will see their way clear to establishing new goals: development within resource limitations and with careful attention to the *quality* of life.

In short, the DCs must not only give unprecedented aid to the UDCs,
they must help the UDCs to avoid the mistakes made by the DCs. Some-

thing like this message must come across: "By making the fundamental error of basing our standard of progress on expansion of the GNP, we have created a vast industrial complex and great mental, moral, and aesthetic poverty. Our cities are disaster areas, our air often unbreathable, our people increasingly regimented, and our spirit increasingly domitable. We require far too large a slice of the world's resources to maintain our way of life. We, in short, are not developed, we are *overdeveloped*. We now realize that our current patterns of consumption and exploitation cannot and should not be sustained. While we are correcting our mistakes and de-developing, we want to help you to semi-develop—not in our image but in whatever way is most appropriate for your culture."

What semi-development might mean in practice would, of course, differ from area to area. Certainly, ecologically sound agricultural development,

---

BOX 12-1   A PROGRAM TO COMBAT MALNUTRITION

One of the most serious problems in many UDCs is widespread malnutrition, particularly protein malnutrition. This is usually most severe in young children, whose protein needs are greater than those of adults in proportion to body weights, but who are, through their parents' poverty, ignorance, or custom, often given quite restricted diets. This is in many ways a different problem from that of insufficient total food, and requires different solutions.

In Haiti, where fatal malnutrition among children was very common, a program that has attempted to meet this problem, especially to help malnourished children, was initiated in 1959 by the Haitian Department of Public Health in collaboration with the Department of Biochemistry and Nutrition at Virginia Polytechnic Institute, with financial support from Research Corporation, a foundation.

Realizing that lack of transportation and economic conditions made the distribution of a food supplement from elsewhere to isolated villages impractical, and that an unfamiliar food, even if accepted, would probably be too complicated an addition for village cooking methods, the project researchers started by looking for suitable supplements among indigenous food plants. Ultimately, they came up with a happy combination of a cereal (corn, rice, or millet) and any of three varieties of beans. Although separately these were low-quality protein foods, each compensated for the other's amino acid deficiencies, resulting in a mixture containing protein of excellent quality, and a superior source of vitamins as well.

Since Haitian mothers ordinarily feed their children a gruel of cereal, in order to improve the children's diets it was only necessary to convince the mothers to add a handful of beans with every two handfuls of cereal when making the gruel. Beans were already a part of the regular diet; they simply were not customarily fed to very young children.

To introduce the use of the new food mixture to the population, "Mothercraft Centers" were established in villages. Each center was run by a girl with a high-school education and six weeks of special training in child care, including nutrition and sanitation. The thirty most malnourished children in the village were invited to join the center with their mothers. The children were expected to spend six days and the rather than industrialization, should receive priority virtually everywhere. In general the DCs would, where needed, supply medical services, educational facilities and teachers, and especially technical assistance, in population control. Roadways, electrification, and communications adequate to the demands of an agrarian society would be an almost universal need as would help in developing improved local systems of agriculture. In all of these endeavors, the most efficient means of meeting the needs should be the first consideration: how to make the limited resources do the most good. Roads can be built without the sort of heavy machine equipment used in DCs. In fact, the simpler techniques of several decades ago would probably be more efficient in poor countries and would provide employment for unskilled labor (an important consideration since most UDCs have serious unemployment problems). The same is true of electrification and communications; a single

mother one day a week at the center. The girl who ran the center was expected to feed the children exclusively from local market produce and to do it at the same cost per child as the villagers spent. While she and the mothers prepared the food for the children, the center supervisor explained the nutritional and economical reasons for her particular food choices. Thus the mothers learned not only how to obtain better food but also more food for their money.

Within about three weeks, the children's symptoms of malnutrition were disappearing. Originally listless and apathetic, the children became alert, lively, and disobedient. The mothers, unaccustomed to such behavior, thought "that these alert and frisky children were either sick or under a curse of some kind." By the time the first group "graduated" after four months at the center, the mothers had begun to regard the changed behavior of their children as normal. Then the next group was invited to the center.

The program proved to be very successful beyond reducing the incidence of fatal malnutrition among young children. The diets of all the villagers were considerably improved through the mothers' new knowledge of nutrition and economical food-buying.

The Haitian food-supplement program has been a model for the development of similar ones in several countries: Algeria, Brazil, Colombia, Costa Rica, Equador, Guatemala, Nigeria, Peru, Uganda, and Venezuela. Programs of this sort, utilizing indigenous foods that are known to be acceptable, and introducing the new ideas in a sympathetic way, may prove to be among the most effective that have been proposed for alleviating malnutrition. The approach is simple, not horrendously expensive, and it causes a minimum of disruption in the society that the program was designed to help.

The method of introducing the new ideas can also serve as a model for the introduction of many other changes for the society, such as birth control and improved agricultural practices. Indeed, the success of the food-supplement program itself, in greatly reducing child mortality from malnutrition, will soon lead to a need for both in these villages.

power supply or telephone for each village, with its use being shared communally, makes more sense than attempting to provide electricity to each home, which is impossible anyway. Transportation should not be designed along DC lines. Busses, whether imported or locally manufactured, make far more sense than cars, where only a fraction of the population can afford the latter. A suitable vehicle should be provided for UDC farmers, low-powered, economical and sturdy. Several owners of small farms might own one communally, or the government might provide the transport of agricultural produce to market on a pickup and delivery basis.

Farm machinery need not be highly mechanized to be efficient; Japan and Taiwan have developed very efficient agricultural systems without mechanization. Economist Bruce F. Johnston of Stanford University's Food Research Institute has written that "simple, inexpensive farm equipment that is well suited to local manufacture in small- and medium-scale rural workshops" would be far more beneficial to the economies of UDCs and more practical than the use of heavy machinery. Not the least benefit of such a system would be its dependence upon abundant farm labor.

Education is an obvious area for aid, but setting up systems that mimic those of the DCs should be avoided. Education must be tailored to the needs of the local culture, not designed to destroy it. One of the great tragedies of Latin America is its university system, which turns out many attorneys, philosophers, poets, and "pure" scientists, but not the agriculturalists, ecologists, and public-health experts which the area so desperately needs. Education for Eskimos or Bushmen should be designed to produce first-class Eskimos or Bushmen, not caricatures of Americans or Russians, although the option to acquire technical or academic educations should remain open to those who may desire them. These special educations could be available to children of affluent classes at their own expense and to the poor through scholarship programs. Education is particularly an area where innovations in methods are sorely needed. In the past two decades, due mainly to the population explosion, the literacy rate in most UDCs has dropped, not risen. Mass education in traditional Western style of so many children is simply beyond the means of most poor countries. It has been suggested that basic education of the masses be deferred to adulthood (or possibly adolescence), when it can be accomplished far more economically in terms of both time and money; an adult can acquire in a year the equivalent of an entire grade-school education. If effort were now concentrated on adults, including mothers, these adults could then begin to teach their children. Some educational resources might profitably be devoted to producing and distributing locally designed versions of the sorts of toys and games that prepare children in Western societies to learn in school.

Above all, the standard for aid and development should not be to make a nation or area "self-sufficient" in terms of today's economic standards. Just as some areas within Western countries today are maintained at economic expense because they supply other values, so in the future some parts of the world will have to be maintained at economic expense because they supply other values: natural beauty, biological or cultural diversity, survival and happiness for fellow human beings, and, in the long run, survival for us all. Similarly, while some states in the U.S. are largely agricultural, others are heavily industrialized. There is no reason why UDC countries could not be developed differentially, some might have considerable industry and others be limited almost entirely to agricultural development. Such disparate economic entities could perhaps be loosely federated in economic associations similar to the Common Market.

INTERNATIONAL POLITICS

The third area of rule-changing is political. Because of their own backgrounds and capabilities the two most powerful DCs, the U.S.A. and the U.S.S.R. have approached aid differently: the U.S.A., with a vast store of capital to draw on, has seen the problems of the UDCs primarily in terms of a shortage of capital. Shortage of capital is, of course, a major problem. The Soviets, on the other hand, because of their relatively recent history of revolution, and the recent success of revolutions in two UDCs, China and Cuba, tend to emphasize the export not of capital but of political change, of revolution. The need for dramatic political change is obvious in many countries. Haiti (with a per capita GNP of $70) has no chance while it is being ground under the heel of a dictator like Francois Duvalier. A reasonable life cannot be available to the majority of the inhabitants of Angola and Mozambique while the Portuguese control their countries; it is not just a coincidence that these two colonies have among the lowest per capita GNPs on the African continent, 40 and 55 dollars respectively. Moreover, in nominal "democracies" land reform unquestionably is badly needed to give the people incentive to improve their agricultural practices. Revolution might be one way to achieve land reform.

Both the capitalist and revolutionary points of view on aid have a certain validity, but both are also sadly deficient. If progress is to be made, both superpowers will have to change their ways. The United States must stop supporting assorted dictators around the world simply because they are "anti-communist." We must face the fact that in many countries the majority of the people might be better off under a regime that we perceive as "communist" than under their present regimes. Instead of viewing with horror the prospect of a "communist" movement to depose Duvalier, we might encourage it, while exerting every possible legitimate effort to remove him. At the very least we could refrain from helping him to stay in power. In Latin America in particular, the need for social justice as a first step toward economic development has been widely recognized. If badly needed reforms do not take place peacefully, they will sooner or later take place by revolution. It is imperative that U.S. officials in the UDCs realize that their contacts within these countries are all too often totally unrepresentative of the people as a whole.

There is, of course, no doubt that corporate interests, sensitive to the resource poverty of the United States and motivated by the desire for profits, play a substantial role in shaping American foreign policy. The interlocking directorates of our government and various industrial giants are well known. Executives move freely from big business into administrative positions in the government, while high level bureaucrats and military men are welcomed into executive positions with corporations doing government business. The significance of the activities of the Central Intelligence Agency in Latin America, our open military intervention in southeast Asia, Cuba, and the Dominican Republic, and such devices as the Hickenlooper amendment (which discourages expropriation by foreign governments of American property within their territories) is not lost on people in the UDCs.

It seems unlikely that there is much to be gained in attempting immediately to break the power of international corporations that, among other things, are busily engaged in the exploitation of UDC resources. A primary reason is that it probably would be impossible in the absence of dramatic changes in DC attitudes. As long as economic standards reign supreme, economic power will tend to become concentrated; only more fundamental changes will suffice. And these changes must be made with great care. International corporations supply planning coordination, capital, and expertise in their operations in UDCs, and considerable economic hardship could result from the sudden dissolution of the giants.

It is, however, equally evident that the UDCs can undertake, and would profit from control over their own resources and destinies. The contrary view is often held as doctrine by the DCs—but recall the dire and erroneous warnings that the Egyptians would be unable to run the Suez canal when they took it over from the British. Some way must be found to make the people wielding the vast economic power of the West's steel, oil, banking, and other empires realize that their own survival depends on a graceful abdication of much of that power. Such a move would be unprecedented, but so are the dangers mankind faces.

On the other side of the coin, Russia should face the facts of life, too. Blaming all the problems of the world on capitalist imperialism simply is not supported by the evidence. For instance, India has, in many ways, gotten deeper into trouble since she gained her freedom from England. Revolution is not the answer; India today is in great need of thoughtful, technically competent help, especially in achieving population control. No kind of revolution can remove the biological and physical constraints upon development. Furthermore, the Soviet Union's intervention in other countries in defense of what she perceives as her vital interests has been fully as blatant and brutal as that of the "Capitalist Imperialists," as the Czech invasion of 1968 so clearly demonstrated. It is ironic that the U.S.S.R., in the Mediterranean and elsewhere, now seems to be emulating the "gunboat diplomacy" pioneered in the last century by Western European powers and the United States.

In attempting to save the world, the U.S.A. and the U.S.S.R. must not merely lead the way by making resources available; rather than try to bury each other, they must bury their compulsion toward destructive competition to an extent that will permit them to lead the way toward cooperative planning. A simple GNP transfer from DCs to UDCs is probably neither possible nor desirable; the United Nations estimates that the UDCs could not usefully absorb more than $20 billion per year in aid. Much more than "aid" in the familiar sense will be necessary if the world is to be restructured, and much thought must go into ways of increasing the "absorptive power" of the UDCs. It is hardly credible that they are unable to utilize more than $10 per capita in assistance annually (as the UN figure indicates) unless one assumes that only the type of economic aid which has become more or less traditional since 1950 should be given. Clearly, material goods alone worth more than $10 could benefit the average UDC citizen a great deal. We must find ways to revolutionize the DC-UDC aid situation, in part by a reorganization of the economic structure of the world. At the same time care must be taken so that aid does not become counterproductive. Food shipments from the United States hindered the modernization of Indian agriculture in the mid-1960's, and the Aswan Dam has lulled Egypt into a false sense of security. Finding ways to supply aid to UDCs without doing harm to their social and economic structure is a major challenge for the future.

An important problem is that of the allocation of resources. How much should go into improving worldwide systems for food distribution and subsidizing redistribution? How many more agricultural research teams must be trained and established in experiment stations in the UDCs? How many paramedical personnel are to be trained to be salesmen of birth control techniques, where are they to be trained, and how are they to operate? How are communications systems to be set up in the UDCs? Who will run them? Where are the anthropologists, economists, and sociologists to be educated who will help plan the aid programs so they are minimally disruptive and maximally acceptable? What is to be done with the dictators who do not want the lives of their people improved? Which countries should receive outright gifts of food? The questions are exceedingly complex and nearly infinite in number. The kind of planning and decision-making which the Paddocks proposed in their book, *Famine—1975!* will have to be adopted by worldwide policy planning groups (Box 12-2).

It seems likely that, at least at first, a great deal of the financial resources of DCs that are allocated to help the UDCs will involve large expenditures within the DCs themselves—a factor which might make the entire program more palatable to DC citizens. The DCs must plan and initiate their own "dedevelopment," to take the pressure off UDC resources and preserve the Earth's environment. At the same time, ships, wheat, bulldozers, fertilizer, condoms, and many other items will have to be procured and moved to UDCs. Vast education and training programs will have to be established, and scarce talent organized into planning and teaching teams. Many people will be employed in new research programs on everything from efficient integrated control of insects and the psychology of food acceptance to worldwide policy planning to maintain the quality of our environment and prevent international conflict. The challenge of carrying out such an idealistic program is immense. The reward could be survival, and hopefully, a much better world for future generations.

BOX 12-2   TRIAGE

William and Paul Paddock in their book *Famine—1975!* considered the difficult question of how the United States might allocate its limited food aid as the world food situation worsens in the 1970's. They suggested a policy based on the concept of "triage" borrowed from military medicine. Briefly the idea is this: when casualties crowd a dressing station to the point where all cannot be cared for by the limited medical staff, some decisions must be made on who will be treated. For this purpose the triage system of classification was developed. All incoming casualties are placed in one of three classes. In the first class are those who will die regardless of treatment, in the second are those who will survive regardless of treatment, and the third contains those who can be saved only if they are given prompt treatment. When medical aid is severely limited it is concentrated only on the third group; the others are left untreated.

The Paddocks suggest that we devise a similar system for classifying nations. Some will undergo the transition to self-sufficiency without enormous aid from us. They will be ones with abundant money for foreign purchases, or with efficient governments, strong population control programs, and strong agricultural development programs. Although our aid might help them, they could get along without it. The Paddocks suggest that Libya is probably such a country. It has the resources, in the form of oil, that will allow it to purchase food as its population expands. If analysis shows them to be correct, food aid should be withheld from Libya in favor of countries with greater needs.

Some nations, on the other hand, may become self-sufficient if we can give them some food to tide them over. The Paddocks think that Pakistan, at least West Pakistan, might be such a country. If their present leadership is as effective in the pursuit of population control and agricultural development as was former President Ayub Khan, then the Paddocks may be right.

Finally there is the last tragic category: those countries that are so far behind in the population-food game that there is no hope that our food aid could see them through to self-sufficiency. The Paddocks say that India is probably in this category. If so, then under the triage system it should receive no more food.

The crucial lesson which the world should learn from the Paddocks' proposal is the need to evaluate rationally any program to help people, to ask how whatever aid is available can be used to the greatest humanitarian effect. That agricultural experts such as the Paddocks are so dispairing of the food production situation that they feel the necessity of proposing triage should jolt the world into some realization of the predicament. The United States cannot feed the world, and the UDCs cannot avoid massive famines for much more than a decade, no matter how successful programs to expand food production may be. If careful analysis shows the Paddocks to be wrong in their evaluations, then we have perhaps bought a little time before we will again be faced by triage. But if they are right, some form of triage would be preferable to thoughtless dispersal of limited food reserves without regard for their long-range effects.

War

In *The Naked Ape* (1967), Desmond Morris observed that ". . . . the best solution for ensuring world peace is the widespread promotion of contraception and abortion . . . moralizing factions that oppose it must face the fact that they are engaged in dangerous war mongering." As this indicates, and as was discussed in Chapter 3, population-related problems seem to be increasing the probability of triggering a thermonuclear Armageddon. Avoiding such a denouement for *Homo sapiens* is the most pressing political-economic problem of our time.

In 1969 the world saw in a microcosm what may be in store for it. Two grossly overpopulated Central American countries, El Salvador and Honduras, went to war. El Salvador had an estimated population of 3.3 million, a population density of 413 people per square mile, and a doubling time of 21 years. Honduras had a population of 2.5 million, a density of only 57 per square mile, and the same doubling time as El Salvador. More significant statistics have been provided by the Latin American Demographic Center; they show that in El Salvador the population density per square mile of *arable* land was 782 persons, while in Honduras it was only 155 persons. Almost 300,000 Salvadorans had moved into Honduras in search of land and jobs because of the population pressure and resulting unemployment at home. Friction developed among the immigrants and the Honduran natives, El Salvador accused Honduras of maltreating the Salvadorans, and the problem escalated into a brief but nasty war. The conflict was ended by the intervention of the Organization of American States (OAS). In a precedent-shattering move the OAS recognized demographic factors in its formula for settling the dispute. An international body acknowledged that population pressure was a root cause of a war.

Systematic analyses of the role of population pressures in generating wars, carried out by political scientist Robert C. North and his colleagues at Stanford, have begun to support earlier conclusions based on anecdotal evidence. Pilot statistical studies of war involvement of major European powers in modern times have revealed very high correlations among rates of population growth, rising GNP, expanding military budgets, and involvement in wars, although technical considerations make drawing conclusions about causes and effects hazardous. In more detailed multivariate analyses, Professor North has shown a rather complex causal chain involving population growth in relation to static or slowly growing resources, technological development, a tendency to invest energy beyond previous boundaries of society, and increases in the presumed "needs" and demands of a populace. In North's own words, "Differential rates (from society to society) of population growth, technological growth, and access to resources gave rise to differential demands, differential capabilities, and differential expansions of interests and influence, to competitions, conflicts, arms races, crises, and wars."

In ancient times such tendencies were buffered to a degree by oceans, mountain ranges, deserts, vast distances, and slow means of travel. Rome could raze Carthage, but not China or the cities of South and Central American Indians. Today, however, with vast increases of population and unprecedented developments in technology, transportation, and communications, the people of the world are cheek by jowl, and there is little geographical buffering left. North points out that states in nonaggressive phases, like modern Sweden, tend to share certain characteristics: "A relatively small and stable population, a relatively high and steadily developing technology, and good access to resources (either domestic or acquired through favorable trade)."

It is in the area of international conflict above all else that the old rules must be changed. Most national leaders still view war as an extension of politics, as Clausewitz did in the early Nineteenth Century. They have not yet learned that thermonuclear war itself is a far more deadly enemy than any other nation; they still talk of winning, when in reality only losing is possible. It is to be expected that older people will have more trouble in adjusting to change than the young, and changes in the world military situation over the past 25 years have been so unprecedented as to constitute a serious test of even the adaptability of the most flexible young people. It is lamentable that at the time of its most extreme crisis the world is still largely ruled not just by old men, but by an unfortunate selection of old men.

In the United States, the leadership consists mainly of those people who are most likely to have the ethnocentrism of their society embedded in their characters. Our images of leadership and our political and elective processes seem to require this. Our leaders are unlikely to be familiar with the values and attitudes of other cultures. They are equally unlikely to know anything about the psychology of aggression. They are most likely to have deep emotional investments in patriotic ideals and the glorification of the American way of life, and to have contempt for other cultures. Few have any insight into the psychological tricks which we have built into our world view in order to conceal reality. They do not understand why we talk of military "hardware" instead of weapons, why we say we can "take out" an enemy city instead of "destroy it, killing every man, woman, and child," why we talk of "casualties" in Vietnam instead of "dead and maimed." They do not understand how our preconceptions about the Russians, the Chinese, the Cubans, and other unfamiliar peoples badly distort our perceptions of their behavior. *Moreover, American leaders do not understand that the leaders of the other countries have equally distorted perceptions of our actions and motives.* They have no way of understanding. If the men now leading most nations really had been sensitive to such things as cultural relativity, it is unlikely that they ever would have become political leaders.

In spite of these handicaps, there has been an increasing attempt on the part of the American establishment to gain some degree of understanding of the motives of the Russians, and even to open communications with them. The existence of a White House–Kremlin "hotline" testifies to progress in the area of communications. It is, of course, a device to help prevent misinterpretation of Soviet actions by Americans and vice versa. Americans seem to have learned something since the 1950's, when rigidity and paranoia set the tone of our relations with the U.S.S.R. Similarly, Russian leadership has been more reality-oriented since the demise in 1953 of Joseph Stalin. But the change has not been great, and a lack of basic understanding still seems to exist on both sides of the Iron Curtain. While American-Soviet relations have improved somewhat, both nations now find themselves in an old-style confrontation with the Chinese.

The conclusion seems inevitable that if nations continue to collect nuclear arms and biological weapons, sooner or later World War III will occur. And it *will* be the war that ends all wars, at least all world wars, for a very long time, if not forever. Unfortunately a great deal of our governmental policy with regard to national defense is founded on the idea of a "balance of terror," the creation of a group of scientists specializing in what has become known as the "theory of nuclear deterrence." What the politicians apparently do not know (or refuse to believe) is that this theory is based on assumptions which have been demonstrated to be untenable, analyses which are inapplicable, and nonexistent or irrelevant data (see Green's *Deadly Logic* for details). A similar foundation has been developed in parallel by the Soviet Union for their military policy.

Why would presumably intelligent men be taken in by transparent theorizing? Simply because the "analysis" can be conveniently arranged to produce desired results. Naturally the answers are engineered to fit precisely the expectations of the apropriate government officials. Leaders of nations believe that their nations must be *strong* if they are to survive. Nuclear weapons fit right into a pattern which has, for all of man's history, dictated arming against an enemy in order to avoid attack. In the past, if a strong society was attacked, it won. But nations have not been able to adjust to the brand new set of rules. With thermonuclear weapons, regardless of which side is stronger and which attacks, both sides will lose.

Four elements make recognition of the new rules and action based on them difficult. First there are always scientists who tell the politicians that nuclear or CBW wars can be won. If the other side is utterly destroyed and 20 million of us survive the conflict, is that not victory? Remember Senator Russell and his "American Adam and Eve."

A second element is the notion that the weapons will not be used; that the balance of terror will be a stable one. This notion has been examined in detail by behavioral scientists, and few of them seem anxious to bet on it. The basic assumption of rational behavior on the part of leaders is not only weak, but has been contradicted by history. Scientists may make guesses about the "probability" of a thermonuclear war, but they are really no better than the guesses of an informed layman. (A good introduction to this problem is to read the three books by Herman Kahn listed in the bibliography of this chapter, followed by Green's *Deadly Logic,* Frank's *Sanity and Survival,* and finally Robert F. Kennedy's *Thirteen Days.* These will provide the reader with some background for his own predictions).

The third element of difficulty in changing the rules is uncertainty about the best way to achieve disarmament and security in a world where security has usually in the past been provided by brute force, either overtly exercised or used as a threat. Unfortunately the effort going into the study of this aspect of the problem has been infinitesimal compared with that going into military research, although almost no area demands greater immediate attention. The basic need is evident: once again it is a change in human attitudes so that the "in group" against which aggression is forbidden expands to include *all* of humanity.

If this could be accomplished, security might be provided by an armed international organization, a global analogue of a police force. Many people have recognized this as a goal, but the way to reach it remains obscure. The first step might involve partial surrender of sovereignty to an international organization. It seems probable that as long as most people fail to comprehend the magnitude of the threat, that step will be impossible. At the very least we must learn to weigh the risks inherent in attempting controlled disarmament against those run by continuing the arms race. An attempt at disarmament could lead to a war, or the destruction or domination of the United States through Chinese or Soviet "cheating." But, if we were successful at disarming and if we achieved an international police force, the reward would be a very much safer world in which resources would be freed for raising the standard of living for all mankind. Few problems deserve more intensive study. The dynamics of disarmament appear to be even more complex than those of arms races.

The fourth element of difficulty involves economics and the military. Although this will be discussed in terms of the United States, there is every reason to believe that an analogous situation exists in the Soviet Union. Civilians should realize that peace and freedom from tension are not viewed as an ideal situation by many members of the military-industrial-government complex. By and large, professional military officers, especially field grade and higher, hope for an end to the Cold War about as fervently as farmers hope for drought. When there is an atmosphere of national security, military budgets are usually small, military power minimal, and military promotions slow. The founders of the United States recognized that the military services were unlikely to work against their own interests, and carefully established ultimate civilian control over the Army and Navy. It worked rather well for a long time. But times have changed. Wars are no longer fought with simple, understandable things like axes, swords, and cannon. Now we need "weapons systems" with complex and often arcane components, such as acquisition radar, VTOL fighters, doppler navigators, MIRVs, heat-seeking missiles, and nuclear submarines. These cannot be produced rapidly, on demand, by a few government contractors. Long-term planning is required, involving not only the military services, but also a large number of different industrial organizations which supply various components. These organizations, not unnaturally, often hire retired military men to help them in their negotiations with the government, where decisions on armament appropriations are made. The necessary intimacy of the military and industry in areas of weapons development and procurement has thus given rise to the term "military-industrial complex." But the term military-industrial-government complex sometimes seems more accurate.

This complex seems to have a certain aversion to peace, but it is not composed of a group of evil, conspiring men determined to napalm babies and keep the world on the edge of thermonuclear disaster. Rather, it is composed of men who, because of their personal history and associations, are convinced that our only hope of survival lies in confronting the Soviet juggernaut with overwhelming strength. On the other side, of course, their Russian counterparts see Soviet preparedness as the only thing preventing an attack by the capitalists who want to destroy their way of life. The Soviets tend to forget that we did not attempt to destroy them when we enjoyed a nuclear monopoly. Americans on the other hand tend not to appreciate the valid roots of Soviet anti-Western paranoia. Members of both complexes are generally not long on introspection; that by keeping the cold war going they are adding to their own prestige and power is not viewed by them as a major factor in their behavior. In individual instances, however, it must be difficult even for members of the complex to avoid admitting the truth to themselves.

With the military budget now in the vicinity of $80 billion annually, one does not have to look far to find a quick $10 billion a year or so that could be used by the United States to try and save itself and the rest of the world. Unfortunately the strategic arms budget is a rather small part of the total military budget, so that potential "savings" by witholding funds for specific weapons systems are not as large as is often thought. Furthermore if large cuts were made in military budgets substantial economic dislocations and unemployment would occur, unless very careful planning preceeded the cuts. It is unrealistic to expect the funds necessary for the solution of our population-environment problems to be diverted in great amounts from military or space programs. Higher taxes will be necessary, at least at the start, to reach the level of effort discussed earlier.

The problem of breaking the power of the military-industrial-government complex (and its analogues in other nations) and the related problem of finding a way to world peace are, as we have seen, among several general problems which mankind must solve if civilization is to survive. Two French scientists, Marcel Fetizon and Michel Magat, have stated, "We must either eliminate science or eliminate war. We cannot have both." One might go even further. Man's science and technology are incompatible with his present attitudes. Either the attitudes must change or science and technology will disappear, and one way or another most of *Homo sapiens* will go with them.

International Controls

It has been apparent for some time that the nations of this planet cannot long survive without a system of controls for dealing with what may be called the "world commons." All of *Homo sapiens* must extract needed materials from the atmosphere and waters of the Earth, and the hydrologic and biogeochemical cycles bind these together into an indivisible entity. Although nations vary in their mineral endowment, it would clearly be wise to consider all supplies of non-renewable resources as a commons also.

Idealistically we might put in a plea here for a surrendering of national sovereignty to a world government, but it is apparent that any movement in that direction will be extremely slow at best. There does seem to be, however, some chance that humanity might be able to move much more rapidly than it has in the past towards international agreements on the control of the world commons. Treaties have been worked out to control the uses of outer space and Antarctica, and there is now growing interest in a treaty to control the use of the oceans. A draft of such a treaty has been prepared by Elisabeth Mann Borgese of the Center for the Study of Democratic Institutions. It is based on previous ocean treaty drafts and the Treaty on Outer Space. The proposed Ocean Treaty would do more than set rules for the behavior of nations, it would establish an *Ocean Regime,* an institution charged with the development of a code of conduct for nations, non-governmental entities, and individuals who use the sea. The Regime would also modify that code in response to changing ecological, economic or technological developments. It would provide for the development, administration, conservation, and distribution of the resources in the seas and in the sea-bed on a cooperative, international basis, limiting all use to peaceful purposes. This would include the regulation of fisheries and sea-farming, exploitation of sea-bed resources, the control of pollution, the supervision of exploration and research, and the settling of disputes among nations or groups regarding ocean use. The Ocean Regime and the proposed route to its establishment are discussed in Mrs. Borgese's article, which is listed in the bibliography.

Should an Ocean Regime be established, it could serve as a model for a future Atmosphere Regime to regulate the use of airspace and to control atmospheric pollution. Perhaps these two might eventually be developed into a Planetary Regime. Experience gained in dealing internationally with the oceans and the atmosphere could, in theory, be combined with that gained within national governments dealing with problems of population and environment. The Planetary Regime might thus incorporate the United Nations into a sort of International Agency for Population, Resources, and Environment.

As an extension of the Ocean and Atmosphere Regimes, the comprehensive Planetary Regime could control the development, administration, conservation and distribution of *all* natural resources, renewable or nonrenewable, at least so far as any international implications exist. Thus the Regime could have the power to control pollution not only in the atmosphere and the oceans, but also in such fresh water bodies as rivers and lakes that cross international boundaries. Any river that discharged pollutants into oceans might also be subject to control by the Regime.

The Regime would also be the logical central agency for regulating all international trade, particularly assistance from DCs to UDCs, and including all food on the international market, as well as all that comes from the oceans.

The Regime could have the responsibility for determining the optimum population for the world and for each region and for arbitrating various countries' shares in their regional limits. Population control might be the responsibility of each government, but the Regime should have power to enforce the agreed limits. As in the ocean regime, all regulations for population sizes, resource development and pollution control should be subject to revision and modification in accordance with changing conditions.

The Planetary Regime might have the advantage over earlier proposed world government schemes in not being primarily political in its emphasis. Since most of the areas it would control are not now being regulated or controlled by nations or anyone else, its establishment would involve far less surrendering of national power. Nevertheless it might function powerfully to suppress international conflict simply because such an interrelated resource-environment structure would not permit such an outdated luxury.

Bibliography

Aron, Raymond, 1957. *On War*. W. W. Norton & Co., Inc., New York. A European view of the influence on international relations of nuclear armaments and planetary politics.

Barnet, Richard J., and Richard D. Falk (eds.), 1965. *Security in Disarmament*. Princeton Univ. Press, Princeton. A collection of essays dealing with such subjects as systems of inspection, violations of arms control agreements, and supernational vs. international models for disarmament.

Bolton, Roger E. (ed.), 1966. *Defense and Disarmament*. Prentice-Hall, Inc., Englewood Cliffs, N.J. A series of essays on the economics of disarmament.

Boulding, Kenneth E., 1962. *Conflict and Defense*. Harper & Row, New York. A pioneering attempt to create a general theory of conflict.

Borgese, Elisabeth Mann, 1968. The Ocean Regime. *Center Occasional Papers*, vol. 1, no. 5. A model statute and program which, if enacted, could go a long way toward solving the problem of the "ocean commons" and perhaps serve as a trial for a similar governing of the "world commons."

Buchan, Alistair (ed.), 1966. *A World of Nuclear Powers?* Prentice-Hall, Inc., Englewood Cliffs, N.J.

Calder, Nigel (ed.), 1968. *Unless Peace Comes*. Viking Press, New York. A description of future weapons systems.

Chedd, Graham, 1969. Famine or sanity? *New Scientist*, Oct. 23.

Coale, Ansley J., and Edgar M. Hoover, 1958. *Population Growth and Economic Development in Low-Income Countries.* Princeton Univ. Press, Princeton.

Daetz, Douglas, 1968. *Energy Utilization and Aid Effectiveness in Nonmechanized Agriculture: A Computer Simulation of a Socioeconomic System.* Univ. of California doctoral dissertation.

Doane, Robert R., 1957. *World Balance Sheet.* Harper and Brothers, New York.

Enke, Stephen, 1966. The economic aspects of slowing population growth. *The Economic Journal,* vol. LXXVI, no. 301 (March), pp. 44–56.

Enke, Stephen, 1969. Birth control for economic development. *Science,* vol. 164. pp. 798–802.

Food and Agriculture Organization of the United Nations, 1968. *Production Yearbook 1967.* FAO-UN, Rome.

Frank, Jerome D., 1967. *Sanity and Survival.* Vintage Books. New York. The psychology of war and peace.

Frederiksen, Harald, 1969. Feedbacks in economic and demographic transition. *Science,* vol. 166, pp. 837–847. An overly optimistic discussion of the possible benefits of death control in motivating people to have smaller families in UDCs.

Green, Philip, 1968. *Deadly Logic.* Schocken Books, New York. An analysis of deterrence theory—a critically important work.

Halperin, Morton H., 1966. *Limited War in the Nuclear Age.* John Wiley & Sons, Inc., New York.

Henkin, Harmon, 1969. Side effects. *Environment,* vol. 11, no. 1 (Jan.–Feb.). More on unexpected ecological results from development projects.

Hersh, Seymour M., 1969. *Chemical and Biological Warfare.* Doubleday (Anchor Book), Garden City, New York.

Hertzog, Arthur, 1965. *The War-Peace Establishment.* Harper & Row, New York. An introduction to the views of those researchers concerned with our military-foreign policy stance.

Illich, Ivan, 1969. Outwitting the "developed" countries. *New York Review of Books,* Nov. 6.

Jarrett, Henry (ed.), 1966. *Environmental Quality in a Growing Economy.* Johns Hopkins Press, Baltimore. An interesting collection—see especially the article by Boulding, "The Economics of the Coming Spaceship Earth."

Kahn, Herman, 1960. *On Thermonuclear War.* Princeton Univ. Press. Princeton. This book brought much unfair personal criticism of Kahn. It is the subject of devastating professional analysis by Greene in *Deadly Logic.*

Kahn, Herman, 1962. *Thinking about the Unthinkable.* Horizon, New York. An able reply to the personal attacks made on Kahn after *On Thermonuclear War* was published.

Kahn, Herman, 1965. *On Escalation.* Penguin Books, Baltimore. The most recent work by the best known of the deterrence theorists.

King, Kendall W., 1969. The world food crisis—a partial answer. *Research Development* (Sept.) Describes a successful program for dealing with malnutrition among children in UDCs.

Melman, Seymour, 1962. *Disarmament, Its Politics and Economics*. American Academy of Arts and Sciences, Boston.

Myrdal, Gunnar, 1968. *Asian Drama*. Pantheon, New York. A three-volume monument on politics, economics, planning, and population in Asia. Comprehensive, and rather depressing.

Paddock, William, and Paul Paddock, 1964. *Hungry Nations*. Little, Brown & Co., Boston. A fine brief treatment by two outspoken agriculturalists.

Pincus, John A. (ed.), 1968. *Reshaping the World Economy*. Prentice-Hall, Englewood Cliffs, N.J. Especially useful source on world trade problems.

Platt, John, 1969. What we must do. *Science,* vol. 166, pp. 1115–1121. A classification of our multiplicity of crises and suggestions on how we might meet them.

Rathjens, George W., 1969. *The Future of the Strategic Arms Race: Options for the 1970's*. Carnegie Endowment for International Peace.

Sakharov, Andrei D., 1968. *Progress, Coexistence and Intellectual Freedom*. W. W. Norton and Co., New York. Heroic statement by the brilliant physicist called "Father of the Russian H-bomb."

Sanders, Sol., 1969. *A Sense of Asia*. Charles Scribner's Sons, New York.

Schelling, Thomas C., 1968. *The Strategy of Conflict*. Oxford Univ. Press, Oxford. Well worth reading. Schelling is one of the brightest of the deterrence theorists.

Spengler, Joseph J., 1960. Population and world development. *Science,* vol. 131, pp. 1497–1502.

American Museum of Natural History, 1969. The unforeseen international ecologic boomerang (supplement to the Feb. 1969 issue of *Natural History*). The misuse of western technology in UDCs.

United Nations, 1968. *Statistical Yearbook 1967,* 19th ed. Statistical Office of the U.N., New York. A gold mine of information on population, manufacturing, agriculture, trade, consumption, etc. Produced annually.

CHAPTER 13

Conclusions

*"The only trouble with our time is that
the future is not what it used to be."*

Paul Valéry
(1891–1945)

*"The future is a cruel hoax . . .
I am terribly saddened by the fact that
the most humane thing for me to do
is to have no children at all."*

Valedictorian Stephanie Mills, 1969
Mills College

Summary

To recapitulate, we would summarize the present world situation as follows:

1. Considering present technology and patterns of behavior our planet is grossly overpopulated now.

2. The large absolute number of people and the rate of population growth are major hindrances to solving human problems.

3. The limits of human capability to produce food by conventional means have very nearly been reached. Problems of supply and distribution already have resulted in roughly half of humanity being undernourished or malnourished. Some 10–20 million people are starving to death annually now.

4. Attempts to increase food production further will tend to accelerate the deterioration of our environment, which in turn will eventually *reduce* the capacity of the Earth to produce food. It is not clear whether environmental decay has now gone so far as to be essentially irreversible; it is possible that the capacity of the planet to support human life has been permanently impaired. Such technological "successes," as automobiles, pesticides, and inorganic nitrogen fertilizers are major causes of environmental deterioration.

5. There is reason to believe that population growth increases the probability of a lethal worldwide plague and of a thermonuclear war. Either could provide an undesirable "death rate solution" to the population problem; each is potentially capable of destroying civilization and even of driving *Homo sapiens* to extinction.

6. There is no technological panacea for the complex of problems composing the population-food-environment crisis, although technology, properly applied in such areas as pollution abatement, communications, and fertility control can provide massive assistance. The basic solutions involve dramatic and rapid changes in human *attitudes,* especially those relating to reproductive behavior, economic growth, technology, the environment, and conflict resolution.

Recommendations: A Positive Program

Although our conclusions must seem rather pessimistic, we wish to emphasize our belief that the problems can be solved. Whether they *will* be solved is another question. A general course of action that we feel will have some chance of ameliorating the results of the current crisis is outlined below. Many of the suggestions will seem "unrealistic," and indeed that is how we view them. But the system has been allowed to run downhill for so long that only relatively idealistic programs offer any hope of salvation.

1. Population control is absolutely essential if the problems now facing mankind are to be solved. *It is not, however, a panacea.* If population growth were halted immediately, virtually all other human problems—poverty, racial tensions, urban blight, environmental decay, warfare—would remain. The situation is best summarized in the statement, "whatever your cause, it's a lost cause without population control."

2. Political pressure must be applied immediately to induce the United States government to assume its responsibility to halt the growth of the American population. Once growth is halted, the government should undertake to regulate the birthrate so that the population is reduced to an optimum size and maintained there. It is essential that a grassroots political movement be generated to convince our legislators and the executive branch of the government that they must act rapidly. The program should be based on what politicians understand best—

votes. Presidents, Congressmen, Senators, and other elected officials who do not deal effectively with the crisis must be defeated at the polls and more intelligent and responsible candidates elected.

3. A massive campaign must be launched to restore a quality environment in North America and to *de-develop the United States*. De-development means bringing our economic system (especially patterns of consumption) into line with the realities of ecology and the world resource situation. This campaign would be largely political, especially with regard to our overexploitation of world resources, but the campaign should be strongly supplemented by legal and boycott action against polluters and others whose activities damage the environment. The need for de-development presents our economists with a major challenge. They must design a low-consumption economy of stability, and an economy in which there is a much more equitable distribution of wealth than in the present one. Marxists claim that capitalism is intrinsically expansionist and wasteful, and that it automatically produces a monied ruling class. Can our economists prove them wrong?

4. Once the United States has clearly started on the path of cleaning up its own mess it can then turn its attention to the problems of the de-development of the other DCs, population control, and ecologically feasible semi-development of the UDCs. It must use every peaceful means at its disposal to bring the Soviet Union and other DCs into the effort, in line with the general proposals of Lord Snow and Academician Sakharov. Such action can be combined with attempts to achieve a general detente with the Soviets and the Chinese. Citizens, through the ballot, letter writing, and continued peaceful protest, must make clear to American leaders that they wish to move toward disarmament in spite of its possible risks. They must demand detailed appraisal of the risks of continuing the "balance of terror" versus the risk that the other side might "cheat" in a controlled disarmament situation. Americans should inform themselves of what is known about the causes and the psychology of conflict and about deterrence theory, and attempt to elect officials who are similarly informed.

5. It is unfortunate that at the time of the greatest crisis the United States and the world has ever faced, many Americans, especially the young, have given up hope that the government can be modernized and changed in direction through the functioning of the elective process. Their despair may have some foundation, but a partial attempt to institute a "new politics" very nearly succeeded in 1968. In addition many members of Congress and other government leaders, both Democrats and Republicans, are very much aware of the problems outlined in this book and are determined to do something about them. Others are joining their ranks as the dangers before us daily become more apparent. These people need public support in order to be effective. The world cannot, in its present critical state, be saved by merely tearing

down old institutions, even if rational plans existed for constructing better ones from the ruins. We simply do not have the time. Either we will succeed by bending old institutions or we will succumb to disaster. Considering the potential rewards and consequences we see no choice but to make an effort to modernize the system. It may be necessary to organize a new political party with an ecological outlook and national and international orientation to provide an alternative to the present parties with their local and parochial interests. The environmental issue may well provide the basis for this.

6. Perhaps the major necessary ingredient that has been missing from a solution to the problems of both the United States and the rest of the world is a goal, a vision of the kind of Spaceship Earth that ought to be and the kind of crew that should man her. Society has always had its visionaries who talked of love, beauty, peace, and plenty. But somehow the "practical" men have always been there to praise the smog as a sign of progress, to preach "just" wars, and to restrict love while giving hate free rein. It must be one of the greatest ironies of the history of *Homo sapiens* that the only salvation for the practical men now lies in what they think of as the dreams of idealists. The question now is: can the "realists" be persuaded to face reality in time?

About this Book

It has been our aim to produce a reasonably comprehensive and reliable sourcebook for the study of questions related to population, resources and environment—a book that can serve the needs of teachers and students as well as the needs of general readers who may not be enrolled in any formal courses.

We have tried to make clear, by providing adequate detail and documentation, our reasons for sharing with many well-informed and concerned citizens of the world a gloomy prognosis for mankind. We have also tried to include many constructive proposals and suggestions that offer possible means of brightening that prognosis.

The wide diversity of sources we have drawn upon is indicated in the annotated bibliographies at the ends of the chapters, and in the general bibliography at the end of the book. We have listed only a small selection of references from technical journals, but these should provide the interested student with adequate guidance for a further exploration of this literature. We have not hesitated to include, in addition, bits of information from such sources as newspapers and the scientist's "grapevine," if such information seemed sufficiently important and timely, even though this might entail some risk of possible small losses in scientific accuracy.

Because, as indicated in the acknowledgments, the various drafts of our manuscript were thoroughly reviewed by a large number of critics who are competent in the various areas covered, we believe that the factual basis of the book is sound throughout. We do not believe that such minor errors as may be revealed in any of our figures, estimates, or interpretations will change the thrust of our major conclusions. In many areas, of course, it is impossible to determine exactly what has happened, or to know what the significance of certain trends may be. Data are often unreliable or unavailable, and our understanding of the complexities of ecological systems and human behavior is still fragmentary. But in dealing with the population-resource-environment crisis, it is important to recognize that people are going to have to learn to make decisions in the face of such uncertainty. Possible benefits will have to be weighed against possible risks, and a great deal of thought given to possible future events which may seem unlikely *but which will be catastrophic if they do occur*. It would be a major step forward for mankind if all people could know the general state of the world and could be informed as to just what chances are being taken with their lives and the lives of future generations.

From the almost limitless number of subjects which might have been included in this book, choices of those that were to be treated in detail had to be made. We have tried to emphasize those which seemed to us to be of the most general importance, and we make no apology either for our selection of subjects or for the personal style and approach we have used throughout. We have not attempted to give equal weight to both sides of all controversial issues; where we think one side is correct we have so indicated. We also make no claim to having tried to detail all exceptions to general rules. We hope that this book will provide concerned readers with enough background to enable them to make informed political decisions about environmental issues and to combat what C. P. Snow has referred to as the "excessive unsimplicity" which, in his words, "crops up whenever anyone makes a proposal which opens up a prospect, however distant, of new action. It involves a skill which all conservative functionaries are masters of, as they ingeniously protect the status quo: it is called the 'technique of the intricate defensive.' "

Finally, we hope that all of our readers will understand that the primary purpose of this book is to inform and convince them about the elements and the dimensions of the environmental crisis, rather than merely to frighten or discourage them. Nothing in this book is intended to cause feelings of guilt, resentment, or defensiveness in anyone who happens to be a parent or a child of a large family. It is not our purpose to offend anyone; in fact, to do so would only help to defeat our own goals. The future is our concern, and clearly, any measures that may help to brighten the prospects for mankind will require the understanding, the goodwill, and the enthusiastic support of all.

Acknowledgments

The members of the Population Biology group in the Department of Biological Sciences at Stanford University have been continually involved in the development of the ideas expressed in this book. Thanks go especially to: Andrew Beattie, David M. Bell, Peter F. Brussard (now at Cornell University), Valerie C. Chase, Douglas Daetz, Peter Dollinger, Marc Feldman, Lawrence E. Gilbert, Jr., Edward Groth, John A. Hendrickson (now at the Academy of Natural Sciences of Philadelphia), John H. Hessel, Richard W. Holm, Andrew R. Moldenke, Harold Mooney, Dennis R. Parnell (now at California State College, Hayward), Peter H. Raven, Michael C. Singer, John H. Thomas, and Ward W. Watt. Our closest associates, Professors Richard W. Holm, Peter H. Raven, and John H. Thomas, have collaborated with us in work on population-resource-environment problems for many years. One could not ask for colleagues more generous with their time, ideas, and support.

Donald Kennedy, Executive Head of the Department of Biological Sciences, has given us continual encouragement and has read drafts of the entire manuscript, making detailed comments on content and presentation. Other colleagues at Stanford who have been helpful in many ways are: H. Russel Hulett (Department of Genetics), Sumner M. Kalman (Department of Pharmacology). Sidney Liebes, Jr. (Department of Genetics), Joshua Lederberg (Department of Genetics), Jonathan L. Freedman (Department of Psychology), and Robert D. North (Department of Political Science).

Among the others to whom we owe thanks for reading part or all of the manuscript critically are: James Bonner, Division of Biology, California Institute of Technology; Georg A. Borgstrom, Department of Food Science, Michigan State University; Lester R. Brown, Overseas Development Council; Preston Cloud, Department of Geology, University of California, Santa

Barbara; Dana Dalrymple, Agricultural Development Service, Washington, D.C.; Frank E. Egler, Aton Forest, Connecticut; Thomas Eisner, Division of Biological Sciences, Cornell University; James Gilluly, Lakewood, Colorado; Garrett Hardin, Department of Biology, University of California, Santa Barbara; Lawrence Hines, Department of Economics, Dartmouth College; E. R. Kanwisher, Department of Biology, Atlantic Community College, New Jersey; Nathan Keyfitz, Department of Demography, University of California, Berkeley; I. Michael Lerner, Department of Genetics, University of California, Berkeley; John W. Marr, Institute of Arctic and Alpine Research, University of Colorado; Roderic B. Park, Department of Botany, University of California, Berkeley; Ralph E. Thorson, Department of Biology, University of Notre Dame; and Kenneth E. F. Watt, Department of Zoology, University of California, Davis. In a great many cases we have incorporated their helpful suggestions into the manuscript, but in others we have not. The ultimate responsibility for all statements in the book must, of course, rest with us.

The cooperation of the Population Reference Bureau has made our task much easier. We are especially grateful to Robert C. Cook and William E. Moran, Jr., of that organization for their help and encouragement. Hugh Moore, Honorary Chairman of the Board of the Population Reference Bureau and pioneer worker for population control has given us his friendship and support. We are grateful for both.

We must also add a word of thanks here to the very large number of colleagues in biology, at many institutions, who have supplied us with information, ideas, and moral support. We hope that this book accurately reflects the growing concern of a large segment of the biological community about the problems of population, resources, and environment.

We are particularly indebted to attorney Johnson C. Montgomery of Palo Alto for his constant aid in developing ideas on the legal aspects of the problem, and to plasma physicist John Holdren (Institute for Plasma Research, Stanford), who has worked closely with us in investigating the role of technology relative to the population-environment crisis. Many of their thoughts have been incorporated directly into the text.

Margaret Craig, Chief Librarian of the Falconer Biology Library, Stanford, and her able assistants, Ferne Barr and Claire Shoens, have been of immense help in running down difficult references and in general making the job of keeping track of the literature easier. Margaret Fuhrman, who operates the Xerox machine in the library, has also been extremely helpful in finding and organizing source material and manuscript. Lewine Beattie has spent hours doing library research, particularly on resources. Mrs. Wendell Duffield, Mrs. Lawrence Gilbert, and Mrs. Michael Singer cheerfully typed and proofread more manuscript than we are sure any of them would care to remember. Our daughter Lisa has also helped with proofreading.

Our friend Mrs. Dorothy Decker, who has been secretary for the Population Biology group for the past decade, has become something of a legend among our colleagues and friends. Her efficiency and cheerfulness in the face of almost continual chaos have been far beyond the call of duty, as have been the many times we have found her working at the office on weekends, "so that things won't be such a mess on Monday."

World Demography

Figures are from the 1969 Data Sheet of the Population Reference Bureau,
except for those on literacy and life expectancy,
which are from the 1968 Data Sheet.

The data include, for each country and continent, current population sizes, birth rates, death rates, growth rates, and doubling times. In addition infant mortality figures, percent of population under 15 years of age, population projection for 1980, and per capita gross national product are also included. These data are compiled from various sources, the United Nations being the principal one. The population figures given are mostly extrapolations from the most recent census data (censuses are not taken annually). Estimates for many countries undoubtedly contain a large margin of error. In many cases census data are extremely unreliable, in others undetected changes in birth or death rates since the latest census may introduce considerable error into extrapolations. And, of course, in some instances the figures may represent faulty extrapolations from incorrect census data.

Nonetheless these are the best estimates available, and because errors in different countries are probably in different directions (and thus cancel each other out) a 1960 U.N. analysis concluded that the world total is probably accurate within plus or minus 50 million. Whether the U.N. analysts were correct is open to question. Needless to say, most of the figures should be considered to represent rough magnitudes. A difference of a point or two in birth rates between two countries may have no significance whatever. The most accurate census data come from the DCs; those of many UDCs are extremely suspect. The per capita gross national product figures should be used with special caution; as ratios of estimates they are especially liable to error. The major features of the current world demographic picture are clear in these data, but in using them their limitations should always be kept in mind.

Region or Country	Population Estimates Mid-1969 (Millions)	Birth Rate per 1,000 population	Death Rate per 1,000 population	Current Rate of Population Growth†	Number of Years to Double Population‡	Infant Mortality Rate (Deaths under one year per 1,000 live births)	Population Under 15 years (percent)	Population Projections to 1980 (millions)‡	Per Capita Gross National Product (US$)§	Life expectancy at birth (years)‡	Population illiterate 15 years and over (percent)‡
WORLD[1]	3551	34	15	1.9	37		37	4368	589	53	39
AFRICA[1]	344	46	22	2.4	28		43	456	140	43	82
Northern Africa											
Algeria	13.3	44	11–14	2.9	24	86	47	19.5	220		75–85
Libya	1.9			3.6	19		44		640		80–87
Morocco	15.0	46	15–19	3.0	23	149	46	22.4	170	50–55	80–90
Sudan	15.2	52	18–22	3.0	23		47	21.0	100		80–88
Tunisia	4.8	45	17	2.8	25	110	41	6.4	200		75–85
UAR	32.5	43	15	2.9	24	120	43	46.7	160	50–55	75–80
Western Africa											
Dahomey	2.7	54	26–31	2.9	24	110	46	3.4	80	30–35	90–95
Gambia	0.4	39	19	2.1	33		38	0.5	90		90–95
Ghana	8.6	47	20	2.5	28	156	45	12.2	230	40–45	70–75
Guinea	3.9	55	35	2.0	35	216	44	5.1	80	25–35	80–90
Ivory Coast	4.2	56	33	2.3	31		43	5.5	220	30–35	85–92
Liberia	1.2	40		1.8	39		37	1.5	210		90–95
Mali	4.9	52	30–32	2.0	35	123	49	6.5	60	30–35	85–95
Mauritania	1.1	45	25–28	2.0	35	187			130	40–45	90–97
Niger	3.7	52	25–27	2.7	26	200	46	4.8	80	35–40	95–99
Nigeria	53.7[2]	50	25	2.5	28		43		80		80–88
Senegal	3.9	43	17	2.5	28	93	42	4.9	210	35–45	90–95
Sierra Leone	2.5	44	22	2.2	32	146	37	3.3	150		80–90
Togo	1.8	55	29	2.6	27	127	48	2.3	100	30–40	80–90
Upper Volta	5.3	53	35	2.0	35	182	42	6.3	50	30–35	85–92
Eastern Africa											
Burundi	3.5	46	26	2.0	35	150	47	4.7	50	35–40	85–92
Ethiopia	24.4			2.0	35			30.1	60		90–95
Kenya	10.6	50	20	3.0	23	132	46	14.6	90	40–45	70–75
Madagascar	6.7	46	22–25	2.4	29	102	46	8.5	90		60–67
Malawi	4.3			2.5	28		45	6.1	50		85–93
Mauritius	0.8	30	9	2.0	35	65	44	1.1	210	58–65	35–40
Mozambique*	7.3	42	31	1.2	58			9.0	100		90–95
Rwanda	3.5	52		2.7	26	137		5.0	40		85–90
Somalia	2.8			3.1	23			4.1	50		90–95
Rhodesia*	4.8	48	14–18	3.0	23	122	47	7.1	210	50–55	70–75
Tanzania	12.9	45	23	2.9	24	189	42		80	35–45	80–90
Uganda	8.3	42	20	2.5	28	160	41		100		65–75
Zambia	4.2	51	20	3.1	23	259	45		180	40–45	55–60

Footnotes for this Appendix are on on page 334.

Region or Country	Population Estimates Mid-1969 (Millions)	Birth Rate per 1,000 population	Death Rate per 1,000 population	Current Rate of Population Growth†	Number of Years to Double Population‡	Infant Mortality Rate (Deaths under one year per 1,000 live births)	Population Under 15 years (percent)	Population Projections to 1980 (millions)‡	Per Capita Gross National Product (US$)§	Life expectancy at birth (years)‡	Population illiterate 15 years and over (percent)‡
Middle Africa											
Angola*	5.4			1.4	50		42		170	40–50	90–97
Cameroon (Western)	5.7	50	26–28	2.2	32	137	39		110	35–40	80–90
Central African Republic	1.5	48	30	1.7	41	190	42		110	35–40	70–77
Chad	3.5	45	31	1.5	47	160	46		70	30–35	75–82
Congo (Brazzaville)	0.9	41	24	1.7	41			1.1	120	35–40	50–55
Congo (Democratic Rep.)	17.1	43	20	2.3	31	104	39		60	35–45	80–85
Gabon	0.5	35	30	0.9	78	229	36		400	25–45	85–90
Southern Africa											
Botswana	0.6			2.0	35		43		60		70–80
Lesotho	0.9	40	23	1.8	39	181	43		60	40–50	
South Africa	19.6	46		2.4	29		40	26.8	550	50–60	65–70
Southwest Africa (Namibia)	0.6			1.7	41		40	0.9			60–70
Swaziland	0.4	36		2.9	24			0.6	290		
ASIA¹	1990	38	18	2.0	35		40	2472	184	50	54
South West Asia											
Cyprus	0.6	25	7	1.8	39	28	35	0.7	690	70	20–25
Iraq	8.9	48		2.5	28		45	13.8	270		75–85
Israel	2.8	25	6.6	2.9	24	25	33		1160	72	10–15
Jordan	2.3	47	16	4.1	17		46	3.3	220		60–70
Kuwait	0.6	52	6	7.6	9	37	38		3410		50–55
Lebanon	2.6			2.5	28			3.6	480		40–50
Saudi Arabia	7.2			1.8	39			9.4	240		85–95
Southern Yemen	1.3	37	8	2.2	32	80		1.6			
Syria	6.0			2.9	24		46	9.2	180		65–70
Turkey	34.4	46	18	2.5	28	161	44	48.5	280	50–60	60–65
Yemen	5.0							6.9	90		90–95
Middle South Asia											
Afghanistan	16.5			2.3	31			22.1	70		85–95
Bhutan	0.8			2.7	26			1.0			
Ceylon	12.3	32	8	2.4	29	56	41	16.3	150	62	25–30
India	536.9	43	18	2.5	28	139	41		90	45	70–75
Iran	27.9	50	20	3.1	23		46	38.0	250		75–85
Nepal	10.9	41	21	2.0	35		40	14.1	70		85–95
Pakistan	131.6	52	19	3.3	21	142	45	183.0	90	45	75–85

Footnotes for this Appendix are on on page 334.

Region or Country	Population Estimates Mid-1969 (Millions)	Birth Rate per 1,000 population	Death Rate per 1,000 population	Current Rate of Population Growth†	Number of Years to Double Population‡	Infant Mortality Rate (Deaths under one year per 1,000 live births)	Population Under 15 years (percent)	Population Projections to 1980 (millions)‡	Per Capita Gross National Product (US$)§	Life expectancy at birth (years)‡	Population illiterate 15 years and over (percent)‡
South East Asia											
Burma	27.0	50	25–31	2.2	32		40	35.0	60	40	30–40
Cambodia	6.7	41	20	2.2	32	127	44	9.8	120	44	60–70
Indonesia	115.4	43	21	2.4	29	125	42	152.8	100	42	55–60
Laos	2.9	47	23	2.6	27				70		70–80
Malaysia (East & West)	10.7	36	7	3.1	23	49	44	14.9	280	44	70–80
Philippines	37.1	50	10–15	3.5	20	73	47	55.8	160	47	25–30
Singapore	2.1	27	5	2.5	28	26	43	3.2	570		40–50
Thailand	34.7	46	13	3.1	23	31	43	47.5	130	65–70	30–35
North Vietnam	21.4			3.1	23		38				
South Vietnam	17.9			2.6	27				120		
East Asia											
China (Mainland)	740.3[3]	34	11	1.4	50			843.0			40–50
China (Taiwan)	13.8	29	6	2.6	24	20	44	17.6	230	65–70	35–45
Hong Kong*	4.0	23	5	2.3	31	26	40	5.5	560	65–70	25–30
Japan	102.1	19	6.8	1.1	63	15	25	112.9	860	71	0–2
North Korea	13.3	38	10–14	2.4	29			17.5			
South Korea	31.2	41	10–14	2.8	25		42	43.4	150	55–60	
Mongolia	1.2	40	10	3.0	23		30	1.7		30	5
NORTHERN AMERICA[1]	225	18	9	1.1	63	22	30	264	3399	71	2
Canada	21.3	18.0	7.3	2.0	35	23.1	33	22.3	2240	72	0–3
United States	203.1	17.4	9.6	1.0	70	22.1	30	240.1	3520	71	0–3
LATIN AMERICA[1]	276[4]	39	10	2.9	24		43	376	385	60	34
Middle America											
Costa Rica	1.7	45	7	3.8	18	70.0	38	2.7	400	62–65	10–20
El Salvador	3.3	47	13	3.3	21	62.0	45	4.9	270	57–61	45–50
Guatemala	5.0	43	15	2.8	25	92.0	46	6.9	320	50–60	60–70
Honduras	2.5	49	17	3.4	21		51	3.7	220		50–60
Mexico	49.0	43	9	3.4	21	63.0	46	71.4	470	58–64	30–35
Nicaragua	2.0	46	16	3.0	23		48	2.8	330		45–50
Panama	1.4	41	8	3.2	22	45.0	43	1.9	500		20–30

Footnotes for this Appendix are on on page 334.

Region or Country	Population Estimates Mid-1969 (Millions)	Birth Rate per 1,000 population	Death Rate per 1,000 population	Current Rate of Population Growth†	Number of Years to Double Population‡	Infant Mortality Rate (Deaths under one year per 1,000 live births)	Population Under 15 years (percent)	Population Projections to 1980 (millions)‡	Per Capita Gross National Product (US$)§	Life expectancy at birth (years)‡	Population illiterate 15 years and over (percent)‡
Caribbean											
Barbados	0.3	30	9	0.9	78	48.0	38	0.3	400	63–68	0–10
Cuba	8.2	27	8	2.0	35	40.0	37	10.1	320		15–25
Dominican Republic	4.2	49	15	3.4	21	80.0	47	6.2	250	57–60	40
Haiti	5.1	44	20	2.4	29		38	6.8	70	35–45	80–90
Jamaica	1.8	40	8–9	2.5	28	35.0	41	2.1	460	63–68	15–20
Puerto Rico*	2.7	26	6	1.1	63	33.0	39	3.1	1090	68–73	15–20
Trinidad & Tobago	1.1	38	8	2.4	29	42.0	43	1.6	630	63–68	15–25
Tropical South America											
Bolivia	4.5	44	19	2.4	29	99.0	44	6.0	160		55–65
Brazil	90.6	38	10	2.8	25	79.0	43	124.0	240		30–35
Colombia	21.4	45	11	3.4	21	80.0	47	31.4	280		30–40
Ecuador	5.8	45	11	3.4	21	90.0	48	8.4	190		30–35
Guyana	0.7	40	9–10	2.7	26	40.0	46	1.0	300	60–65	15–25
Peru	13.2	42	11	3.1	23	63.0	45	18.5	320	55–60	35–40
Venezuela	10.4	41	8	3.3	21	46.0	46	15.0	850	65–70	30–35
Temperate South America											
Argentina	24.0	23	9	1.5	47	58.0	29	28.2	780	63–70	5–8
Chile	9.6	33	10	2.3	31	108.0	40	12.2	510		13–16
Paraguay	2.3	45	11	3.4	21	80.0	45	3.5	200		20–25
Uruguay	2.9	21	9	1.2	58	43.0	28	3.3	570	65–70	8–10
EUROPE¹	456	18	10	0.8	88		25	499	1230	70	5
Northern Europe											
Denmark	4.9	18.4	10.3	0.9	78	16.9	24	5.3	1830	72	0–1
Finland	4.7	16.5	9.4	0.6	117	14.2	27	5.2	1600	69	0–1
Iceland	0.2	22.4	7.0	2.0	35	13.7	34	0.3	1740	73	0–1
Ireland	2.9	21.1	10.7	0.5	140	24.4	31	3.5	850	70	0–1
Norway	3.8	18.0	9.2	0.8	88	16.8	25	4.3	1710	73	0–1
Sweden	8.0	15.4	10.1	0.8	88	12.6	21	8.6	2270	74	0–1
United Kingdom	55.7	17.5	11.2	0.6	117	18.8	23	60.2	1620	71	0–1
Western Europe											
Austria	7.4	17.4	13.0	0.5	140	26.4	24	7.7	1150	70	0–1
Belgium	9.7	15.2	12.2	0.1	700	23.7	24	10.2	1630	71	0–3
France	50.0	16.9	10.9	1.0	70	20.6	25	53.8	1730	71	0–3
West Germany	58.1	17.3	11.2	0.4	175	23.5	23	61.0	1700	71	0–1
Luxembourg	0.3	14.8	12.3	0.1	700	20.4	22	0.4	1920	68	0–3
Netherlands	12.9	18.9	7.9	1.1	63	13.4	28	15.3	1420	74	0–1
Switzerland	6.2	17.7	9.0	0.9	78	17.5	23	5.9⁵	2250	71	0–1

Footnotes for this Appendix are on on page 334.

Region or Country	Population Estimates Mid-1969 (Millions)	Birth Rate per 1,000 population	Death Rate per 1,000 population	Current Rate of Population Growth†	Number of Years to Double Population‡	Infant Mortality Rate (Deaths under one year per 1,000 live births)	Population Under 15 years (percent)	Population Projections to 1980 (millions)‡	Per Capita Gross National Product (US$)§	Life expectancy at birth (years)‡	Population illiterate 15 years and over (percent)‡
Eastern Europe											
Bulgaria	8.4	15.0	9.0	0.6	117	33.1	24	9.2	620	70	10–15
Czechoslovakia	14.4	15.1	10.1	0.5	140	23.7	25	15.8	1010	71	0–5
East Germany	16.0	14.8	13.2	0.1	700	21.2	22	17.7	1220	71	0–1
Hungary	10.3	14.6	10.7	0.3	233	38.4	23	10.7	800	70	0–5
Poland	32.5	16.3	7.7	0.8	88	38.1	30	36.6	730	68	0–5
Romania	20.0	27.1	9.3	1.8	39	46.8	26	22.4	650	68	5–15
Southern Europe											
Albania	2.1	34.0	8.6	2.7	26	86.8		3.0	300	65	20–30
Greece	8.9	18.5	8.3	1.2	58	34.3	25	9.3	660	69	15–20
Italy	53.1	18.1	9.7	0.7	100	34.3	24	58.8	1030	70	5–10
Malta	0.3	16.6	9.4	0.6	117	27.5	32	0.4	510	69	35–45
Portugal	9.6	21.1	10.0	1.1	63	59.3	29	10.9	380	64	35–40
Spain	32.7	21.1	8.7	0.8	88	33.2	27	34.8	640	70	10–20
Yugoslavia	20.4	19.5	8.7	1.1	63	61.3	30	22.8	510	65	15–25
U.S.S.R.	241	18	8	1.0	70	26	32	277.8	890	70	12
OCEANIA[1]	19	24	11	1.8	41	18	30	23	1857	71	0–2
Australia	12.2	19.4	8.7	1.8	39	18.2	29	15.2	1840	71	0–1
New Zealand	2.8	22.4	8.4	1.9	37	17.7	33	3.6	1930	71	0–1

* Nonsovereign country.
† Latest available year.
‡ Assuming continued growth at current annual rate.
§ 1966 data supplied by the International Bank for Reconstruction and Development.
[1] Population totals take into account small areas not listed on Data Sheet.
[2] Official government estimate of 64.8, based on 1963 census, is now considered high.
[3] U.N. estimate. Other estimates range from 800–950 million.
[4] Mid-1969 population estimates for the Latin American countries are taken from the latest figures of the Latin American Demographic Center of the United Nations. These figures are more recent than those of the 1967 U.N. Demographic Yearbook on which most of this Data Sheet is based.
[5] Foreigners with resident permits not taken into account.

World and Regional Population (Millions)

	World	Africa	Asia	North America	Latin America	Europe	Oceania	USSR
Mid-1969 estimate	3,551	344	1,990	225	276	456	19	241
U.N. projections to 2000								
Constant fertility	7,522	860	4,513	388	756	571	33	402
Percent increase	112	150	127	72	174	25	74	67
Medium estimate	6,130	768	3,458	354	638	527	32	353
Percent increase	73	123	74	57	131	16	68	46

Population Estimates, 1960–2000

From "World Population Prospects as Assessed in 1963,"
United Nations Population Studies, no. 41.

Projections of population growth, even more than estimates of population sizes and growth rates, are subject to a substantial margin of error. Besides the problem of scanty or inadequate data to start with, predicting the future reproductive behavior of any society, even one whose population structure may be known in detail, is notoriously difficult. In the past demographers have erred fairly consistently on the low side.

All of these projections, except the "constant fertility, no migration" projection, assume some degree of success for family planning programs and economic development in UDCs. The constant fertility projection assumes a continuation of present fertility rates.

Population Estimates According to the U.N. "Low" Variant, 1960–2000, for Major Areas and Regions of the World

(Population in thousands)

Major areas and regions	1960	1965	1970	1975	1980	1985	1990	1995	2000
WORLD TOTAL	2,998,180	3,265,555	3,544,781	3,840,439	4,147,337	4,462,720	4,782,859	5,109,362	5,448,533
More developed regions[a]	976,414	1,028,862	1,069,745	1,110,340	1,153,323	1,195,026	1,234,313	1,266,219	1,293,175
Less developed regions[b]	2,021,766	2,236,693	2,475,036	2,730,099	2,994,014	3,267,694	3,549,546	3,843,143	4,155,358
A. East Asia	794,144	839,970	883,366	926,689	966,092	1,002,895	1,039,118	1,079,058	1,118,122
1. Mainland region	654,181	689,000	722,000	754,000	782,000	808,000	834,000	864,000	893,000
2. Japan	93,210	97,159	100,328	104,081	107,762	110,750	112,950	114,378	115,326
3. Other East Asia	46,753	53,811	61,038	68,608	76,330	84,145	92,168	100,680	109,796
B. South Asia	865,247	975,777	1,101,743	1,237,117	1,378,496	1,526,188	1,675,465	1,825,655	1,984,435
4. Middle South Asia	587,277	659,977	743,752	832,611	922,138	1,012,824	1,101,103	1,188,439	1,283,065
5. South-East Asia	218,866	248,792	281,465	317,082	356,997	401,363	449,372	499,081	549,594
6. South-West Asia	59,104	67,008	76,526	87,424	99,361	112,001	124,990	138,135	151,776
C. Europe	424,657	439,340	449,988	458,742	467,081	475,079	481,578	486,999	490,777
7. Western Europe	134,536	139,160	142,570	145,452	148,151	150,648	153,132	155,101	156,920
8. Southern Europe	117,488	121,543	124,503	126,838	128,958	131,203	132,707	134,115	134,753
9. Eastern Europe	96,852	101,193	104,439	107,446	110,651	113,653	116,219	118,263	119,700
10. Northern Europe	75,781	77,444	78,476	79,006	79,321	79,575	79,520	79,520	79,404
D. 11. USSR	214,400	230,627	243,486	255,768	268,865	282,387	296,533	307,306	316,464
E. Africa	272,924	305,859	343,633	386,653	434,486	486,730	545,614	611,088	684,132
12. Western Africa	85,973	98,269	112,093	127,711	145,401	165,336	189,339	217,461	250,284
13. Eastern Africa	75,032	81,884	89,773	98,847	109,155	120,572	133,531	148,217	164,976
14. Middle Africa	28,345	30,471	32,969	35,816	39,080	42,755	46,990	51,835	57,395
15. Northern Africa	65,955	75,282	86,119	98,418	111,400	124,770	138,452	152,152	165,899
16. Southern Africa	17,619	19,953	22,679	25,861	29,450	33,297	37,302	41,423	45,578
F. 17. Northern America	198,664	212,028	222,156	234,102	248,250	261,592	274,207	284,736	294,337
G. Latin America	212,431	244,828	281,805	321,313	362,278	404,483	446,466	488,133	532,388
18. Tropical South America	112,479	131,334	153,168	176,533	200,745	225,453	249,924	274,147	299,977
19. Middle America (mainland)	46,811	54,844	64,304	74,908	86,443	98,525	110,699	122,976	136,241
20. Temperate South America	32,796	35,914	38,906	41,633	44,067	46,724	49,463	52,080	54,586
21. Caribbean	20,345	22,736	25,427	28,239	31,023	33,781	36,380	38,930	41,584
H. Oceania	15,713	17,126	18,604	20,055	21,789	23,366	24,878	26,387	27,878
22. Australia and New Zealand	12,687	13,794	14,881	16,014	17,298	18,494	19,582	20,720	21,685
23. Melanesia	2,166	2,332	2,523	2,741	2,991	3,272	3,596	3,967	4,393
24. Polynesia and Micronesia	860	1,000	1,200	1,300	1,500	1,600	1,700	1,700	1,800

[a] Including Europe, the USSR, Northern America, Japan, Temperate South America, Australia and New Zealand.
[b] Including East Asia less Japan, South Asia, Africa, Latin America less Temperate South America and Oceania less Australia and New Zealand.

Population Estimates According to the U.N. "Medium" Variant, 1960–2000, for Major Areas and Regions of the World

(Population in thousands)

Major areas and regions	1960	1965	1970	1975	1980	1985	1990	1995	2000
WORLD TOTAL	2,998,180	3,280,522	3,591,773	3,944,137	4,330,037	4,746,409	5,187,929	5,647,923	6,129,734
More developed regions[a]	976,414	1,031,759	1,082,150	1,135,587	1,193,854	1,256,179	1,318,433	1,379,812	1,441,402
Less developed regions[b]	2,021,766	2,248,763	2,509,623	2,808,550	3,136,183	3,490,230	3,869,496	4,268,111	4,688,332
A. East Asia	794,144	851,520	910,524	975,935	1,041,097	1,104,903	1,167,882	1,228,006	1,287,270
1. Mainland region	654,181	700,000	748,000	799,000	850,000	900,000	950,000	998,000	1,045,000
2. Japan	93,210	97,523	101,465	106,174	111,064	115,169	118,280	120,561	122,400
3. Other East Asia	46,753	53,997	61,059	70,761	80,033	89,734	99,602	109,445	119,870
B. South Asia	865,247	976,341	1,106,905	1,256,352	1,420,258	1,596,329	1,782,525	1,973,889	2,170,648
4. Middle South Asia	587,277	659,977	746,892	846,932	953,709	1,064,374	1,177,133	1,288,246	1,398,810
5. South-East Asia	218,866	249,213	283,035	320,720	364,310	414,686	471,973	535,170	603,272
6. South-West Asia	59,104	67,151	76,978	88,700	102,239	117,269	133,419	150,473	168,566
C. Europe	424,657	440,303	453,918	466,772	479,391	491,891	503,858	515,674	526,968
7. Western Europe	134,536	139,456	143,766	147,876	151,845	155,724	159,769	163,635	167,699
8. Southern Europe	117,488	121,831	125,671	129,205	132,569	136,342	139,238	142,539	145,360
9. Eastern Europe	96,852	101,414	105,354	109,341	113,597	117,414	121,601	125,181	128,426
10. Northern Europe	75,781	77,602	79,127	80,350	81,380	82,411	83,250	84,319	85,483
D. 11. USSR	214,400	231,000	245,700	260,800	277,800	296,804	316,090	334,845	353,085
E. Africa	272,924	306,173	345,949	393,257	448,869	513,026	586,702	671,207	767,779
12. Western Africa	85,973	98,359	112,862	129,851	149,818	173,369	201,832	236,082	277,192
13. Eastern Africa	75,032	81,957	90,397	100,505	112,515	126,518	142,528	161,153	183,119
14. Middle Africa	28,345	30,553	33,299	36,632	40,592	45,225	50,610	56,965	64,519
15. Northern Africa	65,955	75,351	86,712	100,408	116,369	133,920	152,577	172,185	192,148
16. Southern Africa	17,619	19,953	22,679	25,861	29,575	33,994	39,155	44,822	50,801
F. 17. Northern America	198,664	213,150	226,803	242,942	261,629	283,105	305,926	329,186	354,007
G. Latin America	212,431	244,880	283,263	327,584	378,437	435,558	497,920	565,681	638,111
18. Tropical South America	112,479	131,334	153,838	179,798	209,506	242,902	279,613	319,463	361,985
19. Middle America (mainland)	46,811	54,844	64,595	76,359	90,433	106,662	124,655	144,469	165,901
20. Temperate South America	32,796	35,966	39,302	42,708	46,221	49,778	53,227	56,771	60,514
21. Caribbean	20,345	22,736	25,528	28,719	32,277	36,216	40,425	44,978	49,711
H. Oceania	15,713	17,155	18,711	20,495	22,556	24,793	27,026	29,435	31,866
22. Australia and New Zealand	12,687	13,817	14,962	16,191	17,749	19,432	21,052	22,775	24,428
23. Melanesia	2,166	2,338	2,549	2,804	3,107	3,461	3,874	4,360	4,938
24. Polynesia and Micronesia	860	1,000	1,200	1,500	1,700	1,900	2,100	2,300	2,500

a Including Europe, the USSR, Northern America, Japan, Temperate South America, Australia and New Zealand.
b Including East Asia less Japan, South Asia, Africa, Latin America less Temperate South America and Oceania less Australia and New Zealand.

Population Estimates According to the U.N. "High" Variant, 1960–2000, for Major Areas and Regions of the World

(Population in thousands)

Major areas and regions	1960	1965	1970	1975	1980	1985	1990	1995	2000
WORLD TOTAL	2,998,180	3,305,862	3,659,157	4,070,083	4,550,733	5,096,198	5,689,910	6,325,593	6,993,986
More developed regions[a]	976,414	1,038,410	1,102,074	1,170,451	1,244,728	1,321,537	1,402,019	1,485,660	1,574,079
Less developed regions[b]	2,021,766	2,267,452	2,557,083	2,899,632	3,306,005	3,774,661	4,287,891	4,839,933	5,419,907
A. *East Asia*	794,144	869,950	956,283	1,056,589	1,170,951	1,239,018	1,405,321	1,515,953	1,623,170
1. Mainland region	654,181	718,000	791,000	875,000	971,000	1,070,000	1,167,000	1,258,000	1,345,000
2. Japan	93,210	97,865	102,972	109,536	116,554	122,819	128,216	133,311	138,731
3. Other East Asia	46,753	54,085	62,311	72,053	83,397	96,199	110,105	124,642	139,439
B. *South Asia*	865,247	976,550	1,107,569	1,262,512	1,447,692	1,665,607	1,909,998	2,174,390	2,443,531
4. Middle South Asia	587,277	659,977	746,892	850,684	974,841	1,120,290	1,280,930	1,450,581	1,614,152
5. South-East Asia	218,866	249,422	283,699	322,951	369,613	425,211	489,796	563,154	645,358
6. South-West Asia	59,104	67,151	76,978	88,877	103,238	120,106	139,272	160,655	184,021
C. *Europe*	424,657	441,268	457,850	474,801	491,701	508,703	526,139	544,349	563,159
7. Western Europe	134,536	139,752	144,962	150,299	155,539	160,800	166,407	172,168	178,478
8. Southern Europe	117,488	122,119	126,839	131,573	136,180	141,481	145,770	150,962	155,968
9. Eastern Europe	96,852	101,636	106,270	111,236	116,542	121,175	126,983	132,100	137,151
10. Northern Europe	75,781	77,761	79,779	81,693	83,440	85,247	86,979	89,119	91,562
D. 11. *USSR*	214,400	233,853	253,827	274,157	296,032	319,891	346,010	373,775	402,772
E. *Africa*	272,924	306,563	348,468	399,989	462,886	538,972	629,061	736,266	864,282
12. Western Africa	85,973	98,535	114,007	132,973	156,165	184,631	219,799	263,572	317,915
13. Eastern Africa	75,032	82,120	91,342	102,955	117,330	134,780	155,244	179,841	209,946
14. Middle Africa	28,345	30,559	33,548	37,361	42,104	47,971	54,917	63,402	73,792
15. Northern Africa	65,955	75,351	86,712	100,408	116,884	136,236	157,732	180,749	204,982
16. Southern Africa	17,619	19,998	22,859	26,292	30,403	35,354	41,369	48,702	57,647
F. 17. *Northern America*	198,664	215,513	232,746	252,113	274,818	298,182	323,083	348,542	376,141
G. *Latin America*	212,431	244,935	283,436	328,902	383,243	449,815	521,603	600,624	686,084
18. Tropical South America	112,479	131,334	153,842	180,327	211,871	251,892	294,611	343,866	386,113
19. Middle America (mainland)	46,811	54,845	64,597	76,595	91,522	109,223	128,856	149,725	171,574
20. Temperate South America	32,796	36,020	39,469	43,184	47,236	51,704	56,479	61,542	67,077
21. Caribbean	20,345	22,736	25,528	28,796	32,614	36,996	41,657	46,491	51,320
H. *Oceania*	15,713	17,230	18,978	21,020	23,410	26,010	28,695	31,694	34,847
22. Australia and New Zealand	12,697	13,891	15,210	16,660	18,387	20,238	22,092	24,141	26,199
23. Melanesia	2,166	2,339	2,568	2,860	3,223	3,672	4,203	4,853	5,648
24. Polynesia and Micronesia	860	1,000	1,200	1,500	1,800	2,100	2,400	2,700	3,000

[a] Including Europe, the USSR, Northern America, Japan, Temperate South America, Australia and New Zealand.
[b] Including East Asia less Japan, South Asia, Africa, Latin America less Temperate South America and Oceania less Australia and New Zealand.

Population Estimates According to U.N. "Constant Fertility, No Migration," 1960–2000, in Major Areas and Regions of the World

(Population in thousands)

Major areas and regions	1960	1965	1970	1975	1980	1985	1990	1995	2000
WORLD TOTAL	2,998,180	3,297,482	3,640,970	4,042,761	4,519,146	5,088,112	5,763,577	6,564,584	7,522,218
More developed regions[a]	976,414	1,037,209	1,100,340	1,168,202	1,241,660	1,319,857	1,401,980	1,488,187	1,580,049
Less developed regions[b]	2,021,766	2,260,273	2,540,630	2,874,559	3,277,486	3,768,255	4,361,597	5,076,397	5,942,169
A. East Asia	794,144	863,258	942,256	1,034,364	1,142,609	1,272,236	1,424,527	1,601,016	1,810,678
1. Mainland region	654,181	711,000	776,000	852,000	942,000	1,051,000	1,180,000	1,330,000	1,509,000
2. Japan	93,210	98,011	103,341	108,861	114,055	118,457	121,948	124,809	127,160
3. Other East Asia	46,753	54,247	62,915	73,503	86,554	102,779	122,579	146,207	174,518
B. South Asia	865,247	975,940	1,105,563	1,259,456	1,446,153	1,674,235	1,952,050	2,290,246	2,701,865
4. Middle South Asia	587,277	660,148	746,062	848,430	972,506	1,123,880	1,308,534	1,534,394	1,811,220
5. South-East Asia	218,866	248,641	282,523	322,149	370,409	430,006	502,966	590,983	696,620
6. South-West Asia	59,104	67,151	76,978	88,877	103,238	120,349	140,550	164,869	194,025
C. Europe	424,657	442,416	460,136	478,209	496,448	514,820	533,108	551,655	570,785
7. Western Europe	134,536	139,157	143,583	148,036	152,284	156,621	161,183	166,123	171,520
8. Southern Europe	117,488	123,273	129,224	135,221	141,304	147,498	153,492	159,291	164,962
9. Eastern Europe	96,852	101,654	106,234	111,105	116,313	121,475	126,498	131,411	136,213
10. Northern Europe	75,781	78,332	81,095	83,847	86,547	89,226	91,935	94,830	98,090
D. 11. USSR	214,400	233,411	252,498	272,415	294,594	318,896	345,084	372,800	402,077
E. Africa	272,924	306,563	347,791	397,830	458,251	531,213	619,748	728,013	860,462
12. Western Africa	85,973	98,535	114,007	132,973	156,165	184,631	219,799	263,572	317,915
13. Eastern Africa	75,032	82,120	90,910	101,579	114,355	129,384	146,976	167,803	192,725
14. Middle Africa	28,345	30,559	33,303	36,578	40,444	45,001	50,389	56,832	64,427
15. Northern Africa	65,955	75,351	86,712	100,408	116,884	136,843	161,215	191,104	227,748
16. Southern Africa	17,619	19,998	22,859	26,292	30,403	35,354	41,369	48,702	57,647
F. 17. Northern America	198,664	213,840	230,409	249,840	272,238	297,348	324,955	354,914	388,264
G. Latin America	212,431	245,080	283,899	330,488	386,856	455,131	537,450	636,447	755,579
18. Tropical South America	112,479	131,334	153,838	180,933	213,792	253,728	302,118	360,626	431,302
19. Middle America (mainland)	46,811	54,926	64,775	76,878	91,921	110,535	133,312	161,037	194,816
20. Temperate South America	32,796	35,896	39,287	43,018	47,123	51,647	56,587	61,966	67,786
21. Caribbean	20,345	22,924	25,999	29,659	34,020	39,221	45,433	52,818	61,675
H. Oceania	15,713	16,974	18,418	20,159	21,997	24,233	26,655	29,493	32,508
22. Australia and New Zealand	12,687	13,635	14,669	15,859	17,202	18,689	20,298	22,043	23,977
23. Melanesia	2,166	2,339	2,549	2,800	3,095	3,444	3,857	4,350	4,931
24. Polynesia and Micronesia	860	1,000	1,200	1,500	1,700	2,100	2,500	3,100	3,600

[a] Including Europe, the USSR, Northern America, Japan, Temperate South America, Australia and New Zealand.
[b] Including East Asia less Japan, South Asia, Africa, Latin America less Temperate South America and Oceania less Australia and New Zealand.

The Essential Nutrients

Carbohydrates and Fats

Energy for the life processes and for activity is obtained through "burning" food in the process known as metabolism. Usually this energy is provided by carbohydrates and fats, although if they are undersupplied, proteins may be utilized to make up the deficit. This potential energy from food is measured in "calories." One calorie is the amount of energy (in the form of heat) required to raise the temperature of one kilogram of water one degree centigrade.

Carbohydrates are sugars and starches. They are both made of the same elements, carbon, hydrogen, and oxygen. In digestion, starch (which is a structurally more complicated kind of molecule) is broken down to simple sugars. These may then be metabolized at once or stored for future needs.

Sugars are found most commonly in fruits, and to a lesser extent in vegetables, milk, and milk products. Refined sugars, which are used in cooking, baking, and preserving, come from sugar cane or sugar beets. Starches are found in grains and vegetables, especially such root vegetables as potatoes and yams.

Fats are present in both plant and animal foods, as well as eggs and dairy products. Besides being a source of energy, whether used directly or stored as a reserve, fats are important structural constituents of cell membranes. They provide the sheaths that surround nerves, help to support internal organs, and assist in the utilization of fat-soluble vitamins.

When insufficient supplies of carbohydrates and fats are eaten, the stored reserves are consumed, and weight is lost. There is usually an accompanying curtailment of physical activity. If the weight loss continues until the reserves are gone, the individual starves. Calorie starvation is very hard to separate from other deficiencies. Even if enough protein is provided in the diet to meet protein needs, it will be metabolized for its caloric value, and protein deficiencies will result. Vitamins and minerals are also likely to be under-supplied when intake of carbohydrates and fats is insufficient.

A diet deficient in fats is likely to produce nervous irritability and possibly deficiencies in the fat-soluble vitamins.

Proteins

Proteins are the structural materials of life, including human life. They also serve in many other roles, as enzymes (biological catalysts), and as oxygen transport compounds (hemoglobin). Most of the parts of the body, muscles, bones, skin, even hair and blood are made up largely of proteins. While there are millions of different proteins, all of them are built from about 20 amino acids. The differences are in the arrangements and proportions of the amino acids. These subunits, in turn, are composed primarily of carbon, nitrogen, oxygen, and hydrogen. The complicated protein molecules we eat are broken down in digestion into their constituent amino acids, which are then reassembled in our bodies to meet our protein needs. Nine of these amino acids (eight for adults) are essential in our diets; the others can be synthesized from simple precursors.

Proteins are essential for growth and development, for tissue maintenance and repair and for healing and recovery from disease. They also play a part in regulating the metabolism of sugar. Infants and children need higher proportions of protein relative to their body weight than adults. So, for similar reasons, do pregnant and lactating (nursing) women.

Proteins are found in virtually all foods, but in enormously differing quantities and qualities. "Complete protein" foods, those whose proteins contain all of the nine essential amino acids, are found primarily in animal foods: meat, fish, poultry, eggs, and dairy products. Nuts and soybeans also provide complete proteins, but of lower quality. This means that while all essential amino acids are present, they do not occur in ideal proportions for meeting nutritional needs. Protein of the highest quality (except for mother's milk) is found in eggs, cow's milk being second.

Substantial amounts of incomplete proteins are found in cereal grains and pulses, such as lentils, peas, and beans. By combining these with other foods (for example, cereal combined with milk), a meal of very high quality protein can be achieved. Additional amino acids can be obtained from other fruits and vegetables, thus supplementing the diet further.

A diet deficient in protein results in a lack of energy, stamina, and resistance to disease. In children the result is retarded growth and development. If the deficiency is severe and continues over a long period of time, the child may never fully recover. The severe form of protein starvation in children is called "kwashiorkor." This form of malnutrition is discussed in greater detail in chapter 4.

Vitamins

Vitamins are essential nutrients needed in minute amounts compared with carbohydrates, fats, and proteins. They fill a variety of needs in the regulation of life processes. The lack of any of the 13 or more essential vitamins leads to problems of cellular metabolism, which may lead to a serious deficiency disease and ultimately death.

Vitamins fall into two general classes: the fat-soluble (vitamins A, D, E, and K) and the water-soluble (B-complex and C) ones. The fat-soluble vitamins can be absorbed only in the presence of bile salts, which are brought into the digestive system by fat in the diet.

Many vitamins are depleted or destroyed by exposure to light, air, heat, or alkaline conditions. They are therefore often lost from food through improper storage or cooking methods.

Vitamin A exists in vegetables and fruits in a precursor form known as carotene, which is converted in the liver to vitamin A. It is found as vitamin A most abundantly in animal liver, eggs, and dairy foods. It is needed for normal vision, healthy skin, gums, and soft tissues and resistance to respiratory illnesses. Vitamin A is a precursor of retinene, which together with a protein makes up visual purple, the photosensitive substance of the retina.

A lack of vitamin A first shows up in "night blindness," skin problems, and susceptibility to colds. When it is more extreme, the visual and skin problems intensify, and blindness may ultimately result (xerophthalmia).

The B vitamin complex consists of at least eight separate essential vitamins. They were originally thought to be only one when first discovered. Although they perform different functions, they seem to act somewhat synergistically, and they occur in many of the same foods, the richest sources being liver, whole grains, yeast, and unpolished rice. Deficiencies often occur that involve several of them simultaneously. The lack of one also may interfere with the action of the others. These vitamins are necessary for efficient metabolism.

Thiamin (vitamin B_1), besides having an important role in carbohydrate metabolism, is necessary in regulating growth, maintaining the health and functions of the circulatory, digestive, and nervous systems. Its absence leads to the disease known as beriberi, whose symptoms are lack of energy, nervous and emotional disorders, and digestive and circulatory disturbances.

Riboflavin (vitamin B_2) is also involved in carbohydrate metabolism, functioning as a coenzyme. Deficiency leads to problems with eyes, central nervous system, and skin (ariboflavinosis). This deficiency frequently appears together with vitamin A deficiency. Riboflavin is found in the usual B vitamin foods, plus milk and eggs.

Pyridoxin (vitamin B_6) also functions as a coenzyme involved in protein and fat metabolism. It is needed for healthy skin, nerves, and muscles.

Vitamin B_{12} is, unlike the other B vitamins, not found in vegetable sources. It is obtained mainly from milk and liver. It is used mainly for treatment of pernicious anemia, and probably normally prevents its occurrence.

Niacin (nicotinic acid) participates in a wide variety of metabolic processes as part of the NAD $\rightleftharpoons$ NADP electron transfer system. It is essential for normal function of the nervous system, soft tissues, skin, and the liver. The symptoms of deficiency include mental disorders, skin problems, swollen gums and tongue. The severe deficiency disease, pellagra, is characterized by the "three D's"—diarrhea, dermatosis, dementia.

Choline is essential for normal functioning of several glands, the liver and kidneys, and for fat metabolism.

Pantothenic acid functions as a component of coenzyme A, involved in carbohydrate, fat, and protein metabolism. It is needed for growth, for the health of the skin, the digestive tract, and the adrenal gland.

Folic acid is involved in the regulation of red blood cells and the function of the liver and glands. Deficiency may lead to liver and digestive disturbances.

Biotin is essential to cellular metabolism, functioning, among other places, in the Krebs cycle. Deficiency produces an anemia, skin and heart disorders, sleeplessness, and muscular pain.

Other B vitamins are para-aminobenzoic acid (PABA) and inositol. PABA is an intermediate in folic acid synthesis, and inositol is involved in the metabolism of fats.

Vitamin C (ascorbic acid) is essential for healthy skin, gums, and blood vessels. It is also built into cell walls and is necessary for their continuing strength. Vitamin C also is an important factor in resistance to stress and infection. This vitamin is widely found in fruits and leafy green vegetables, the richest sources being the citrus fruits. It is relatively unstable, being destroyed by heat, and cannot be stored in the body for any length of time.

Symptoms of vitamin C deficiency include bleeding gums, a tendency for small blood vessels to break and hemorrhage, and low resistance to infection. Extreme deficiency is the familiar disease of sailors and explorers, scurvy.

Vitamin D is sometimes known as the "sunshine" vitamin. The precursor ergosterol, which we obtain from green plants, is changed to vitamin D in the skin when it is exposed to sunlight. Today in developed countries milk is enriched with vitamin D through irradiation. The only satisfactory source of converted vitamin D, if sunshine and irradiated milk are unavailable, is fish liver oils. It is quite likely that the thick blanket of smog hanging over American cities interferes with the manufacture of vitamin D in urban populations, which has implications for adults who do not drink milk.

Vitamin D is intimately involved in the absorption and utilization of calcium and phosphorus, and consequently in the growth and maintenance of the bone structure. Rickets is a disease of children who lack vitamin D and/or calcium and phosphorous. In these children the growth and development of the bones is disturbed and retarded. The corresponding disease in adults is osteomalacia. This occurs when calcium is being drawn from the bones to meet daily needs, and is not sufficiently replaced in the diet.

Vitamin E seems to be involved in reproductive functions; lack of it may lead to repeated miscarriage. It is obtained from vegetable oils, particularly wheat germ oil.

Vitamin K is essential to normal blood-clotting activity. This vitamin is ordinarily manufactured by intestinal bacteria, and is also found in green leaves, fat, and egg yolks. The intestinal supply may be cut off temporarily following an antibiotic regime, especially if it is orally administered.

Minerals

Some 17 essential nutrients are minerals, some of them required in very minute amounts.

Bones and teeth are composed primarily of calcium and phosphorous. Calcium also plays a part in the regulation of nerves and muscles, and is necessary for healthy skin and for blood-clotting. The best source of calcium is milk, followed by yellow cheeses. It can also be obtained from the bones of fish and other animals and from green vegetables, shellfish, and lime, which is sometimes used in the preparation of food. Hard water used for drinking or in cooking also contributes calcium.

Phosphorous is closely involved with calcium in bone-building and nerve and muscle regulation. It is also important in sugar metabolism and the utilization of vitamins, and is critically involved in transfers of energy in living systems. Phosphorous is found in dairy foods, poultry, eggs, and meat. Deficiency is relatively uncommon.

Iron is an essential component of hemoglobin, the protein in red blood cells which carries oxygen to the cells of the body. Iron-deficiency anemia is the commonest kind of anemia. Its symptoms include lack of energy and stamina. It is more common among women, whose iron needs are higher due to blood loss in menstruation and the demands of pregnancy. Anemic women are susceptible to stillbirth and miscarriage, and are likely to produce anemic children. Iron is found most abundantly in liver, other organ meats, eggs, molasses, oysters, and apricots. Smaller amounts are found in meat and green vegetables.

Sulphur is necessary for the building of some proteins in the body and must be ingested in amino acids. It is found in many high protein foods, both plant and animal.

Sodium chloride—ordinary table salt—is essential to life, although toxic in too large doses. It occurs naturally in sea foods, meat, and a few fruits and vegetables. It is also found in processed foods such as cheese and bread. Vegetarians may have difficulty getting enough salt; otherwise deficiency is unlikely except where there is danger of heat prostration.

Potassium is a widely available mineral found in meat and many dried fruits and vegetables. It is needed most during periods of rapid growth.

Iodine is an essential component of thyroid hormones which regulate growth, development, and metabolic activities. It is found in foods grown in iodine-rich soil and in iodized salt. Its lack results in goiter, characterized by a swelling of the thyroid gland in the neck. In extreme forms of this disease, cretinism or deaf-mutism may be produced in children.

Zinc is a component of insulin and therefore involved in utilization of carbohydrates and protein. It is found in pulses (peas and beans), organ meats, and green vegetables.

Magnesium is necessary for the utilization of both calcium and vitamin C. It is found in a wide variety of foods.

Manganese is necessary for lactation and some other glandular functions. It is obtained from a variety of nuts and vegetables.

Some other trace elements that are necessary for health are: chromium, cobalt, copper, molybdenum, and selenium.

It is quite possible that other essential nutrients exist that have not yet been isolated. The importance of trace elements cannot be overemphasized. Because they are often required in such minute amounts, and perhaps because there seems to be considerable individual variation in requirements, there is some tendency to overlook them. Yet without them human life would cease.

The Fire Ant Program: An Ecological Case Study

The fire ant is a nasty, but not-too-serious pest in the southeastern United States. Its nests form mounds that interfere with the working of fields. Its stings may cause severe illness or death in sensitive people, but it is a considerably smaller menace in this regard than are bees and wasps. The ant is best described as a major nuisance. After limited and inadequate research on the biology of the fire ant, the USDA in 1957 came up with the astonishing idea of carrying out a massive aerial spray campaign, covering several states, against the ant. Along with other biologists, including those most familiar with the fire ant, I protested the planned program, pointing out, among other things, that the fire ant would be one of the *last* things seriously affected by a broadcast spray program. A quote from a letter I wrote concerning the problem to Ezra Taft Benson, then Secretary of Agriculture, follows:

> To any trained biologist a scorched earth policy involving the treatment of 20 million acres with a highly potent poison such as dieldrin should be considered as a last ditch stand, one resorted to only after all of the possible alternatives have been investigated. In addition such a dangerous program should not even be considered unless the pest involved is an extremely serious threat to *life* and property.
>
> Is the Department of Agriculture aware that there are other consequences of such a program aside from the immediate death of vast numbers of animals? Are they aware that even poisoning the soil in a carefully planned strip system is bound to upset the ecological balance in the area? We are all too ignorant of the possible sequelae of such a program. Has it been pointed out that an adaptable and widespread organism such as the Fire Ant is one of the least likely of the insects in the treated area to be exterminated? It is also

highly likely that, considering its large population size, the Fire Ant will have the reserve of genetic variability to permit the survival of resistant strains.

I would strongly recommend that the program be suspended: 1) until the biology of the ant can be thoroughly investigated with a view toward biological control, baiting, or some other control method superior to broadcast poisoning, and 2) until trained ecologists can do the field studies necessary to give a reasonable evaluation of the chances of success, and the concomitant damage to the human population, wildlife, and the biotic community in general of *any* contemplated control program.

I hope that the United States will learn from the disastrous Canadian Spruce Budworm program and hesitate before carrying out a program whose consequences may be a biological calamity.

This reply came from C. F. Curl, then Acting Director of the USDA Plant Pest Control Division. Note the emphasis on "eradication" in this excerpt:

Surveys do indicate that the imported fire ant infests approximately 20,000,000 acres in our southern states. This does not mean, however, that the eradication program is embarked on a "scorched earth policy." The infestation is not continuous and the insecticide is applied only to areas where it is known to exist. The small outlying areas are being treated first to prevent further spread and of the large generally infested areas only a portion is treated in any one year.

The method of eradication, namely, the application of granular form of two pounds of either dieldrin or heptachlor per acre is based on an analysis of research information compiled from State and Federal sources. Use experience on other control programs such as the white-fringed beetle and Japanese beetle was also taken into consideration before the final decisions were made. All the data indicated that a program could be developed which would be safe and would present a minimum of hazard to the ecological balance in the areas to be treated.

To date approximately 130,000 acres have been treated. This includes a block of 12,000 acres at El Dorado, Arkansas, treated nearly a year ago. Reports indicate the program is successful in eradicating the ants. No active mounds have been found in the El Dorado area and the results look equally good in other locations treated to date. Observers vitally interested in the impact of this program to other forms of life have not reported serious disturbances in the area as a whole.

Close liaison has been established with the Fish and Wildlife Service to continue their observations and to keep us informed currently as to the effect this program may have on fish and wildlife in the area. Experience to date indicates that a successful program can be carried out with a minimum hazard to the beneficial forms of life present.

We believe that the points mentioned in your letter were given ample consideration before the initiation of the fire ant eradication program. We recognize of course that in any program where insecticides are used, certain precautions are necessary. Our experience has shown that insecticides can be applied successfully using very definite guidelines which can be established to minimize the hazard to fish and wildlife and to preclude any hazard to domestic animals and human health. Such guidelines are being followed in the operation of all control and eradication programs in which the U.S. Department of Agriculture participates.

In order to permit you to judge for yourself who was right, here are parts of an article on the results of the program by Dr. William L. Brown, Jr., of the Department of Entomology of Cornell University. Dr. Brown, an outstanding biologist and a world authority on ants, wrote:

> With astonishing swiftness, and over the mounting protests of conservation and other groups alarmed at the prospect of another airborne 'spray' program, the first insecticides were laid down in November, 1957. The rate of application was two pounds of dieldrin or heptachlor per acre . . . Dieldrin and heptachlor are extremely toxic substances—about 4–15 times as toxic to wildlife as is DDT. Many wildlife experts and conservationists as well as entomologists both basic and economic, felt a sense of forboding at the start of a program that would deposit poisons with 8–30 times the killing power of the common forest dosage of DDT (one pound per acre in gypsy moth control).
>
> . . .The misgivings of the wildlife people seem to have been justified, since the kill of wildlife in sample treated areas appears to have been high in most of those that have been adequately checked. The USDA disputes many of the claims of damage, but their own statements often tend to be vague and general.
>
> . . .Although the USDA claims that the evidence is inconclusive in some cases, there does exist contrary information indicating that stock losses from ant poisons may sometimes be significant.
>
> . . .A serious blow was dealt the program in late 1958, when treatments were only one year old; Senator Sparkman and Congressman Boykin of Alabama asked that the fire ant campaign be suspended until the benefits and dangers could be evaluated properly. Then, in the beginning of 1960, the Food and Drug Administration of the Department of Health, Education, and Welfare lowered the tolerance for heptachlor residues on harvested crops to zero, following the discovery that heptachlor was transformed by weathering into a persistent and highly toxic derivative, heptachlor epoxide, residues of which turn up in milk and meat when fed to stock. Some state entomologists now definitely advise farmers against the use of heptachlor on pastures or forage.
>
> . . .The original plan set forth in 1957 called for eradication of the ant on the North American continent, by rolling back the infestation from its borders, applying eradication measures to more control foci in the main infestation, and instituting an effective program of treatment of especially dangerous sources of spread, such as nurseries. Nearly four years and perhaps 15 million dollars after the plan was announced, the fire ant is still turning up in new counties, and is being rediscovered in counties thought to have been freed of the pest in Arkansas, Louisiana, Florida, and North Carolina.

Recently a bait has been found which gives effective fire-ant control on a rate of insecticide application of less than one tenth ounce per acre. It is claimed that the insecticide, Mirex (a chlorinated hydrocarbon) is virtually harmless to vertebrates and bees. Even if it is not, this program shows what improvement is possible if one pays some attention to the ecology of a situation, rather than launching vast broadcast spray programs. Note that baiting was suggested to the USDA before 1960.

This rather lengthy discussion should give you some insight into two of the government agencies which should be most active in preserving the quality of our environment. The USDA, against the advice of the most competent people in the field, launched a fruitless eradication campaign which could only have positive results for the stockholders of pesticide companies, and the FDA discovered that another of its tolerance levels was set too high.

Some Important Pesticides

(Adapted from Bulletin of Entomological Society of America)

The left-hand column below gives the commonest name for the insecticide, other names by which it is known, and the chemical designation. Sometimes on labels the chemical designation may be simplified. For instance, aldrin will sometimes be listed simply as "hexachlorohexahydro-*endo, exo*-dimethanonaphthalene. The second column gives the general use of the chemical, coded as follows.

> Acar.   = Acaracide (used against mites)
> Ins.   = Insecticide (used against insects)
> Syn.   = Synergist (makes insecticide more potent)
> MP   = Moth Proofer
> C. Fum. = Commodity or space fumigant
> S. Fum. = Soil fumigant
> Sys.   = Systemic insecticide (taken up by plant)
> Nem.   = Nematocide (kills roundworms)

The right-hand column indicates mammalian toxicity judged by experiments on rats (no symbol), rabbits (Rb), white mice (M) or dogs (D). They are mostly given as LD_{50}, that is the dose level which killed 50% of the experimental animals. The doses used in studying acute toxicity are in parts per million of live animal weight. AO = acute oral toxicity; AD = acute dermal (skin application) toxicity. Chronic oral toxicity (CO) is the highest level (parts per million in diet) at which no effect is seen in 90 days or more.

Fumigant toxicities: VA = acute vapor toxicity, the highest level in ppm thought not to be dangerous to man with 60 minutes exposure; VC = chronic vapor toxicity, same for 8 hours per day, five days per week.

For example, chlordane killed 50 percent of rats tested in different experiments at oral doses of 283–590 milligrams per kilogram (mg/kg) of body weight. When chlordane was applied to the skin, 50 percent of the rats died at doses of 580 mg/kg in at least one experiment, but in another a dose of 1600 mg/kg did not produce 50 percent deaths. In rabbits more than 50 percent were killed with a skin dose of 780 mg/kg. In mouse experiments diets with greater than 25 or less tran 150 ppm did not produce symptoms in 90 days or more.

As a general rule there will be a reasonable correlation between other mammals and man in the toxicity of these compounds. Thus TEPP with an AO of 0.5–2 in rats in exceedingly toxic to man. An amount equal to about one-millionth of your body weight will kill you. DDT, on the other hand, is much safer as far as acute exposure is concerned.

Note that the chlorinated hydrocarbons appear in several groups: Chlorinated Aryl Hydrocarbons, DDT relatives, and Fumigants (paradichlorobenzene).

Common and Technical Names	Use	Mammalian Toxicity
ACTIVATORS OR SYNERGISTS FOR INSECTICIDES		
Piperonyl butoxide (Butacide^R)	Ins.	AO>7500, M3800
α–[2–(2–butoxyethoxy)-ethoxy]–4,5–methylenedioxy–2–propyltoluene	Syn.	D>7500
		Rb>7500
		AD Rb>1880
		CO 1000, D700
BOTANICALS		
Rotene powder and resins (derris) (cubé)	Ins.	AO 60–1500, M350
		AD Rb>1000–3000
1,2,12,12α,tetrahydro–2–iso–propenyl–8,9–dimethoxy–[1]benzopyrano–[3,4–b]furo[2,3–b][1] benzopyran–6 (6aH)one		CO 25, D>400
Pyrethrins (cinerin)	Ins.	AO 200–2600
Pyrethrum (principally from plant species chrysanthemum cinariaefolium)		AD>1800
		CO 1000
Allethrin (synthetic pyrethrins)	Ins.	AO 680–1000
2–allyl–4–hydroxy–3–methyl–2–cyclopenten–1–one ester of 2,2–dimethyl–3–(2–methylpropenyl)–cyclopropanecarboxylic acid		M480, Rb4290
		AD>11200
		CO 5000, D 4000
Nicotine (sulfate)	Ins.	AO 50–91, M24
Black Leaf 40^R		AD 140, Rb50
ℓ–1–methyl–2–(3–pyridyl)–pyrrolidine		
CHLORINATED ARYL HYDROCARBONS (containing 6 or more chlorines)		
Benzene hexachloride (BHC)	Ins.	AO 600–1250
1,2,3,4,5,6–hexachloro-cyclohexane, mixed isomers and a specified percentage of gamma		CO 10
		(Toxicity depends on ratio of isomers)

Common and Technical Names	Use	Mammalian Toxicity

CHLORINATED ARYL HYDROCARBONS (*continued*)

Lindane (gamma BHC)
 	
1,2,3,4,5,6–hexachlorocyclo-hexane, 99%
  or more gamma isomer
	Ins.	AO 76–200, M86
		  Rb60–200, D40
		AD 500–1200
		  Rb300–4000
		CO 50, 25(m)
		  D>15

Chlordane
 	
1,2,4,5,6,7,8,8–octachloro–3α,4,7,7α–
  tetrahydro–4,7-methanoindane
	Ins.	AO 283–590
		AD 580–>1600
		  Rb<780
		CO>25–<150(m)

Heptachlor
 	
1,4,5,6,7,8,8–heptachloro–3α,4,7,7α–tetra-
  hydro–4,7–methanoindene
	Ins.	A040–188, M68
		AD 119–320
		  Rb2000
		CO 0.5->5(m)
		  D4–5(m)

Aldrin
 	
Not less than 95% of 1,2,3,4,10,10–hexa-
  chloro–1,4,4α,5,8,8α–hexahydro–1,4–endo–
  exo,5,8–dimethano-naphthalene
	Ins.	AO39–60, M44
		  D65–90, Rb50–80
		AD 80–>200
		  Rb<150
		CO 0.5, 25(m), D1

Dieldrin
 	
Not less than 85% of 1,2,3,4,10,10–hexa-
  chloro–6,7–epoxy–1,4,4α,5,6,7,8α–octa-
  hydro–1,4–endo–exo–5,8–dimethano–
  naphthalene
	Ins.	A040–100
		  D65–95, M38
		  Rb45–50
		AD 52–117, Rb250–
		  360
		CO 0.5, Dcal

Endrin
 	
1,2,3,4,10,10–hexachloro–6,7–expoxy–
  1,4,4α,5,6,7,8,8α–octahydro–1,4–endo–endo–
  5,8–dimethano–naphthalene
	Ins.	AO 3–45, Rb7–10
		AD 12–19, Rb60–
		  120
		CO >1–<25(m)

Endosulfan (Thiodan[R])
 	
6,7,8,9,10,10–hexachloro–1,5,5α,6,9,9α–
  hexahydro–6,9–methano–2,4,3–benzodioxa-
  thiepin 3–oxide
	Acar.
	Ins.
		AO 30–110
		AD 74–130, Rb360
		CO 30, D30

Toxaphene
 	
Chlorinated camphene containing 67–69%
  chlorine
	Ins.	AO 40–283, M112
		  D15, Rb<780
		AD 600–1613
		  Rb780–4000
		CO 10, 25(m)
		  Dca400

Mirex Dodecachlorooctahydro–1,3,4–methano– 1H–cyclobuta[cd]pentalene	Ins.	AO 235–702 AD Rb800

DDT RELATIVES
(Diphenyl Aliphatics)

DDT (dichloro diphenyl trichloro-ethane)
1,1,1–trichloro–2,2–bis-(p–chlorophenyl)
  ethane
	Ins.
	MP
		AO 87–500
		  M150–400
		  Rb250–400
		AD 1931–3263
		  Rb2820
		CO 5, 1(m), D400

Common and Technical Names	Use	Mammalian Toxicity

DDT RELATIVES (continued)		
DDD (TDE) Dichlorodiphenyl dichloro-ethane 1,1–dichloro–2,2–bis-(p–chlorophenyl) ethane	Ins.	AO 400–3400 M2500 AD Rb 4000–>5000 CO ca100–900(m)
Kelthane^R (dicofol) 4,4′–dichloro–α–(tri-chloromethyl)– benzhydrol	Acar.	AO 575–1331 D>4000 Rb1810 AD 1000–1230 Rb2100 CO 20–100, D300 D100(m)
Methoxychlor 1,1,1–trichloro–2,2–bis-(p–methoxyphenyl) ethane	Ins.	AO 5000–7000 M1850, Rb>6000 AD >2820->6000 CO 100, >200(m) D>4000

FUMIGANTS		
Methyl bromide Bromomethane	C. fum. S. fum.	VA 200 VC 20
Cyanide (prussic acid) (HCN) Hydrocyanic acid	C. fum. S. fum.	AO Rb4 CO >300 VA 40 VC 10
Paradichlorobenzene (PDB) p–dichlorobenzene	C. fum. MP	AO 500–5000 M2950 AD Rb>2000 VA 500 VC 75
Naphthalene	C. fum. MP	VC 10
Carbon disulfide	C. fum.	VA 200 VC 20
Vapam^R Sodium methyldithio-carbamate	Nem. S. fum.	AO 820, M285 AD Rb800

ALIPHATIC DERIVATIVES OF PHOSPHORUS COMPOUNDS		
Tepp (TEPP) Tetraethyl pyrophosphate	Ins.	AO 0.5–2, M1–7 AD 2–20, Rb5
Dipterex^R (trichlorfon) Dimethyl (2,2,2–trichloro–1–hydroxyethyl) phosphonate	Ins.	AO 450–699 M300–500 AD>2800, Rb5000 CO<100–125(m)
DIBROM^R (naled) 1,2–dibromo–2,2–dichloroethyl dimethyl phosphate	Acar. Ins.	AO 430 AD Rb1100 CO D7.5 mg/kg(m)
Vapona^R (dichlorvos) 2,2–dichlorovinyl dimethyl phosphate	C. fum. Ins.	AO 25–170 AD 59–900, Rb107 CO <50(m)

Common and Technical Names	Use	Mammalian Toxicity

ALIPHATIC DERIVATIVES OF PHOSPHORUS COMPOUNDS (*continued*)

Phosdrin[R] (mevinphos)	Ins.	AO 3–7, M8–200
Methyl 3–hydroxy–alpha–crotonate, dimethyl phosphate	Sys.	AD 3–90, Rb13–55 CO 0.8, D1
Azodrin[R]	Ins.	AO 21
3–hydroxy–N–methyl–cis–crotonamide dimethyl phosphate	Sys. Acar.	AD Rb354 CO 1.5(m)
Systox (demeton)	Acar.	AO 2–12
Mixture of 0,0–diethyl S–(and 0)–2–[(ethylthio)ethyl] phosphorothioates	Ins. Sys.	AD 8–200, Rb24 CO 1, D1, D2(m)
Malathion	Ins.	AO 885–2800
Diethyl mercaptosuccinate, S–ester with 0,0– dimethyl phosphorodithioate		M720–4060 AD >4000->4444 Rb4100 CO 100–1000, D100

ARYL (PHENYL) DERIVATIVES OF PHOSPHORUS COMPOUNDS

Methyl parathion	Ins.	AO 9–42, M32
0,0–dimethyl 0–p–nitrophenyl phosphorothioate		AD 63–72, Rb1270
parathion	Acar.	AO 3–30, M6–25
0,0–diethyl 0–p–nitrophenyl phosphorothioate	Ins.	Rb10, D3 AD 4–200 Rb40–870 CO 1, 50(m), D1

HETEROCYCLIC DERIVATIVES OF PHOSPHORUS COMPOUNDS

Diazinon	Acar.	AO 66–600
0,0–diethyl 0–(2–isopropyl– 4–methyl–6–pyrimidyl) phosphorothioate	Ins.	M80–135 Rb130–143 AD 379–1200 Rb 4000 CO 1, D 0.75

SULFONATES

Mitin FF[R]	MP	AO 750–1380
Sodium 5–chloro–2–(4–chloro–2–(3–(3,4– dichlorophenyl)–ureido)phenoxy)benzenesulfonate		

CARBAMATES

Baygon[R]	Ins.	AO 95–175
0–isopropyoxyphenyl methylcarbamate		AD >1000 CO 800(m)
SEVIN[R]	Ins.	AO 307–986
Carbaryl		D>759, Rb710
1–naphthyl methylcarbamate		AD >500->4000 Rb >2000 CO 200, D200–400

355

Reproductive Anatomy and Physiology

According to those who have been involved in the Planned Parenthood movement, the two greatest obstacles to successful birth control are ignorance and prudery. In fact, the two often go together. Women who have been raised to fear and dislike sex will often resist learning the facts of reproduction and be very reluctant to discuss any aspect of the subject, including birth control, with their doctors or anyone else. Women without such psychological problems, who are ignorant of their own anatomy and the significance of the menstrual cycle, are still very likely to have failures in their birth control programs, simply because they do not understand how they work or why. Here is one more argument for good sex education programs in schools, churches, and in the home. A sound understanding of the reproductive process is essential to the effective use of at least the conventional methods of birth control. There is even enough uncertainty among educated persons about human reproductive biology and contraception to make a brief review appropriate here.

Conception occurs when a spermatozoan (sperm cell) from a man meets and fertilizes an ovum (egg cell) within a woman's body. The various forms of contraception are designed to prevent that occurrence in a number of different ways, either by erecting a physical or chemical barrier between sperm and egg or through adjustment of the hormone system.

Spermatozoa are manufactured continuously by the millions daily in a man's testes. This goes on from the age of puberty, around fourteen, until very old age. Each spermatozoon contains the genetic information which the man passes on to the child in the event conception takes place. But unless it meets and fertilizes an egg cell, it dies within a few days. These microscopic, active cells which resemble minute tadpoles, are emitted in the hundreds of millions each time a man ejaculates. The testes are also the source of production of the male hormone, testosterone, which is released to the blood

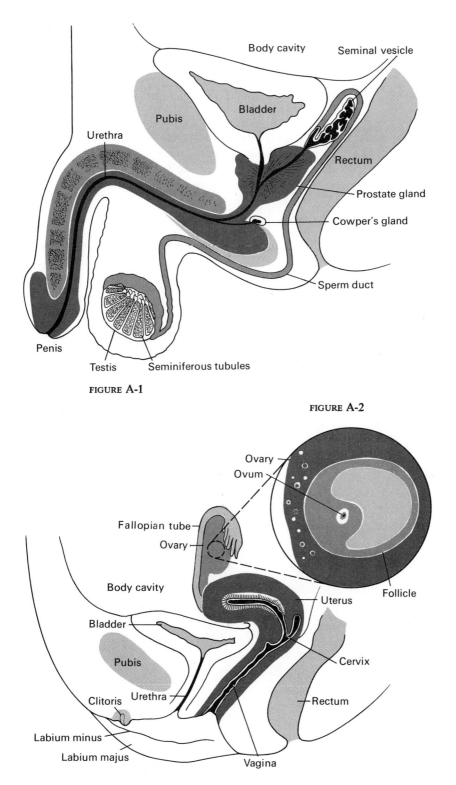

FIGURE A-1

FIGURE A-2

stream and is responsible for sexual activity and for the development of a man's secondary sexual characteristics such as a deep voice, a beard, and typically male body structure.

When the spermatozoa are mature, they are moved upward through one of a pair of tubes called a vas deferens to the seminal vesicle (Fig. A-1). This acts as a reservoir for storage until the man ejaculates. Each vas deferens opens into the urethra, a tube which extends the length of the penis. During intercourse when the man experiences his climax, or orgasm, a series of muscular contractions force the sperm cells in a fluid matrix known as semen through the urethra, injecting it into the vagina. The semen is a mixture produced in several glands including the prostate. It provides the spermatozoa with protection after they are deposited in the vagina, which is a relatively hostile environment.

The woman's reproductive cells (ova) are present in immature form in her ovaries from birth (Fig. A-2). From puberty (around 13) until she reaches menopause, somewhere around the age of 45 or 50, one egg cell or *ovum* (or occasionally two or more, which may result in multiple births, usually twins or triplets) is brought to maturity approximately every 28 days. A single ovum is so small it would be visible to the naked eye only as a tiny speck, yet it is many thousands of times larger than a spermatozoan. Besides the mother's genetic contribution to the potential child, the egg cell contains nourishment to support the early development of the embryo, should the ovum be fertilized.

Besides being the source of ova, the ovaries also secrete the female hormones, which, along with certain pituitary hormones, regulate the woman's menstrual cycle and the successful completion of a pregnancy. Estrogen, which is also responsible for the secondary sexual characteristics of a woman, such as the developed breasts and the pelvic bone structure adapted for the bearing of children, initiates the maturation of the ovum and the preparation of the uterus for pregnancy. In one of the two ovaries each month, an ovum, which is surrounded by a group of cells called a follicle, ripens and is released (ovulation). It enters the adjacent flared end of a trumpet-shaped structure known as a fallopian tube and travels slowly down it towards the uterus (womb). If fertilization does not take place during the one or two days of this journey, the ovum begins to deteriorate and eventually dissolves.

After the ovum is discharged from the follicle, the latter develops into a structure called a corpus luteum, which begins to secrete the other female hormones, including progesterone. Progesterone further stimulates the buildup of a lining of cells and extra blood vessels in the uterus, in preparation to receive a developing embryo for implantation. If conception (fertilization) does not occur, the corpus luteum degenerates and ceases to produce progesterone. In the absence of fertilization, about 14 days after ovulation the lining of the uterus is sloughed away through the vagina over a period of 5 or 6 days in the process of menstruation (Fig. A-2). Then the cycle begins again.

Spermatozoa which have been deposited in the vagina during coitus still have a long way to go relative to their size and vulnerability before fertilization can take place. The mucus lining of the vagina is acid, and the sperm cells cannot live long in such an environment. They must find their way into and through the thick mucus filling the cervical canal of the uterus. They are equipped with an enzyme capable of dissolving the mucus, but apparently it requires large numbers of them to dissolve enough to allow them to reach the uterus. Many, of course, are lost along the way. The uterus provides a favorable, alkaline environment, but the spermatozoa must still find their way into the fallopian tubes. If an ovum is descending one of the fallopian tubes as the remaining several thousand spermatozoa swim up it, one of them may succeed in penetrating the capsule of the egg cell. Once one has penetrated, the fertilized ovum is impervious to all of the others. The ovum continues to descend the tube, undergoing cell division as it goes. When it reaches the uterus and is implanted in the wall of the uterus, it is a rapidly developing embryo.

Within several weeks, the growing embryo is about an inch long and has established its placenta, the organ through which food and oxygen from the mother and wastes and carbon dioxide from the fetus, as it is now called, are exchanged. Nine months from conception, the infant is born. With powerful contractions from the uterus, the child is forced through the cervix and vagina, which expand to accommodate it.

Throughout the pregnancy, the corpus luteum continues to secrete progesterone, which protects the implantation of the early fetus and suppresses ovulation and menstruation. During lactation (the period when the mother is producing milk) menstruation is also usually suppressed, although ovulation may or may not occur.

General Bibliography

Appleman, Philip, 1965. *The Silent Explosion*. Beacon, Boston. An excellent general treatment, strong on attitudes toward control of population.

Bates, Marston, 1960. *The Forest and the Sea, a Look at the Economy of Nature and the Ecology of Man*. Random House, New York.

Blake, P., 1964. *God's Own Junkyard, the Planned Deterioration of America's Landscape*. Holt, Rinehart & Winston, New York.

Borgstrom, Georg, 1967. *The Hungry Planet*. Collier, New York. Excellent.

Borgstrom, Georg, 1969. *Too Many, A Story of Earth's Biological Limitations*. Macmillan, New York. A fine, impassioned treatment of the population-food crisis.

Bronson, W., 1968. *How to Kill a Golden State*. California Tomorrow.

Brown, Harrison, 1954. *The Challenge of Man's Future*. Viking, New York. A classic work on population and resources.

Brown, Harrison, J. Bonner, and C. Weir, 1957. *The Next Hundred Years*. Viking, New York.

Brown, Harrison (ed.), 1967. *The Next Ninety Years*. California Institute of Technology, Pasadena. Updates *The Next Hundred Years*.

Calder, Nigel, 1967. *Eden Was No Garden*. Holt, Rinehart & Winston, New York. An interesting, over-optimistic look into the future.

Chase, Stuart, 1968. *The Most Probable World*. Harper & Row, New York. Another very interesting "futurist" book which suffers from a lack of appreciation of the magnitude of environmental problems and constraints.

Cloud, Preston E., Jr. (ed.), 1969. *Resources and Man*. W. H. Freeman and Company, San Francisco.

Cole, LaMont C., 1968. Can the world be saved? *BioScience,* vol. 18, no. 7. (July).

Comfort, Alex, 1966. *The Nature of Human Nature*. Discus Books (Avon), New York.

Commoner, Barry, 1967. *Science and Survival*. Viking, New York. Technology and survival.

Darwin, C. G., 1952. *The Next Million Years*. Doubleday, New York.

Dasmann, Raymond, 1965. *The Destruction of California*. Collier, New York.

Day, L. H., and A. T. Day, 1965. *Too Many Americans*. Delta, New York. Important work on overpopulation in the United States.

Dubos, Rene, 1965. *Man Adapting*. Yale Univ. Press. New Haven. Deals with all aspects of the individual's adaptation to his environment.

Ehrlich, Paul R., 1968. *The Population Bomb*. Ballantine, New York.

Environment (formerly *Scientist and Citizen*). An official publication of the Scientists' Institute for Public Information, this journal is published monthly by the Committee for Environmental Information, 438 N. Skinker Blvd., St. Louis, Mo. 63130. The best source of sound, relatively nontechnical information on environmental problems.

Fagley, R. M., 1960. *The Population Explosion and Christian Responsibility*. Oxford Univ. Press, Oxford. A Protestant perspective on population control.

Foreign Policy Association, 1968. *Toward the Year 2018*. Cowles Corp., New York. A set of essays on subjects as diverse as weaponry, economics, population, and oceanography.

Freeman, O. L., 1968. *World Without Hunger*. Frederick A. Praeger, New York. An optimistic book which views American efforts through rose-colored glasses and has neither "ecology" nor "environment" in its index.

Hardin, Garrett (ed.), 1969. *Population, Evolution, and Birth Control*. W. H. Freeman and Company, San Francisco. A superb collection of readings, including numerous gems by the editor.

Hauser, Philip M., 1963. *The Population Dilemma*. Prentice-Hall, Englewood Cliffs, N.J.

Heer, David M. (ed.), 1968. *Readings on Population*. Prentice-Hall, Englewood Cliffs, N.J. A good collection of demographic papers, most of which will be understandable to the layman.

Heer, David M., 1968. *Society and Population*. Prentice-Hall, Englewood Cliffs, N.J.

Hopcraft, Arthur, 1968. *Born to Hunger*. Houghton Mifflin, Boston. An excellent and personalized account of hunger in the world.

Jarrett, Henry (ed.), 1969. *Environmental Quality in a Growing Economy*. Johns Hopkins Press, Baltimore.

Kahn, H., and A. J. Wiener, 1967. *The Year 2000, a Framework for Speculation on the Next Thirty-Three Years*. Macmillan, New York. Virtually ignores population and environment problems, probably over-optimistic on international conflict, but with much interesting material nonetheless.

McHarg, Ian, 1969. *Design with Nature*. Natural History Press, Garden City, New York.

Marsh, George P., 1874. *The Earth as Modified by Human Action*. Charles Scribner's Sons, New York. An early classic showing that environmental concerns are nothing new.

Morris, Desmond, 1967. *The Naked Ape*. McGraw-Hill, New York. In spite of some errors of fact and interpretation this is an excellent book for putting man in perspective. Highly recommended.

Myrdal, Gunnar, 1968. *Asian Drama* (3 vols.). Pantheon (Random House), New York.

National Advisory Commission on Civil Disorders, 1968. *Report of the National Advisory Commission on Civil Disorders.* Bantam Books, New York.

Ng, L. K. Y., and S. Mudd (eds.), 1965. *The Population Crisis, Implications, and Plans for Action.* Indiana Univ. Press, Indianapolis. Although somewhat dated, this is still a useful collection of readings.

Osborn, Fairfield, 1948. *Our Plundered Planet.* Little, Brown & Co., Boston. An early warning which, unhappily, was ignored. See the comments on DDT, pp. 61–62.

Paddock, W., and P. Paddock, 1964. *Hungry Nations.* Little, Brown & Co., Boston. An excellent work on the UDCs.

Paddock, W., and P. Paddock, 1967. *Famine—1975! America's Decision: Who Will Survive?* Little, Brown & Co., Boston. Everyone must read this controversial work.

Petersen, Wm., 1965. *The Politics of Population.* Doubleday (Anchor Book), New York. A collection of essays on how population relates to social psychology.

Population Reference Bureau, Inc., 1775 Massachusetts Ave. N. W., Washington, D.C. 20036. Publishes the *Population Bulletin, PRB Selections,* and the *World Population Data Sheet.* Everyone interested in population should subscribe to all three.

President's Science Advisory Committee, 1965. Restoring the quality of our environment. Report of the Environmental Pollution Panel. Washington, D.C. An important source on environmental deterioration and what might be done about it. The recommendations of this report have been largely ignored.

President's Science Advisory Committee, 1967. *World Food Problem* (3 vols.). Washington, D.C.

Rattray-Taylor, Gordon, *The Biological Time Bomb.* World Publishing Co., New York. A very competent popular treatment of the revolution in the biological sciences. Highly recommended.

Reinow, R., and L. T. Reinow, 1967. *Moment in the Sun.* Dial, New York. A superb popular work on the deterioration of the American environment.

Rudd, R. L., 1964. *Pesticides and the Living Landscape.* Univ. of Wisconsin Press, Madison.

Sax, K., 1955. *Standing Room Only.* Beacon, Boston. Another excellent "early warning."

Shepard, Paul, and Daniel McKinley (ed.), 1969. *The Subversive Science.* Houghton Mifflin Co., Boston.

Stenhouse, David, 1966. *Crisis in Abundance.* Heinemann, Melbourne, Sydney, London. Heinemann Educational Books Ltd., 33 Lonsdale St., Melbourne.

Stewart, George R., 1968. *Not So Rich as You Think.* Houghton Mifflin Co., Boston.

Stockwell, E. G., 1968. *Population and People.* Quadrangle, Chicago.

Stycos, J. M., 1968. *Human Fertility in Latin America.* Cornell Univ. Press, Ithaca.

Udall, Stewart, 1963. *The Quiet Crisis.* Holt, Rinehart & Winston, New York. The history and future of the fight to save the American environment.

Udall, Stewart, 1968. *1976, Agenda for Tomorrow*. Harcourt, Brace, and World, Inc., New York. A superb book outlining a positive action program for Americans. Should be read by everyone.

United Nations, 1966–1967. *World Population Conference, 1965* (vol. 1, Summary Report; vol. 2, Fertility, Family Planning, Mortality; vol. 3, Projections, Measurement of Population Trends; vol. 4, Migration, Urbanization, Economic Development). U.N., New York. The papers by Soviet scientists A. Y. Boyarsky and B. Y. Smvlevich (vol. 2) are especially noteworthy. Their attacks on "Malthusianism" show interesting parallels with those of old-time Catholic dogmatists such as Colin Clark.

United Nations, 1968. *United Nations Statistical Yearbook, 1967*. U.N., New York.

United States Dept. of Health, Education, and Welfare. *Vital Statistics Report*. Health Services and Mental Health Adm., Washington, D.C.

United States Senate, 1968. *Population Crisis* (part 3). Hearings held before the Subcommittee on Foreign Aid Expenditures of the Senate Committee on Government Operations, 90th Cong., 2nd sess., Feb. 1.

Vogt, William, 1948. *Road to Survival*. Sloane, New York. *Time* magazine thought this book was alarmist, but time has shown Vogt to have been right.

Vogt, William, 1960. *People, Challenge to Survival*. Hillman-McFadden, New York. Another fine book to which people should have paid attention.

White, L., 1967. The historical roots of our ecological crises. *Science*, vol 155, pp. 1203–1207.

Whyte, William H., 1968. *The Last Landscape*. Doubleday, Garden City, New York.

Wrigley, E. A., 1969. *Population and History*. McGraw-Hill, New York.

Young, L. B. (ed.), 1968. *Population in Perspective*. Oxford Univ. Press, Oxford.

List of Abbreviations

ACLU	American Civil Liberties Union
AEC	United States Atomic Energy Commission
BHC	benzene hexachloride, a chlorinated hydrocarbon insecticide
BWU	blue whale unit
CBW	chemical and biological warfare
CIAT	International Center for Tropical Agriculture
CIMMYT	International Maize and Wheat Improvement Center
CSM	corn, soya, milk
DDD	dichloro-diphenyl-dichloroethane, a breakdown product of DDT
DDE	dichloro-diphenyl-dichloroethylene, a breakdown product of DDT
DDT	dichloro-diphenyl-trichloroethane, a chlorinated hydrocarbon insecticide
DPE	Department of Population and Environment
EDF	Environmental Defense Fund
FAO	United Nations Food and Agriculture Organization
FDA	United States Food and Drug Administration
FPC	United States Federal Power Commission
GNP	gross national product
2,4-D	a herbicide
2,4,5-T	a herbicide
HEW	United States Department of Health, Education, and Welfare
IITA	International Institute for Tropical Agriculture
INCAP	Institute for Nutrition for Central America and Panama
IPPF	International Planned Parenthood Federation
IR-8	a rice developed by International Rice Research Institute
IRRI	International Rice Research Institute
IWC	International Whaling Commission
NAWAPA	North Atlantic Water and Power Alliance
OAS	Organization of American States
OEQ	United States Office of Environmental Quality
PCBs	polychlorinated biphenyls; chlorinated hydrocarbon industrial solvents related to DDT
TEPP	an organic phosphate insecticide
UAR	United Arab Republic
UN	United Nations
UNCTAD	United Nations Conferences on Trade and Development
UNESCO	United Nations Educational, Scientific and Cultural Organization
USAID	United States Agency for International Development
USDA	United States Department of Agriculture
WHO	World Health Organization

Index